# 01
# Management of health

## Contents



## Supporting information

### GT 700 Toolbox talks

B 01

## Overview

**At any one time there are far more construction industry workers off work due to work-related ill health than there are through accidents.**

**Figures from the Health and Safety Executive (HSE) show, beyond any doubt, that ill health caused by work leads to more deaths, long-term illness and lost time.**

**The actual costs to industry, and the individual companies within it, are significantly more than what are regarded to be the costs of accidents.**

**Good employee health is good for business, as anything else will involve the employer in extra work and extra costs somewhere along the line.**

## 1.1 Introduction

One of the reasons why employers have safe systems of work is to avoid accidents and keep employees at work, instead of them being off sick. Exactly the same reasoning should be applied to the prevention of health problems that may arise from work.

The prevention of ill health on site can clearly be seen to benefit the employer as well as employees. Employees will be able to work to their full capacity, rather than being off work sick or working under the limitations (physical or physiological) imposed by an illness or other condition (such as stress or musculoskeletal problems).

For many years the focus of health and safety legislation has tended to be on the issue of safety on building and construction sites, rather than on the subject of occupational health. Employers should give the same attention to occupational health as they do to preventing accidents at work.

The introduction of the Health and Safety at Work Act 1974 marked a major change in emphasis, acknowledging that ill health arising from work was a problem and giving it equal importance to safety.

A number of regulations on subjects such as the control of substances hazardous to health (COSHH), lead and asbestos regulations have been introduced to further address health issues, as it has become clearly recognised that health is an important subject on building and construction sites.

The legal duties require employers to make provisions to safeguard the health of employees.

- ☑ The construction industry has the largest number of occupational cancer with over 40% of occupational cancer registrations from construction.
- ☑ The most significant carcinogen is still past exposure to asbestos (69%), followed by silica (17%) and diesel engine exhaust/ environmental tobacco smoke (6–7% each). Solar radiation, coal tars and pitches are responsible for about 1,300 cancer registrations, mostly causing non-melanoma skin cancers.
- ☑ 5,000 people die each year from asbestos-related illnesses.
- ☑ In 2012 11 people died from silicosis (dust from cutting blocks, kerbs, and others).
- ☑ In 2013-14 there were an estimated 31,000 new cases of work-related ill health.
- ☑ 76,000 people whose current or most recent job in the last year was in construction, suffered from an illness (longstanding and new cases), which was caused or made worse by their job.
- ☑ In 2013-14 an estimated 2.3 million working days were lost, 1.7 million due to work-related ill health and a further 592,000 due to workplace injuries, making a total of 1.1 days lost per worker.
- ☑ Painters and decorators are at high risk of ill health, possibly due to solvent exposure.
- ☑ Injuries and new cases of ill health resulting from current working conditions in the construction industry cost society more than £1.1 billion each year.
- ☑ Vibration white finger, carpal tunnel syndrome, occupational deafness and dermatitis are the most common cases of non-lung diseases in the construction industry.

**Whilst an injury caused by an accident is in most cases instantly obvious, the symptoms of occupational ill health, and therefore knowledge of it, can take months or years to show.**

Occupational ill health can result in the sufferer having long periods off work or having to give up work completely, and even short-term sickness absence can have an adverse effect on business.

## Contents

The prevention of occupational ill health is easily achievable when the following requirements are met.

- ☑ A suitable assessment of the risks to health is carried out and reviewed as necessary.
- ☑ Adequate control measures are identified, put in place and adjusted as necessary.
- ☑ The persons at risk fully use the control measures provided.

In some circumstances employers have a legal duty to provide health surveillance to employees.

Raising the awareness of managers, supervisors and workers to ensure effective control measures are always put in place and followed is fundamental to help reduce these numbers.

**! At any one time there are far more people off work through occupational ill health than there are because of a work-related accident.**

## 1.2 Legislative requirements

### 1.2.1 Management of Health and Safety at Work Regulations

Employers have a duty to assess the risks to health that arise out of their work and to introduce measures that control the risks to an acceptable level.

The following information is explained within a risk assessment.

- ☑ Health hazards of the job (for example, silica dust created when mechanically cutting a block).
- ☑ Risks (such as a person breathing in the silica dust).
- ☑ Control measures needed to minimise the health risk to a safe level (such as wet cutting the slab and wearing a suitable respirator).

The regulations indicate the general principles of prevention that must be adhered to when making decisions on appropriate risk control measures. Some examples are shown below.

- ☑ Avoiding the risk (such as ordering pre-cut slabs or using a block splitter).
- ☑ Combating risks at source (such as suppressing dust by wet techniques rather than relying solely on PPE).
- ☑ Adapting to technical progress (such as buying new work equipment that is designed to produce a cleaner cut or which incorporates a dust extraction system).

The regulations impose the following legal duties on employers.

- ☑ Provide employees with comprehensive information of the risks identified by the assessment and the measures implemented to control those risks.
- ☑ Ensure that employees are capable in all respects of carrying out the work that they are required to do in a safe manner and without risks to health.
- ☑ Co-operate with other employers, where the employees of more than one employer share a workplace, in the interests of health and safety.

**! It should not be forgotten that a near-miss today could be an accident tomorrow. Managers have an important role to play in both proactive and reactive monitoring.**

### 1.2.2 The Reporting of Injuries, Diseases and Dangerous Occurrences Regulations (RIDDOR)

These regulations cover fatalities and specified injuries, incapacity to work for more than seven days, occupational diseases and dangerous occurrences.

The people covered are employers, employees, self-employed, trainees and members of the public injured on the premises. Specified injuries and reportable occupational diseases are shown in the table overleaf.

| Specified injuries | Occupational diseases |
|---|---|
| ▪ Fractures, other than to the fingers, thumbs and toes.<br>▪ Amputation of an arm, hand, finger, thumb, leg, foot or toe.<br>▪ Any injury likely to lead to permanent loss of sight or reduction in sight.<br>▪ Chemical or hot metal burn to the eye or any penetrating injury to the eye.<br>▪ Injury resulting from an electric shock or electrical burn leading to unconsciousness or requiring resuscitation or admittance to hospital for more than 24 hours.<br>▪ Any other injury arising from working in a confined space leading to hypothermia or heat-induced illness; or requiring resuscitation or admittance to hospital for more than 24 hours.<br>▪ Unconsciousness caused by asphyxia or head injury.<br>▪ Burn injury (including scalds) covering more than 10% of the body's surface or where it causes significant damage to the eyes, respiratory system or other vital organs.<br>▪ Crush injury to the head or torso, causing damage to the brain or internal organs.<br>▪ Scalping, requiring hospital treatment. | ▪ Carpal tunnel syndrome, where the person's work involves regular use of percussive or vibrating tools.<br>▪ Cramp of the hand or forearm, where the person's work involves prolonged periods of repetitive movement of the fingers, hand or arm.<br>▪ Occupational dermatitis, where the person's work involves significant or regular exposure to a known skin sensitiser or irritant.<br>▪ Hand-arm vibration syndrome, where the person's work involves regular use of percussive or vibrating tools, holding materials subject to percussive processes, or processes causing vibration.<br>▪ Occupational asthma, where the person's work involves significant or regular exposure to a known respiratory sensitiser.<br>▪ Tendonitis or tenosynovitis in the hand or forearm, where the person's work is physically demanding and involves frequent, repetitive movements.<br>▪ Any occupation cancer.<br>▪ Any disease attributed to occupational exposure to a biological agent. |

#### 1.2.2.1 Social Security Act and RIDDOR

- ☑ Every accident involving personal injury to an employee must be entered in the accident book by the employee or someone acting on behalf of the employee.
- ☑ The accident book must be easy to get to.
- ☑ An employer must investigate all accidents reported.

### 1.2.3 Occupational health

There are no specific legal requirements that state that employers must provide occupational health services. However, there is relevant legislation.

#### 1.2.3.1 Health and Safety at Work Act

Section 2 of this act places a duty on every employer to ensure, so far as is reasonably practicable, the health, safety and welfare at work of all employees.

#### 1.2.3.2 Management of Health and Safety at Work Regulations

Regulation 6 requires every employer to ensure that their employees are provided with the appropriate health surveillance, having regard for the risks to their health and safety, as identified by the risk assessment (required by Regulation 3).

Regulation 7 requires every employer to appoint one or more persons to assist in undertaking the measures needed to comply with the requirements and prohibitions imposed upon them by or under the relevant statutory provisions.

***Note:*** *self-employed employers are exempt from this requirement.*

#### 1.2.3.3 Control of Substances Hazardous to Health Regulations

Regulation 11 requires that, where it is appropriate for the protection of the health of their employees who are, or are liable to be, exposed to a substance hazardous to health, the employer shall ensure that such employees are under suitable health surveillance. (The regulation goes on to specify the circumstances in which health surveillance is appropriate and when health surveillance has to include medical surveillance under the supervision of an (HSE) employment medical adviser or an appointed (by HSE) doctor.)

#### 1.2.3.4 Other relevant legislation

- ☑ Control of Lead at Work Regulations.
- ☑ Ionising Radiations Regulations.
- ☑ Control of Asbestos at Work Regulations.

## 1.3 Health risk management

The management of health and safety at work principles apply to work-related health risks as well as safety, and require the following of employers.

- Identify the potential health risks (short, medium and long-term) arising from the work to be carried out.
- Investigate what can be done about them and decide how they are going to be addressed.
- Give staff information, instructions and training on the health risks and the control measures to be followed.
- Monitor work to make sure that the procedures are being implemented and are effective.
- Introduce health surveillance where necessary.
- Look for benefits and improvements.

One of the most difficult parts of managing health is understanding and assessing the impact an activity can have on an individual. When assessing risk it is therefore important to have an understanding of the short, medium and long-term health impacts.

It is not about assessing the health risk on a given day, but the cumulative effect over time. This difficulty is compounded by the transient nature of the workforce, which can move from employer to employer and from site to site. Regardless of this, the controls on any given day should minimise the risk of work-related ill health.

**Health, safety and the environment must be proactively managed, in the same way that a good supervisor and manager will manage people, quality and productivity.**

### Health and wellbeing practices on a major contractor's site

The following examples of health and wellbeing practices on a major contractor's site are part of their health risk management programme.

- Toolbox talks, linked to occupational health trends, identified from their web-based safety management system.
- Exercise equipment, including fitness challenges, available for use by their workers on site.
- Health checks and advice open to all workers on their sites.
- Advanced extrication equipment available on site.
- Regular health and wellbeing campaigns, many linked with trends identified from their web-based safety management system and national campaigns.

## 1.4 Risk assessments

**The Management of Health and Safety at Work Regulations** require that a risk assessment is carried out for every work task to be undertaken. This assessment is intended to identify any risks to health and safety that may be inherent in the task and detail any control measures necessary to reduce the risks to an acceptable level.

Risk assessments must be carried out by someone competent in the work activity being assessed to enable all the risks and hazards to health and/or safety to be identified. Risk assessments must be suitable and sufficient and take into account such factors as the complexity of the task and the competency of the person(s) undertaking the work.

The findings of the assessment must be recorded so that any person with an interest in its content can check that statutory requirements have been met and potential risks and problems identified. They should also be in a format so that the operative understands the risks and the necessary controls required to carry out the task safely. Written risk assessments may be stored in an electronic format, as long as copies can be retrieved and printed as requested.

Ideally, the risk assessment process would identify methods of working that would not put anyone's health or safety at risk. In practice, however, this is not always possible, although a good knowledge of the work techniques available to those involved in the installation process can significantly reduce the risks.

The following list, which is not exhaustive, highlights areas that should be considered when carrying out a risk assessment.

- The competence and experience of the person(s) who will carry out and/or supervise the work.
- The adoption of safe and healthy work procedures and practices, means of access and egress, availability of manufacturers' information and training that has been undertaken or is required.
- The physical environment in which the work is to be carried out (for example, an occupied domestic property).
- Fire precautions and procedures – availability of fire extinguishers, means of escape and alarms.
- The possible need for health surveillance through exposure to hazardous substances, noise or vibration.
- The avoidance of potentially harmful manual handling, but where manual handling is unavoidable, the use of correct lifting procedures.

- The control and suppression of harmful dust/fibres or other materials.
- The adoption of other control measures in preference to using personal protective equipment (PPE).
- Confined spaces (lack of ventilation, fire trap/risk).
- Structural stability of external walls.
- Falls from height.
- Possible asbestos/disturbed asbestos from fire curtains or lagging.
- Competence, knowledge, skills/training and experience.

**Do not rely on generic risk assessments. As a manager or supervisor it is your responsibility to make sure that your workplace is safe.**

The following health risks need to be considered.

- Personal injury caused by inadequate manual handling techniques (such as carrying materials and equipment into the premises).
- Respiratory problems, the potential for contracting serious respiratory diseases (such as occupational asthma) resulting from the inhalation of existing harmful substances or insulation materials in the course of insulation and cutting operations.
- Noise-induced hearing loss caused by failing to protect the ears when working in noisy environments.
- Dermatitis and other skin complaints, resulting from the failure to protect exposed skin from contact with adhesives, cement mixes, harmful dusts or persistently working with wet hands.
- Asbestos-related illness caused by contact with harmful asbestos materials.

**For further information refer to Chapter A05 Risk assessments and method statements.**

## 1.5 Safety policy or health and safety policy?

Under the requirements of the Health and Safety at Work Act 1974, all employers who have five or more employees must:

> **... prepare, and, as often as may be appropriate, revise a written statement of general policy with respect to the health and safety of employees, and the organisation and arrangements, for the time being in force, for carrying out that policy.**

It can be clearly seen that the requirement is for a written policy statement that must set out the employer's aims and objectives for improving work-related health as well as safety at work. It must also set out the organisation and arrangements currently in force for achieving those objectives. *Organisation* can be taken to mean people and their responsibilities; *arrangements* can be taken to mean systems and procedures.

In the past many companies have considered the safety issues within their safety policy document and have carefully devised safe working procedures. However, it is also important to look at the health hazards involved in the work that is carried out and to devise an equally efficient policy to deal with them.

With an accident on site, the injury or other effects are usually immediate and obvious.

The effects of exposure to most work-related ill health hazards are not immediate or not even felt (unlike an accident that causes injury). Workers may go home from work feeling more or less the same each day and are none the wiser. It can take many weeks, months or even years before symptoms of exposure become a problem to them and irreversible damage may well have occurred.

Work-related ill health can often result in employees being unable to work as hard or as efficiently as before and sometimes they may never work again. Having an effective health and safety policy will ensure consideration is given to managing work-related ill health issues as they are identified.

The health and safety policy should be reviewed if ill health issues become apparent.

## 1.6 Health surveillance

Health surveillance should be considered if there is a risk from noise, vibration, asbestos, lead, dust, fumes or other COSHH substances. It will help to confirm whether control measures identified in the risk assessment are sufficient.

There is a requirement for health surveillance in the following circumstances.

- When there is an identifiable disease or adverse health effect and evidence of a link with workplace exposure.
- If it is likely that a disease or health effect may occur.
- Where there are valid techniques for detecting early signs of the disease or health effect.
- If these techniques do not pose a risk to employees.

Depending on the findings of the risk assessment health surveillance could involve employees checking themselves for signs or symptoms of ill health (for example, looking for signs of dermatitis if working with cement). Employees will need to be trained on what to look out for and who to report any symptoms to. A responsible person can be trained to perform basic checks but, for more complicated risks, an occupational health nurse or doctor could be employed.

There are some high hazard substances and agents where the law requires that the health surveillance programme includes **statutory medical surveillance**. This involves a medical examination. It can also involve tests by a doctor (who must have been appointed by the HSE), who has the appropriate training and experience.

## 1.7 Health risks that can lead to ill health

Many employees leave the industry due to ill health. Often a person's illness is not traced back to the construction industry, so the actual incidence of ill health caused by work in the industry is probably more than the official figures tell us. Some typical illnesses are shown below.

- Stress.
- Skin cancers.
- Dermatitis.
- Respiratory diseases:
  - diffuse pleural thickening
  - asbestosis
  - mesothelioma
  - asthma
  - silicosis.
- Noise-induced hearing loss/deafness.
- Vibration white finger/hand-arm vibration syndrome (HAVS).
- Spine and back disorders.
- Upper and lower limb disorders.

### 1.7.1 Stress

In the workplace, stress is a growing problem but one that has not been widely recognised or generally accepted within the building and construction industry.

Stress can cause physical problems, such as:

- high blood pressure
- heart disease
- depression.

As well as behavioural problems, such as:

- anxiety
- irritability
- failure to cope as usual
- bad time-keeping.

Some of the causes of stress are shown below.

- Too much work or long working hours.
- Confusion as to what is expected.
- Uncertainty as to responsibilities.
- Conflict of interests.

Work-related factors that lead to stress can be managed but this will require appropriate training for management and operatives. If left unchecked, signs of stress may quickly emerge at the workplace and cause problems.

While a reasonable degree of challenge and stress is acceptable as providing an added incentive to work, excess stress among employees is counterproductive and should be avoided if employees are to work to their best potential.

**For further information refer to Chapter B03 Work-related stress.**

### 1.7.2 Radiation and sunshine

Whenever any work is being carried out that involves the use of ionising radiation, regulations require that competent persons ensure that the detailed requirements of the Ionising Radiation Regulations are properly complied with. This usually means the placing of signs and barriers on site and excluding all but authorised or classified employees from controlled areas. If all the signs and other procedures are obeyed, no-one should be at risk from ionising radiation.

One area of risk that does exist is the radiation from sunshine. The short-term dangers are blisters and sunburn while the well known long-term danger is skin cancer.

On site it is tempting for employees to take their shirts off on sunny days to get a suntan, but a suntan does not protect against the risk of skin cancer.

Advice from the HSE and other bodies is that workers on site should 'keep their shirts on'. Operatives should also adhere to contractors' site rules or their employer's policies, which cover appropriate clothing to be worn at work.

People most at risk include those with fair or freckled skin that does not tan easily or that burns before it tans. People with red or fair hair, light-coloured eyes, and those who have a large number of moles (more than 50), are also at a higher level of risk.

As well as protecting against the possibility of sunburn and the long-term risk of skin cancer, a shirt will also provide protection against minor cuts, abrasions and some of the chemicals or dusts that can be found on site.

## 1.7.3 Dermatitis

Occupational dermatitis causes more time to be lost in the building and construction industry than any other prescribed disease. Yet with proper attention to risk assessments, control measures and good working practices, it could be avoided.

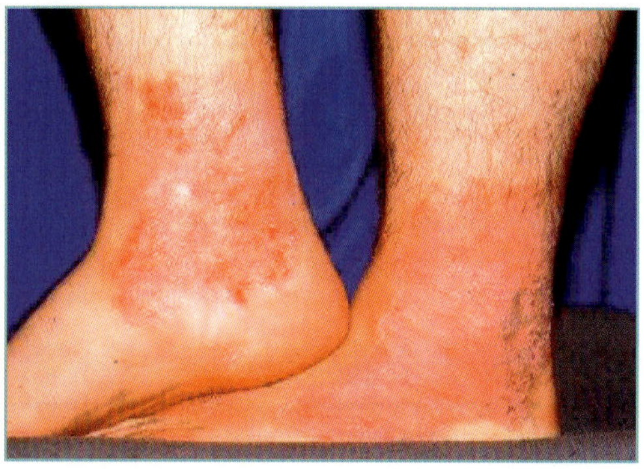

The prevention of dermatitis would save the industry and employers large amounts of money, and also assist in improved productivity on site, as well as improving conditions for the workers.

The agents that cause dermatitis can be divided into five classes.

- ☑ Mechanical factors (such as friction, pressure and trauma).
- ☑ Physical factors (including heat, cold, electricity, sunlight and radiation).
- ☑ The use of some chemicals.
- ☑ Contact with some plants and their products.
- ☑ Contact with biological agents, organisms, insects and mites.

There are two main types of dermatitis, commonly known as contact dermatitis and allergic dermatitis.

### 1.7.3.1 Contact dermatitis

This is sometimes also called irritant dermatitis. It is the commonest form of occupational dermatitis and results from repeated contact with any substance that irritates the skin. Such substances can include cement, lime, plaster, paint, solvents, adhesives, sawdust, oils, pitch, tar, fibreglass, white spirit, thinners and most acids and alkalis.

The effect of the substances is usually to cause the skin to dry out and crack due to the removal of the natural oils. Skin damaged in this way is very vulnerable to other infections.

### 1.7.3.2 Allergic dermatitis

This is sometimes also called sensitive dermatitis. It is an allergic reaction by the skin to a specific substance that the skin has been exposed to in the past, and which the skin has become especially sensitive to. Once a person's skin has become sensitised, any future exposure to the substance will cause an immediate skin reaction.

The main sensitising substances on site are cement, resins, glues, hardeners, hardwoods and chrome and nickel compounds. The allergic response is usually specific to an individual as opposed to affecting everyone, and can also appear suddenly after many years' exposure.

The prevention of dermatitis is basically one of good personal hygiene, good housekeeping, safe systems of work that avoid contact with substances that are known to cause dermatitis, and the use of PPE (as a control measure of the last resort), in the appropriate cases.

**For further information on radiation, sunshine and dermatitis refer to Chapter B08 Skin protection.**

## 1.7.4 Asbestos

More occupation-related deaths are caused by exposure to asbestos than by any other single substance used in the building and construction industry.

Information published by the HSE highlights the problem of asbestos, particularly for tradespeople (such as plumbers, painters, carpenters, electricians, shopfitters, maintenance workers, general operatives and demolition workers) who may come into contact with asbestos while carrying out their work.

It can be said that virtually every building constructed before the 1990s may contain some asbestos in one form or another, ranging from insulation on boilers, pipework or steelwork to gutters and floor tiles.

Even in domestic houses, asbestos can be found as soffits and insulation panels in airing cupboards, and so on. Exposure to asbestos can cause mesothelioma, (which is always fatal), lung cancer (almost always fatal), asbestosis (not always fatal but it can be very debilitating) and diffuse pleural thickening (not fatal). There have been a number of successful civil court cases for damages and compensation brought by employees against their employers and, as a result, substantial awards have been made against employers.

**For further information refer to Chapter B09 Asbestos.**

**Asbestos waste must carry a warning label. The label can also be used to identify and manage known in-situ asbestos.**

## 1.7.5 Respiratory problems

### 1.7.5.1 Dust

Virtually all types of dust are hazardous to health and there are is no such thing as general dust. The effect dust has depends upon what it is made of, the airborne concentration levels and length of time that it is breathed in.

When dust is present in the air, equal to or greater than:

- ☑ ten milligrams per cubic metre (10 mg/m$^3$) of inhalable dust
- ☑ four milligrams per cubic metre (4 mg/m$^3$) of respirable dust

as a time weighted average over an eight hour period it becomes a substance hazardous to health in accordance with the COSHH Regulations.

Good occupational hygiene practice recommends that these levels are the highest concentrations of dust that employees should be exposed to. These are known as workplace exposure limits (WELs). For example, the WEL for respirable crystalline silica is 0.1 mg.m$^{-3}$ and hardwood dust is 5 mg.m$^{-3}$.

Some construction work (such as the examples shown below) can cause respiratory disease.

- ☑ Cutting kerbs, slabs, bricks, blocks.
- ☑ Stone-masonry.
- ☑ Scabbling, surface grinding and grit blasting.
- ☑ Tunnelling.
- ☑ Crushing and screening demolition material.
- ☑ Clearing and removing rubble or sweeping up general dust.
- ☑ Chasing out mortar before repointing or chasing walls.
- ☑ Laying epoxy floors.
- ☑ Carpentry (softwood, hardwood, MDF, glues).
- ☑ Painting and decoration (solvents, rubbing down).
- ☑ Mixing up and rubbing down plaster.

The inhalation of any dust will eventually cause respiratory problems, including or contributing to such conditions as asthma, bronchitis, pneumoconiosis and certain types of lung cancer. Some dusts cause an allergic reaction causing breathing problems immediately after a dust is breathed in. As well as presenting a health hazard, many airborne dust clouds are also flammable or explosive.

Whenever practicable, the generation of dust should be avoided and, where it cannot be avoided, it should be controlled by ventilation or extraction. The use of PPE by employees must be regarded as the very last resort when all other methods of control have been examined and found not to be practicable.

### 1.7.5.2 Fumes, including solvent fumes

The vapour given off by many substances has the potential to cause respiratory illness or other symptoms of ill health if not adequately controlled. Other symptoms include headaches, coughing, feeling sick, feeling light-headed, shortness of breath or feverishness.

As well as being inhaled and causing direct problems in the lungs, many fumes can be absorbed into the bloodstream and bring about complications in other parts of the body.

An example of this type of response is cancer of the bladder, which can be caused by inhaling certain aniline fumes (a chemical made for use in textile dyes).

Below are some potential sources of hazardous fumes, which may be inhaled if control measures are not taken.

- Solvent-based adhesives, spirit-based or solvent-based paints.
- Welding, especially welding galvanised metals.
- Oxyacetylene cutting.
- Engine exhausts.

If the generation or release of the fumes cannot be avoided, for example by using a water-based solvent or paint instead, then adequate natural or mechanical ventilation should be used. The use of PPE for employees must be regarded as the last resort.

**For further information refer to Chapter B10 Dust and fumes.**

## 1.7.6 Noise

Regulations exist on the control of noise at work because of the unacceptable damage that noise can cause to the health of employees. The damage can range from temporary hearing loss to total deafness. As well as hearing problems, excess noise is also known to cause the following.

- Annoyance and irritation.
- Loss of concentration.
- Reduced efficiency.
- Fatigue.
- Increased accident risk.
- Masking of other warning signals.

On site, the failure of an employee to understand instructions that have been given, or to hear a warning signal, can have serious consequences, both for them and for the employer.

**For further information refer to Chapter B13 Noise.**

**Employers have a duty to reduce the risk of damage to employees' hearing to the lowest level that is reasonably practicable.**

## 1.7.7 Vibration

A considerable number of the tools and other equipment that are currently used in the building and construction industry have a rotary or percussive action and so can cause **hand-arm vibration**. This is also known as vibration white finger. This even applies to some widely used small tools (such as hand drills with a hammer action). Other examples of tools that create vibration include pneumatic breakers, vibrating pokers, vibrating rollers, plate compactors and scabbling machines.

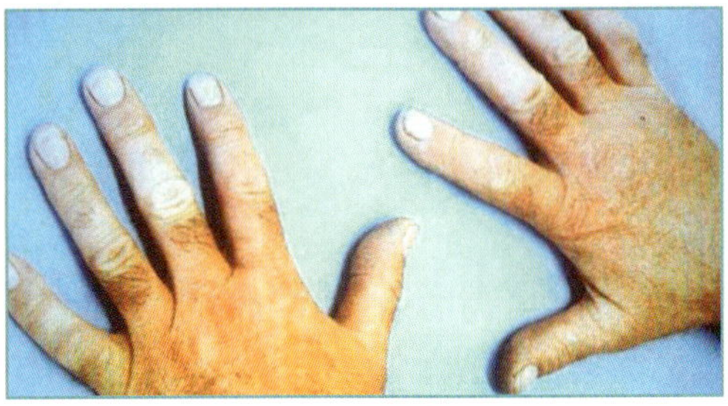

*Vibration white finger*

The most commonly caused ill health effect is vibration white finger, where the effect of the vibration damages the nerves and blood vessels in the fingers. The fingers become white and there is a loss of feeling that prevents smaller tools from being held or used properly.

Hand-arm vibration is also known to cause other vascular, neurological and muscular damage in the hands, wrists, elbows and shoulders.

**Whole-body vibration**, which is caused by the transmission of vibration to the body from sources such as moving plant or vehicles, can bring about long-term back pain.

The effects of both hand-arm vibration and whole-body vibration can be reduced by carrying out risk assessments, appropriate purchasing policies, the correct use of the equipment and the use of the appropriate anti-vibration devices (such as special handles or grips).

**For further information refer to Chapter B14 Vibration.**

## 1.7.8 Repetitive strain injury

The Chartered Society of Physiotherapy (CSP) has indicated that there has been a sharp rise in the number of cases of repetitive strain injury (RSI) in the workforce in general. The people in construction who are most likely to experience RSI are plumbers, carpenters, painters and plant operators.

Methods by which workers can limit the potential for RSI are shown below.

- ✓ Avoiding long periods of repetitive tasks (job rotation).
- ✓ Alternating the use of the hands (picking up left then right-handed).
- ✓ Taking more short breaks rather than one long break.
- ✓ Wearing looser clothing to increase ease of movement.
- ✓ Keeping warm (cold muscles don't expand properly).
- ✓ Not overstretching (move closer to the task).
- ✓ Reporting pain or other symptoms immediately – RSI is easier to treat in the early stages.

Employers can make a big difference to the health of their workers, which will have business benefits, by taking the following actions.

- ✓ Assessing each job for the potential for RSI.
- ✓ Encouraging early reporting.
- ✓ Allowing workers to organise their work and take breaks as necessary.

## 1.7.9 Carpal tunnel syndrome

Carpal tunnel syndrome causes pain, numbness and a burning or tingling sensation in the hands and fingers. The carpal tunnel runs from the base of the wrist to the lower palm. Several tendons that help the fingers to move pass through the carpal tunnel, as does the median nerve. The median nerve controls the sensation and movement of the hand. When the median nerve becomes compressed, this can disrupt the nerve signals and affect your sense of touch and hand movements. The median nerve can become compressed if the tendons that run through the carpal tunnel are swollen and inflammed.

## 1.7.10 Manual handling

Nearly a quarter of all accidents reported to the HSE involve manual handling in some form. Yet, if the guidance offered in the Manual Handling Operations Regulations had been followed, most if not all of the accidents could have been prevented.

More often than not, manual handling is not adequately assessed or planned, relying instead on the workers making do with the equipment to hand or providing their own solutions, thus increasing the risk of injury and the knock-on effects of this.

Giving employees the appropriate training in the correct manual handling techniques and the use of suitable mechanical lifting aids is highly cost effective.

Adequate supervision is necessary to ensure that employees then use the proper equipment and techniques and do not take shortcuts. This will reduce accidents, the amount of time lost on site, and the disruption to work that is caused when something goes wrong.

The part of the body most vulnerable if bad manual handling techniques are used is the back, particularly the lower back. Once it has been damaged, it is usually weakened for the rest of a person's life.

All the other major joints and muscle groups can also be easily damaged if the correct manual handling techniques are not used.

The consequences of an injury due to bad manual handling, or a musculoskeletal injury or illness as they are often called, can be a long-term or permanent inability to work. The cost to the employer is reduced productivity and having to find others to carry out the work.

**For further information refer to Chapter B15 Manual handling.**

### 1.7.11 Bird and bat droppings

The presence of large populations of roosting birds, particularly pigeons, or a bat colony, can present significant risks to health if their droppings are disturbed. This has obvious implications for some types of construction work and preliminary work such as surveys.

The main hazard is the inhalation of fungus spores that become airborne as a result of disturbance of the droppings. However, skin contact with pigeon droppings has been known to cause an acne-like skin condition and ulcers.

The HSE has taken enforcement action against companies who fail to undertake an adequate risk assessment and protect employees against the associated risks of working with bird droppings.

**For further information refer to Chapter B07 Control of substances hazardous to health.**

### 1.7.12 Leptospirosis (Weil's disease)

When working near to water or on sites that are otherwise wet, consideration must be given to the health implications associated with the presence of rats.

Leptospirosis is an occupational hazard for anyone working near water, damp areas or anywhere else where rats might be present. It is a disease caused by bacteria that is present mainly in the urine of infected rats and is therefore also in the water where they live. The bacteria thrives in damp conditions, of riverbanks or streams, and can enter the body through unprotected cuts and scratches, by swallowing infected water and through the lining of the nose.

If anyone thinks they may have come into contact with the disease, they should be aware that the early symptoms closely resemble the symptoms of influenza, namely fever, headache and chill.

Later symptoms include the following.

- Tightening of the skin.
- A yellowing of the skin (similar to jaundice).
- Internal bleeding.

WARNING!
LEPTOSPIROSIS
HEALTH HAZARD
FRESH WATER STREAMS AND MUD POSSIBLY POLLUTED WITH BACTERIA
EXERCISE CAUTION

It is essential that anyone who is at risk, and who becomes unwell with flu-like symptoms, should visit their doctor, describe where they have been working and say that they are at risk from leptospirosis. Persons regularly at risk (for example, canal or sewage workers) should carry a card explaining their occupation and the occupational hazard of leptospirosis.

The following personal precautions should be taken.

- Discouraging the presence of rats on site (do not leave food lying around and do not throw away food scraps).
- Not handling the carcasses of dead rats.
- Avoiding inadvertent entry or immersion in water that could be infected: if this happens and you think that you may be infected, particularly if you swallowed any water, see a doctor as a matter of urgency.
- Wearing appropriate PPE.
- Prior to entering the work area, washing any cuts or grazes in clean water, applying antiseptic to the wound, then covering with gauze, a waterproof dressing and PPE as necessary.
- Upon completion of work, washing hands, forearms and all other exposed areas of skin thoroughly, and removing any wet protective clothing as soon as possible to dry it.
- Avoiding rubbing your nose, mouth or eyes with your hands during work.
- Not smoking, eating or drinking without first washing your hands.

Leptospirosis can be fatal, typically within four to six weeks, if the early symptoms are not recognised and treated.

Another form of leptospirosis can be caught from the urine of infected dairy cattle. Anyone involved in construction work on dairy farms must be aware of this hazard.

Further advice on leptospirosis can be obtained from the Employment Medical Advisory Service of the HSE or by contacting any local office of the HSE.

**For further information refer to Chapter B02 Welfare facilities.**

## 1.7.13 Needlestick injuries

A needlestick injury is an accidental puncture of the skin by a hypodermic needle.

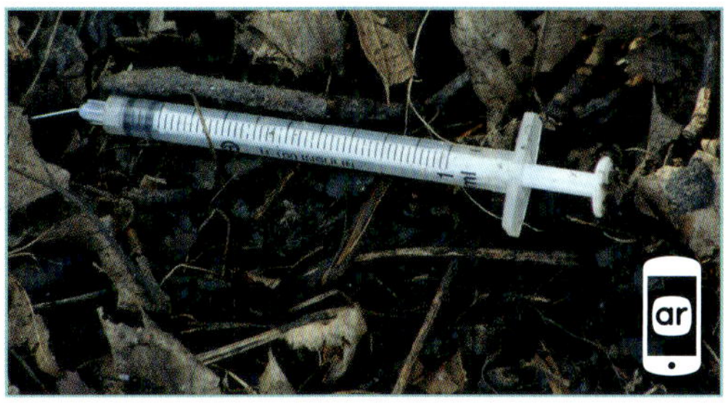

It is a sad fact that the drug culture affects the construction industry as much as other industrial sectors. The abuse of both legal and illegal drugs brings with it the risk of discovering discarded hypodermic syringes or discarded needles.

Employees in the refurbishment sector of the industry are probably at greatest risk, especially if the property is derelict or has been occupied by squatters. However, any work in occupied or previously occupied premises carries with it some risk of finding needles that have been randomly discarded or hidden away in areas where they are difficult to see, until it is too late.

If not handled in a safe manner, discarded needles can pose serious health risks to anyone whose skin is accidentally pricked. Blood on a needle could be infected with a hepatitis or HIV virus.

As part of site induction in the appropriate circumstances, employees should be told to assume that any needle they find has been used by a drug user and is potentially contaminated by infected blood.

Company and site procedures should cover the actions that employees and supervisors should take whenever discarded needles are found. The removal and disposal of such items should be properly covered. Advice may be sought from the site nurse (if there is one) or the Local Authority Environmental Health Department. The local police may also offer guidance.

Generally, employees should be clearly told not to touch or move any needles or hypodermic syringes they find, but to ask a responsible person to guard it whilst reporting the matter to their supervisor.

If a needle or syringe **must** be moved then some examples of suitable instructions to employees are shown below.

- ☑ If possible, use a pair of pliers to pick it up.
- ☑ Carry it with the needle pointing downwards.
- ☑ Do **not** wrap it in paper or put it into a household waste bin.
- ☑ If available, place it in a sharps bin, or otherwise a clear glass bottle or jar.
- ☑ Place the sharps bin, bottle or jar in a secure location.
- ☑ Carefully follow site or company procedures regarding disposal.
- ☑ Wash hands thoroughly.

Employees should not panic if a needle punctures their skin. Encourage the wound to bleed, but **do not suck the wound**. Wash the site of the injury thoroughly with soap and water at the first opportunity and obtain medical assistance as soon as possible, from either the site nurse or the nearest hospital with an Accident and Emergency Department. If it is safe to do so, take the syringe or needle with you. Inform the employer so it can be recorded in the accident book and the correct preventative action can be taken to prevent reoccurrence.

If dealt with properly and promptly, the risks of a resulting health problem are small.

**For further information refer to Chapter B07 Control of substances hazardous to health.**

## 1.7.14 Smoking

Smoking is now prohibited in all enclosed workplaces (such as site cabins, canteens and company premises). Different legislation applies to England, Wales, Scotland and Northern Ireland.

Although smoking is totally prohibited on many sites, employers or the person in control of a site may make provision for smoking in areas that are not enclosed or substantially enclosed, as long as non-smokers are not exposed to tobacco smoke.

**For further information refer to Chapter B02 Welfare facilities.**

## 1.7.15 Contaminated ground

As the drive continues to develop brownfield sites, the magnitude of the health hazard arising from the disturbance of contaminated ground is almost certain to increase.

The disturbance of contaminated ground can release hazardous fibres (such as asbestos), hazardous gases or fumes and even hazardous micro-organisms (such as anthrax spores).

Where ground that has been previously used is to be disturbed, a risk assessment must be carried out to determine whether there will be residual risks to health.

The findings of a thorough assessment of the risks will determine exactly what the hazards are and how the risks can be eliminated or controlled to an acceptable level. Given the wide range of contaminants possible, the potential for ill health may result from inhalation, ingestion or skin contact with the hazardous substance.

**For further information refer to Chapter E08 Contaminated land.**

## 1.8 Occupational health support services

### 1.8.1 Employment Medical Advisory Service

The Employment Medical Advisory Service (EMAS) is an integral part of the HSE that is staffed by specialist occupational health professionals (both doctors and nurses).

In many ways, the functions of EMAS are similar to those of the HSE. EMAS exists to offer advice to employers and employees and take enforcement action where necessary on workplace health issues.

EMAS doctors are medical inspectors and EMAS nurses are occupational health inspectors. Both have the same powers as other HSE inspectors under The Health and Safety at Work Act 1974, where the HSE is the enforcing authority.

The functions of EMAS staff are shown below.

- Investigate complaints and concerns of ill health from employers, employees, trade unions, members of the public and other health care professionals.
- Investigate ill health reports received from employers under RIDDOR.
- Help other HSE inspectors and Local Authorities to make sure that other people comply with health and safety law.
- Provide advice in the workplace to employers, employees and trade unions.
- Provide expert advice to doctors and nurses in general health care and occupational health.
- Provide support for the HSE's occupational health campaigns.

**EMAS staff are based in some but not all HSE offices. Check the HSE website for your local contact.**

### 1.8.2 Scottish Centre for Healthy Working Lives

The Healthy Working Lives website offers employers and workers free confidential advice to help improve health and safety and the wellbeing of everyone at work. They offer free events throughout Scotland.

**Full details are available on the Healthy Working Lives website.**

### 1.8.3 Constructing Better Health

Constructing Better Health (CBH) is a not for profit, although not free, organisation, with a remit to deliver the construction industry's occupational health scheme. As such, CBH has developed occupational health standards and other resources to assist employers in managing occupational health on site.

**Further details can be obtained on the Constructing Better Health website.**

### 1.8.4 Employees returning from sickness absence

In April 2010 fit notes came into force, replacing the old sick-note system. The new system requires general practitioners to categorise patients as *fit for work*, or *may be fit for work*.

The purpose of the new system is to encourage communication between an employee who is categorised as *may be fit for work* and their doctor and employer, to establish what work the employee might be able to do if returning to work. Fit notes are designed to encourage a controlled return to work, with compromises being made on both sides, as necessary, particularly after prolonged periods of sickness absence. Alternative working hours, adaptations to the workplace and alternative types of work are options available to the employer.

However, ultimately it is the employer's decision regarding what course of action to take in these circumstances. If poor decisions are made and the employee's health deteriorates as a consequence, the employer may be challenged to explain why they took the decisions they did.

# 02
# Welfare facilities

**Contents**



## Supporting information

**GT 700 Toolbox talks**

## Overview

**The availability of welfare facilities, their location on site and regular maintenance must be considered at the planning and preparation stages of every construction project, before construction work (including demolition) starts.**

**This chapter describes the minimum welfare facilities that should be provided or made available during all types of construction activity to comply with the Construction (Design and Management) Regulations.**

## 2.1 Introduction

Construction site workers need adequate toilet and washing facilities, a place to warm up and eat their food and somewhere to store clothing. However, these basic requirements are often neglected. Good facilities can have a positive benefit on health and wellbeing and can help prevent dermatitis.

**Details of the minimum welfare facilities required on all construction sites can be found within Schedule 2 of the CDM Regulations. A summary has been provided at Appendix A.**

### 2.1.1 Welfare requirements

Welfare facilities in general should be kept clean, adequately lit, ventilated as necessary and kept in a good state of repair.

Washing facilities must include the following.

- ☑ A supply of hot (or warm) and cold water, ideally from a running supply.
- ☑ Soap or other cleansers.
- ☑ Towels or another means of drying.
- ☑ Separate facilities for men and women except where they:
  - are in a separate room that can be locked from the inside
  - can only be used by one person at a time
  - are only used for washing the hands, forearms and face.

The provision of toilets must include separate facilities for men and women, except where each toilet is in a separate room that can be locked from the inside.

### 2.1.2 Induction on site

During the site induction the following information must be explained.

- ☑ The location of the welfare facilities.
- ☑ If appropriate, the opening hours of site canteens.
- ☑ Responsibilities for the cleaning and maintenance of the facilities.
- ☑ The provision of barrier creams and rehydrating lotions.
- ☑ The need for good personal hygiene.
- ☑ The company policy regarding damage and graffiti.
- ☑ The location of facilities for men and women.
- ☑ The arrangements (if any) made for smokers.

### 2.1.3 Smoking

Smoking in enclosed and substantially enclosed workplaces is now banned by different legislation in England and Wales, Scotland and Northern Ireland.

Broadly, the differing legislation has similar aims in that:

- ☑ the act of smoking in smoke-free premises is an offence
- ☑ the act of **permitting** smoking in smoke-free premises (or a smoke-free vehicle) is an offence
- ☑ generally, vehicles used for work must be smoke-free
- ☑ smoke-free premises must have an official no smoking sign, with the approved text prominently displayed at each entrance
- ☑ smoke-free vehicles must have at least one official no smoking sign prominently displayed.

## 2.2 Important points

- ☑ Suitable and sufficient sanitary conveniences (toilets) must be provided or made available at easy to access places.
- ☑ Suitable and sufficient washing facilities, including showers if required, must be provided or made available at easy to access places.
- ☑ An adequate supply of drinking water, conspicuously marked with the appropriate sign, should be provided or made available at easy to access places.
- ☑ Suitable facilities must be provided for the accommodation of clothing not worn at work and for clothing worn at work but not taken home. Such facilities shall include provisions for drying clothing when it gets wet.
- ☑ Facilities must be provided to enable people to change clothing where a person has to wear special clothing for special work and cannot change elsewhere. The facilities shall be separate for men and women, where necessary, for reasons of privacy.
- ☑ Suitable and sufficient facilities for rest (such as a site canteen) must be made available at easy to access places, including:
  - sufficient tables and chairs (with backs)
  - suitable arrangements to protect non-smokers from discomfort caused by tobacco smoke
  - where necessary, suitable facilities for pregnant women and nursing mothers
  - a means for boiling water and suitable arrangements to ensure that meals can be prepared and eaten.

## 2.3 Welfare facilities at fixed construction sites

If you have overall control of the site, you are responsible for making sure that legal requirements for welfare are met for the site. In practice, this means the principal contractor or other person in control of the site will often either provide or arrange for common facilities for everyone.

If work is carried out in occupied premises (for example, offices, factories, and so on) it may be possible to make arrangements with the client to use the permanent facilities at the premises.

### 2.3.1 Planning

- ☑ Make sure welfare arrangements are clearly addressed in the health and safety plan.
- ☑ Consider welfare facilities, their location on site and regular maintenance during the planning and preparation stage of any project in accordance with CDM Regulations.
- ☑ Arrange for equipment to be available, provided, sited and connected to services before construction work (including demolition) starts or when additional numbers of workers start on site.
- ☑ Make sure the facilities reflect the site size, nature of the work, and numbers of people who will use them. If a large number of people are working on site or the work being carried out is particularly dirty or involves a health risk (for example, pouring concrete) you will need more washing facilities, which may include showers, toilets, and so on.

### 2.3.2 Toilets

- ☑ Make sure that an adequate number of toilets are provided at all times.
- ☑ Men and women may use the same toilet, provided it is in a lockable room and partitioned from any urinals that may also have been provided, otherwise separate toilets will be required.
- ☑ Wherever possible connect toilets to a mains drainage system and ensure they are water flushing. If you cannot do this, use facilities with built in supply and drainage tanks.
- ☑ Only use chemical toilets as a short-term measure. When they are used, it is important that they are of robust construction, regularly emptied and maintained. Access will need to be provided and kept for emptying and maintaining chemical toilets. Suppliers of portable facilities will be able to advise you.
- ☑ Make sure that an adequate supply of toilet paper is always available.
- ☑ Sanitary waste disposal should be provided in facilities used by female workers.

## 2.3.3 Drinking water

- ☑ Ensure that there is a supply of drinking water. Whenever possible it should be supplied direct from the mains; otherwise use bottles or tanks of water. If water is stored, protect it from possible contamination and make sure it is changed often enough to prevent it from becoming stale or contaminated.
- ☑ Clearly mark the drinking water supply to prevent it being confused with water that is not fit to drink or hazardous liquids.
- ☑ Provide cups or other drinking vessels at the water tap, unless the water is supplied in an upward jet that can be drunk easily (such as a drinking fountain).

## 2.3.4 Washing facilities

- ☑ Put washing facilities next to both toilets and changing areas and make sure they include:
  - basin(s) or sink(s) large enough for people to wash their face, hands and forearms
  - a supply of hot (or warm) and cold water running water
  - soap and towels (either cloth or paper) or dryers.
- ☑ If mains water is not available, use clean water supplied from a tank.
- ☑ You may need more washing facilities, including showers, where the work is particularly dirty or when workers are exposed to especially hazardous substances (such as development of contaminated land, or demolition of old industrial buildings that are contaminated with toxic substances). These will need to be separate from the main facilities.
- ☑ Men and women can share basins used for washing hands, face and arms.
- ☑ A shower may be used by both men and women as long as it is in a separate, lockable room that can be used by one person at a time.

## 2.3.5 Storing and changing clothing

- ☑ Every site should have arrangements for storing:
  - clothing not worn on site (such as jackets and training shoes)
  - protective clothing needed for site work (such as wellington boots, overalls and reflective jackets).
- ☑ Separate lockers might be needed, although on smaller sites the site office may be a suitable storage area, provided it is kept secure.
- ☑ Where there is a risk of protective site clothing contaminating everyday clothing, store items separately.
- ☑ Men and women should be able to change separately.
- ☑ Make sure that wet site clothing can be dried.
- ☑ Many fires have been caused by placing too much clothing to dry on electrical heaters, making the heater overheat. If electrical heaters are used, ensure they are properly ventilated and, if possible, fitted with a high temperature cut-out device.

## 2.3.6 Rest facilities

- ☑ Provide facilities for taking breaks and meal breaks. The facilities should provide shelter from the wind and rain, be heated as necessary and contain:
  - tables and chairs (with backs)
  - a kettle or urn for boiling water
  - a means for warming up food (for example, a gas or electrical heating ring, or microwave oven).
- ☑ On small sites, the site office or hut can make a suitable rest area, especially if it is one of the common portable units.
- ☑ Do not store plant, equipment or materials in rest areas.

### 2.3.7 Heating

Rest facilities will normally require heating. Using properly maintained electrical equipment can eliminate the risks associated with LPG heaters. Inadequately ventilated LPG cookers and heaters can produce carbon monoxide, with potentially fatal results. Flammable gas may escape from leaking cylinders that have not been properly turned off. If LPG is used take the following actions to reduce the risks.

- ☑ Use and store the cylinders in safe, well-ventilated places outside the accommodation (including overnight) or in purpose-built ventilated storage areas.
- ☑ Ensure that the appliances have been properly installed, checked and maintained by a competent person.
- ☑ Provide adequate combustion ventilation (fixed grilles at high and low level).
- ☑ Check that the ventilation provided is not blocked (for example, fixed grilles blocked by newspaper or rags in cold weather to stop draughts).
- ☑ Check that cylinders are properly turned off when not in use.
- ☑ Use wall or ceiling-mounted carbon monoxide detectors.

### 2.3.8 First-aid rooms

On a large building or construction site, a first-aid room, suitably staffed and equipped, should be provided. The need for such a room cannot be decided purely on the numbers of persons employed, but should be assessed on the type of work being carried out and whether a hospital or other emergency facilities are close to hand.

The first-aid room will normally be under the control of the first aider who should be nearby or on call, with access to the room when employees are at work. The name of this person should be displayed, together with the names and locations of all other first aiders and appointed persons. On some larger sites, the first-aid room will be staffed by a qualified nurse.

The room should be clearly identified, available at all times and used only for rendering first aid. It should be of sufficient size to contain a couch with adequate space around it to allow people to work, and provided with an access door to allow the passage of a stretcher or other carrying equipment. Pillows and blankets should be provided and be frequently cleaned.

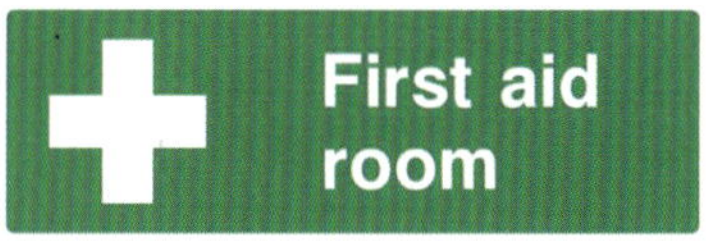


The room itself should be cleaned each working day, have smooth-topped, impermeable working surfaces and provision for privacy and refuse disposal.

Heating, lighting and ventilation should be effective. In addition to the first-aid materials that should be stored in a suitable cabinet, the following items should also be provided.

- ☑ A sink with running hot (or warm) and cold water.
- ☑ Drinking water.
- ☑ Soap, nail brush and paper towels.
- ☑ Clean garments for use by first-aid personnel.
- ☑ A suitable container for disposal of clinical waste (yellow bags).

In first-aid rooms that are supervised by the site nurse, other items may be provided on their advice. The room should have a telephone, where possible, and a siren or klaxon to alert personnel on call.

If the first-aid room cannot be reserved exclusively for first aid, employers need to make sure that the first-aid facilities can be quickly made available, if necessary.

Consideration should be given as to whether:

- ☑ the furnishings and equipment can be moved easily and quickly
- ☑ the activities carried out in the room can be stopped immediately
- ☑ there is a storage room for first-aid equipment.

**For further information on first-aid requirements refer to Chapter B05.**

## 2.4 Welfare facilities at transient construction sites

For the purpose of this chapter, a transient construction site is either where short duration work (up to a week) is carried out at one or many locations, or is of a longer duration carried out while moving over a continuous geographical area (such as major roadworks, cable laying contracts, and so on).

In such cases, it may be appropriate to make arrangements to use facilities provided by the owner of existing premises in which the work is being done, local public facilities or the facilities of local businesses.

Clear agreement should be made with the provider of the facilities; it should not be assumed that local commercial premises can be used without their agreement.

Facilities must be easy to get to at the worksite, open at all relevant times, be at no cost to the workers, be of an acceptable standard in terms of cleanliness and have hand-washing facilities.

Workers need to be made aware of the arrangements to use them and be informed of their location.

When planning welfare provision, consider the following.

- The nature of the work to be carried out and the health risks associated with it. For example, consider the provision of showers if the project involves hazardous substances or very dirty work (such as sewer maintenance, dusty demolition work, work with contaminated land or concrete pouring).
- The distance workers will have to travel to the welfare facilities.
- The duration of the work and number of different locations.
- The numbers of people who will use them.
- The cleaning and maintenance of the welfare facilities.
- Whether they need to be relocated during the construction phase.

You need to plan how welfare units will be moved from delivery vehicles into position. It is preferable to mechanically move these units; if manual handling cannot be avoided then you should manage the risk effectively. Your plans should cover safe lifting practices and ensure proper protection of workers from falls from vehicles or portable units. You should site welfare units and manage traffic effectively to ensure adequate segregation of pedestrians and vehicles.

**For further information on provision of welfare facilities at both fixed and transient construction sites refer to the HSE website.**

## 2.4.1 Use of private and public facilities

Where the construction activity is a long way from central facilities, use of facilities in private premises (such as in cafes) is not considered suitable as permanent alternative arrangements. The use of private facilities may be acceptable in limited circumstances (for example, where there is no alternative and the work is of no more than a week's duration). Permission, preferably in writing, should be obtained from the proprietor in advance of the work starting.

Use of public toilets is acceptable only where it is impractical to return to facilities provided at the main base, or to use a portable installation at the worksite.

Where public or private toilets are used they need to be easy to get to at the worksite, open at all relevant times, be at no cost to the employee, be of an acceptable standard in terms of cleanliness and have hand-washing facilities. Workers need to be made aware of the arrangements to use them and be informed of their location in advance of the work starting.

## 2.4.2 Toilets

So far as is reasonably practicable you need to provide flushing toilets and running water, connected to mains water and drainage systems. If this is not possible, facilities with a built-in water supply and drainage tanks should be used. Portable chemical toilets are acceptable only if it is not reasonably practicable to make other adequate provision.

Portable toilets have a limited capacity and will need emptying. The number of portable toilets needed depends on the number of persons and the frequency of emptying.

## 2.4.3 Drinking water

There is no differential to the requirements for a fixed construction site. *(Refer to 2.3.3 Drinking water.)*

### 2.4.4 Washing facilities

There is no differential to the requirements for a fixed construction site. *(Refer to 2.3.4 Washing facilities.)*

### 2.4.5 Heating

There is no differential to the requirements for a fixed construction site. *(Refer to 2.3.7 Heating.)*

## 2.5 Food safety legislation

Food safety legislation only applies in circumstances where food is prepared, or handled, to be eaten by others. Getting food hygiene wrong can have severe implications for other people.

- ☑ Food hygiene is usually monitored by Local Authority environmental health officers (EHO), who:
  - have similar rights of entry to site as HSE inspectors
  - can issue hygiene improvement and hygiene emergency prohibition notices and instigate prosecutions
  - can close down unsatisfactory catering facilities.
- ☑ Anyone who handles food for consumption by others:
  - must have training in basic food handling techniques
  - must report to their supervisor details of any illness that they may be suffering from
  - may have to be suspended from work if they contract an infectious illness.
- ☑ Premises in which food is handled, prepared and served must conform to certain standards of construction and cleanliness.
- ☑ Food poisoning is caused by bacteria (germs or bugs) that have lain dormant in most uncooked or unprepared foods, whether meat, fish, poultry or some vegetables. It keeps people off work through sickness, just as accidents do.
- ☑ Complying with food safety legislation, and applying appropriate hygiene standards on site, are essential because of the potential for:
  - time lost through sickness absence
  - lost production
  - enforcement action (such as hygiene improvement notices, hygiene emergency prohibition notices and even prosecution by Local Authorities) when your food handling does not come up to the required standard.

### 2.5.1 Food Safety Act

The Food Safety Act provides the framework for all food legislation in Great Britain. Similar legislation applies in Northern Ireland. The Food Safety Act and regulations apply to all workplaces. This includes building or construction sites where food or drink is supplied, provided or sold by you or anyone else for the benefit of employees and others working on site.

- ☑ Toilets adjacent to food rooms must be separated by a lobby. A notice stating 'Now wash your hands' must be displayed.
- ☑ Employees in food rooms must not smoke. A notice must be displayed to that effect.
- ☑ Checks and inspections of equipment and staff training should be recorded.
- ☑ Certificates of staff training in food hygiene and handling must be displayed.
- ☑ A building or construction site that has a canteen or mess room where food is stored, sold, supplied or provided (whether for profit or not) is classified as a **business** and the rooms are classified as **premises** for the purposes of the Act.
- ☑ All food businesses that prepare, cook or sell food for the benefit of others must be registered with the Local Authority. This involves completing the appropriate form available from the Environmental Health Department of that authority. (Registration is only applicable if food is handled on five days in five consecutive weeks. If in doubt, contact the Local Authority.) There should be no charge for registration.

#### Food Safety Act

**Food** – food or drink of any description, or any of the ingredients used in the preparation of food.

**Food room** – any room in which a person is involved in the handling of food, including a servery or counter.

### 2.5.2 Food Safety and Hygiene (England) Regulations

The regulations do not apply to sites where employees only consume their own food and drink. Nevertheless, in accordance with the Health and Safety at Work Act, and the Construction (Design and Management) Regulations, these areas must be kept in good order and in a reasonable state of cleanliness.

Food safety legislation is enforced by the Environmental Health Department of the Local Authority, and any doubt regarding the application of the regulations should be referred to the EHO.

Food inspectors, usually EHOs, may visit the site, with or without prior notice, on either a one-off or regular basis.

Every facility and assistance must be afforded to the inspecting officers. Obstruction in any form is an offence.

**These regulations implement European Community Regulations with respect to food hygiene. The relevant Community Regulations are listed in Schedules 1 and 2 of the Hygiene Regulations.**

The European Community Regulations set out basic hygiene principles. They focus on how to identify and control food safety risks at each stage of the process of preparing and selling food. Controls do not have to be complex; a simple example would be the use of refrigeration to prevent the growth of harmful bacteria on perishable, ready-to-eat foods.

The regulations require all food businesses to have a written food safety management system based on the principles of Hazard Analysis and Critical Control Points (HACCP). Such a system should be proportionate to the food safety risks of the business.

The proprietor of the food business must ensure the following.

- ☑ Food is supplied or sold in a hygienic way.
- ☑ Food safety hazards are identified.
- ☑ Knowledge of which steps in the work are critical for food safety.
- ☑ Safety controls are in place, maintained and reviewed.
- ☑ Appropriate documentation is maintained.

**Refer to the Food Standards Agency booklet *Food hygiene – a guide for businesses* for good food hygiene practice; essential reading if you sell food.**

### 2.5.2.1 Premises

The siting, design and construction of the premises must aim to avoid the contamination of food and harbouring of pests. It must be kept clean and in good repair so as to avoid food contamination.

Surfaces in contact with food must be easy to clean and, where necessary, disinfected. This will require the use of smooth, washable, non-toxic materials unless you can prove to the EHO other materials are appropriate.

Adequate provision must be made for cleaning foodstuffs, and the cleaning and (where necessary) disinfection of utensils and equipment. You must take all reasonable, practical steps to avoid the risk of contamination of food or ingredients.

Washbasins must be designated for washing hands, have hot and cold (or appropriately mixed) running water, and be equipped with soap and suitable hand-drying facilities (such as disposable towels). Lavatories must not lead directly into food rooms and they must be kept clean, maintained in good repair and ventilated.

Adequate arrangements and facilities for the hygienic storage and disposal of hazardous and inedible substances and waste (whether liquid or solid) must be available. Food waste must not be allowed to accumulate in food rooms and should be deposited in closable containers.

Adequate facilities and arrangements for maintaining and monitoring suitable food temperature conditions must be available.

### 2.5.2.2 Food

Stored raw materials and ingredients must be kept in appropriate conditions that will prevent harmful deterioration and be protected from contamination likely to make them unfit for human consumption.

### 2.5.2.3 Water

There must be an adequate supply of potable (clean, drinkable) water that must be used whenever necessary to ensure foodstuffs are not contaminated. This includes the use of ice, which must also be made, handled and stored in a way that protects it from contamination.

### 2.5.2.4 Temperature control

The Hygiene Regulations state that foods intended for sale or supply, which need temperature control for safety must be held either **hot** (at or above a minimum temperature of 63°C) or **chilled** (at or below a maximum temperature of 8°C). Rather than providing a long list of food items, the regulations apply the requirement for temperature control to all types of food that might support the growth of harmful (pathogenic) bacteria or the formation of poisons (toxins).

**Some of the requirements are different in Scotland; please contact the local Environmental Health Department for details.**

### 2.5.2.5 Food handlers

Anyone who works in a food handling area must maintain a high degree of personal cleanliness. The way in which they work must also be clean and hygienic. Food handlers must wear clean and, where appropriate, protective over-clothes. Adequate changing facilities must be provided where necessary.

Food handlers must protect food and ingredients against contamination, which is likely to render them unfit for human consumption or create a health hazard. For example, uncooked poultry should not contaminate ready-to-eat foods, either through direct contact or via work surfaces or equipment.

Anyone whose work involves handling food should adhere to the following.

- ✓ Observe good personal hygiene.
- ✓ Routinely wash their hands before handling foods.
- ✓ Never smoke in food handling areas.
- ✓ Report any illness (such as infected wounds, skin infections, diarrhoea or vomiting) to their manager or supervisor immediately.

If any employee reports that they are suffering from any condition or illness, the business may have to exclude them from food-handling areas. Such action should be taken urgently. If there is any doubt about the need to exclude, seek urgent medical advice or consult the local Environmental Health Department.

Food handlers must receive adequate supervision, instruction and training in food hygiene. Each food business must decide what training or supervision their food handlers need by identifying the areas of work most likely to affect food hygiene.

Local colleges of higher and further education and private training companies provide food hygiene training courses.

**? To determine whether you have complied with all legislative requirements, ask yourself the following questions**

- ✓ Have you carried out a hazard analysis of food handling and production techniques?
- ✓ Are your standards of food hygiene good?
- ✓ Are your foods stored properly and kept at the correct temperatures?
- ✓ Have your staff been adequately and properly trained?
- ✓ Do you understand your food safety responsibilities?

If you can answer **yes** to each of these questions, your standards are probably satisfactory.

## Appendix A – Welfare requirements

The table summarises the requirement for the client, contractors and principal contractors to ensure that adequate welfare facilities are provided, as required by the CDM Regulations.

| | |
|---|---|
| **Sanitary conveniences** | Suitable and sufficient sanitary conveniences must be provided or made available at easy to get to places. So far as is reasonably practicable, the rooms containing sanitary conveniences must be:<br>■ adequately ventilated and lit<br>■ kept in a clean and orderly condition.<br>Separate rooms containing sanitary conveniences must be provided for men and women except where each convenience is in a separate room, the door of which can be locked from the inside. |
| **Welfare facilities** | Suitable and sufficient washing facilities, including showers, if required by the nature of the work or for health reasons, must, so far as is reasonably practicable, be provided or made available at easy to get to places.<br>Washing facilities must be provided adjacent to:<br>■ sanitary conveniences, whether or not provided elsewhere<br>■ changing rooms, where provided, whether or not provided elsewhere.<br>Washing facilities must include:<br>■ a supply of clean cold and hot (or warm) water that, so far as is reasonably practicable shall be running water<br>■ soap or other suitable skin cleansers<br>■ towels or other suitable means of drying.<br>Rooms containing washing facilities must be lit and sufficiently ventilated.<br>Washing facilities and the rooms containing them must be kept in a clean and orderly condition.<br>Except for washing facilities that are intended for the washing of hands and forearms only, separate rooms must be provided for men and women except where:<br>■ they are in a room, the door of which can be locked from the inside<br>■ the room is intended to be used by one person at a time. |
| **Drinking water** | An adequate supply of wholesome drinking water, conspicuously marked with the appropriate sign, should be provided or made available at easy to get to places.<br>Sufficient cups or other drinking vessels must be provided, unless the water supply is in the form of a jet (drinking fountain) from which a person can easily drink. |
| **Changing rooms and lockers** | Suitable facilities must be provided or made available at easy to get to places if:<br>■ the worker has to wear special clothing for the purposes of work<br>■ for reasons of health or personal privacy, changing cannot be carried out elsewhere.<br>Where necessary, in the interests of personal privacy, separate changing rooms for men and women must be provided. Changing rooms must:<br>■ contain seating<br>■ include, where necessary, facilities to dry clothing and personal effects<br>■ include, where necessary, facilities for locking away:<br>– special clothing that is not taken home<br>– a person's own clothing that is not worn at work<br>– personal effects (property). |
| **Facilities for rest** | Suitable and sufficient facilities for rest must be provided at easy to get to places. They must:<br>■ be equipped with an adequate number of tables and adequate seating with backs (not benches)<br>■ where necessary, include facilities for any pregnant woman and nursing mother to rest, lying down<br>■ include a means of boiling water and suitable arrangements to ensure that meals can be prepared and eaten<br>■ be maintained at an appropriate temperature. |

# 03

# Work-related stress

Contents



## Supporting information

**GT 700 Toolbox talks**

## Overview

**Badly managed exposure to pressure caused by work or other demands can result in stress.**

**Workers who experience stress, anxiety or depression are unlikely to perform effectively in the workplace.**

**This can be financially costly to employers and, in industries where safety is a core factor (such as construction), stress can create more general health and safety risks.**



## 3.1 Introduction

Stress takes many forms. As well as leading to anxiety and depression it can have a significant impact on an employee's physical health. Research links longer term stress to heart disease, back pain, headaches, gastrointestinal disturbances and alcohol and drug dependency.

This has an impact for organisations in a number of different areas, and notably in terms of managing their health, safety and wellbeing policies.

There is a clear distinction between stress and pressure. Pressure can be a motivating factor and is often a part of everyday work.

Figures from the Health and Safety Executive (HSE) show that stress is a significant factor for UK organisations and workers overall.

- ☑ The total number of cases of stress in 2010-11 was 428,000 (40%) out of a total of 1,073,000 for all work-related illnesses.
- ☑ Each case of stress-related ill health leads to an average of 30 days off work.
- ☑ A total of almost 11 million working days were lost in Great Britain in 2005-06 due to stress, depression and anxiety, costing in excess of £530 million.
- ☑ Approximately one in seven people say they find their work either very or extremely stressful.
- ☑ When stress leads to absence the average length of sick leave is 30 days.
- ☑ The main work activities that cause, or make worse, work-related stress are work pressure, lack of managerial support and work-related violence and bullying.

Stress is therefore a serious problem and tackling it can have significantly beneficial effects for organisations and their workers. Stress is a management issue that managers can help to resolve.

Stress is often a symptom of poor employment relations and can seriously affect productivity.

Organisations that talk regularly with their employees and have sound systems and procedures in place for dealing with issues (such as absence and discipline) are much more likely to avoid work-related stress, and to be able to deal with potentially stressful situations when they arise.

Work can have a positive impact on our health and wellbeing. Healthy, well-motivated employees can have an equally positive impact on the productivity and effectiveness of a business.

Stress can cause many challenges within the workplace. Some examples are shown below.

- ☑ A fall in a manager's productivity and that of employees.
- ☑ Risks to health and safety.
- ☑ Poor decision-making.
- ☑ An increase in mistakes that may in turn lead to more customer complaints.
- ☑ Increased sickness absence.
- ☑ High staff turnover.
- ☑ Poor workplace relations.

Stress often has a cumulative effect. If one member of staff becomes ill through stress, it places added pressure on those covering for them. Equally, a stressed manager may find it difficult to create a positive working environment and monitor stress levels in others.

The Work Foundation has proposed the following benefits to business in terms of encouraging a healthy workforce.

- ☑ Reduced sickness.
- ☑ Fewer accidents.
- ☑ Higher commitment.
- ☑ Improved brand.
- ☑ Improved retention.
- ☑ Improved resilience.
- ☑ Higher productivity.

Organisations must risk assess for the potential of stress at work. This will be covered in more detail later.

### The construction industry's top five causes of work-related stress

More specifically to the construction industry, research has identified the top five causes of work-related stress as:

- having too much work to do in the time available
- travelling or commuting
- being responsible for the safety of others at work
- working long hours
- having a dangerous job.

Equally, issues external to the workplace can all impact on our ability to cope with pressure at work; these might include personal relationships, financial concerns or domestic issues, including caring responsibilities and bereavement.



## 3.2 Legislative requirements

Organisations have a legal responsibility to protect their employees from stress under the following legal principles and general guidance.

- Health and Safety at Work Act.
- Management of Health and Safety at Work Regulations.
- Protection from Harassment Act.
- Equality legislation.
- The Employment Equality Act.
- Employment Rights Act.
- Consultation with Employees and Safety Representatives.
- Construction (Design and Management) Regulations.
- Common law negligence.
- Protection of Freedoms Act.

Under health and safety legislation, employers have a duty to undertake risk assessments and manage work to reduce the incidence of stress at work. However, this is a complex area of law and there are also cases brought within civil law where individuals have successfully applied cases against employers.

It is recommended that legal advice is always sought by the individual and the employer should the need arise.

### 3.2.1 Health and Safety at Work Act

The Health and Safety at Work Act imposes general duties on employers to secure the health, safety and welfare of people at work and protect others against risks arising from the work activity. The act makes it the duty of every employer to ensure, as far as is reasonably practicable, the health, safety and welfare at work of all employees. This includes provision and maintenance of plant and systems of work that are safe and without risks, information, instruction and training.

### 3.2.2 Management of Health and Safety at Work Regulations

The Management of Health and Safety at Work Regulations place a legal requirement on employers to assess the risks to health and safety that arise out of their work and to introduce measures that control the risks to an acceptable level.

The following information is explained within a risk assessment.

- The hazards of the job (for example responsibility for the safety of others).
- The risks (such as stress).
- The control measures needed to minimise the risk of stress to a safe level (such as support through other welfare services).

The regulations indicate the general principles of prevention that must be adhered to when making decisions.

### 3.2.3 Employment Equality Act – disability discrimination provisions

This act encompasses mental illness. Anxiety, stress and depression may be sufficient to qualify a person as disabled and therefore they will be covered by the act, as long as there is a substantial and long-term effect (for at least a year) on their ability to carry out normal day-to-day duties. Those with clinically recognised mental health diagnoses are very likely to be covered by the act.

If an employee is covered by the act, the organisation has a responsibility to make reasonable adjustments to accommodate the needs of that employee.

**A full explanation of this act can be found online.**

### 3.2.4 Employment Rights Act

The Employment Rights Act is relevant to issues regarding work-related stress. This may be particularly so for situations where there are challenges made by employees in relation to their rights under this act.

## 3.3 Signs and symptoms of work-related stress

Anyone can suffer from work-related stress, no matter what work they do or what level they operate at.

In the construction industry the people who tend to report stress more than others are those within the following occupations.

- ☑ Managers.
- ☑ Road workers.
- ☑ Designers.
- ☑ Administration staff.

Some of the signs of stress are listed overleaf; this is by no means exhaustive and individuals will vary in terms of how their own symptoms manifest in the workplace.



### 3.3.1 Behaviour

If an individual reports any of the following behaviours, this may indicate that they are under stress and this can be noticeable within the workplace.

- ☑ Find it hard to sleep.
- ☑ Have altered eating habits, including food cravings.
- ☑ Smoke or drink more.
- ☑ Avoid friends and family.
- ☑ Are generally quiet and withdrawn.
- ☑ Have a lack of assertiveness.
- ☑ Are frequently tearful.
- ☑ Cannot show their true feelings.
- ☑ Have a disproportionate response to things.
- ☑ Do not have a problem.
- ☑ Avoid difficult situations.

### 3.3.2 Physical symptoms

Symptoms of stress can vary considerably from one person to another, but some examples are shown below.

- ☑ Tiredness.
- ☑ Indigestion.
- ☑ Headaches.
- ☑ Aching muscles.
- ☑ Palpitations.
- ☑ High blood pressure.
- ☑ Breathlessness.
- ☑ Chest pains.
- ☑ Nausea.
- ☑ Tendency to sweat.
- ☑ Constipation and diarrhoea.
- ☑ Restlessness.

### 3.3.3 Mental symptoms

People can exhibit the following tendencies.

- ☑ Be more indecisive.
- ☑ Have poor judgement.
- ☑ Find it hard to concentrate.
- ☑ Suffer loss of memory.
- ☑ Feel inadequate or have low self esteem.
- ☑ Dread the future.
- ☑ Dread failure.
- ☑ Feel isolated.
- ☑ Have a lack of interest in others.

### 3.3.4 Emotional symptoms

Individuals are likely to:

- ☑ get irritable or angry
- ☑ lose their sense of humour
- ☑ be anxious
- ☑ feel numb
- ☑ be hypersensitive
- ☑ feel drained and listless.

## 3.4 Assessing whether stress is a problem at work

Carrying out a **stress audit** is one of the best ways to identify whether stress is an issue in your workplace. It will also help you to assess the risks of stress that people in your business may face as part of your health and safety risk assessment.

A stress audit can involve talking informally to staff (either individually or in groups) to find out if they have any concerns. Let employees know why you are carrying out the exercise and what you are trying to achieve (for example, that you hope to prevent future problems or cure any existing ones).

Safety representatives should also be involved in any relevant plans and decision making and ensure that people are confident and assured that the confidentiality of any information gathering will be respected.

A useful starting point for an audit is to ask staff to list the three best and worst things about their job, and whether any of these put them under excessive pressure.

You can also use **questionnaires** to gather the same information. Although there is a range of commercially available questionnaires, you may be better off developing your own checklist of areas that are particularly relevant to the needs and working conditions of your business.

A number of important areas you should consider are shown below.

- Work scheduling and the type and design of work.
- Working relationships with colleagues.
- The level of communication and reporting.
- The physical working environment.
- Employees' expectations of their work.

www. **The HSE produces a useful checklist, designed to help organisations to clarify whether their own risk assessment approach to stress is appropriate and sufficient. This can be accessed through the HSE website.**



## e.g. Is my risk assessment approach suitable and sufficient?

Answering **yes** to all of the questions below would indicate that your approach is likely to be considered a suitable and sufficient risk assessment for work-related stress.

- Do you include all the steps in the risk assessment process?
- Do you focus on prevention and organisational level solutions?
- Do you include provision for dealing with other issues (for example, personal issues)?
- Do you ensure commitment from all parties (senior management, employees and their representatives)?
- Do you have arrangements to identify those aspects of the work, work organisation or environment that are known to be risk factors for work-related stress?
- Does your approach highlight the extent and nature of the gap, if any, between the current situation, and what is seen as good practice (such as the stakes to be achieved in the management standards), for each of the identified stress risk areas?
- Do you involve the workforce:
  - by asking about their views regarding good and bad features of workplace conditions?
  - by seeking their suggestions, advice and comments on potential solutions to problems (such as improvements to working conditions, changes in the way work is organised, and so on)?
  - by ensuring that people are empowered to contribute and feel that their views are listened to and acted upon?
  - by communicating outcomes (such as action plans)?
- Do you seek to develop and adopt solutions that are reasonably practicable?
- Do you provide documentation to show what you have done at each stage of the process and that you are implementing the recommended actions?

*Risk assessment exercise – combined thinking helps*

The HSE recommends that the process is documented, whatever the approach to carrying out a risk assessment for work-related stress. Documenting the process provides an audit trail to help you demonstrate to any relevant authorities that what has been done represents a suitable and sufficient risk assessment.

## 3.4.1 The role of the line manager

Managers have a significant impact on the work-related stress of people with whom they work, notably their team.

- They can both prevent and cause stress simply through their behaviour towards employees.
- The manager's influence or lack of it can protect or expose employees to working conditions that may cause stress. This can be the case for both internal (organisational) factors and for those that are external (perhaps customer related).
- Managers can identify (or miss) the signs of stress at an early stage.
- If an employee is suffering from work-related stress, the manager is likely to be involved in supporting and helping to deliver change that could result in a solution.
- Increasingly, managers are responsible for the uptake and delivery of risk assessments for work-related stress in relation to their team and department.

**Refer to the HSE website for real case study videos of individuals who have been affected by stress.**

## 3.5 Dealing with stress

Anyone can suffer from stress, in any role and at any level of an organisation. People who work alone or who may have particular responsibilities that set them apart from their work colleagues could be particularly vulnerable.

If an individual feels that they may have the symptoms of stress, there are a number of things that they can be advised to do in order to address the challenges that are facing them.

- Identify and tackle the underlying causes.
- Talk to someone trusted, with whom they can share issues and challenges.
- Practise relaxation techniques (these might include meditation or mindfulness, which have been shown through research to benefit individuals suffering from stress and depression).
- Improve their diet; avoid foods high in refined sugars and cut down where appropriate on alcohol, smoking and caffeine.
- Avoid regularly working long hours if at all possible.
- Do regular exercise.
- Take time off work for holidays.
- Seek additional support and guidance.

**Signs and symptoms of stress can vary for individuals. More guidance on dealing with the symptoms of stress can be found on the MIND website.**

## 3.6 Management standards for work-related stress

Six main causes of work-related stress have been identified across all organisations and a framework of management behaviours or competencies has been created. The HSE describes the standards as follows.

> **The management standards define the characteristics, or culture, of an organisation where the risks from work-related stress are being effectively managed and controlled.**

The six management standards *(shown below)* cover the primary sources of stress at work.

1. **Demands.** Issues that should be considered include workload, work patterns and the working environment.
2. **Control.** How much control the individual has over the way they do their work.
3. **Support.** Whether workers feel that adequate encouragement and resources are provided by the company, managers and colleagues, and whether there are easy access systems to respond to individual concerns.
4. **Role.** Workers at all levels must understand their role and how they fit into the organisation, and have the skills, experience and support to deliver. There must not be any conflicting roles.
5. **Change.** People can be suspicious of the real motives behind organisational change which, whether large or small, must be well-managed and effectively communicated.
6. **Relationships.** Workers at any level must not be subjected to unacceptable behaviours by anyone at work and conflicts must be effectively dealt with. Bullying is a potentially significant factor for workplace relationships and can take many forms; what appears to be light-hearted banter to one person may be perceived as bullying by another. Personal and work-related bullying behaviours may both be evident within a workplace. Examples of these are shown in the table below.

| Personal behaviours | Work-related behaviours |
|---|---|
| ▪ Ignoring/excluding/silent treatment/isolating.<br>▪ Malicious rumours or gossip.<br>▪ Belittling remarks.<br>▪ Undermining integrity.<br>▪ Lies told about you.<br>▪ Sense of judgement questioned.<br>▪ Opinions marginalised. | ▪ Public humiliation.<br>▪ Being shouted or yelled at.<br>▪ Giving unachievable tasks/impossible deadlines/unmanageable workloads.<br>▪ Giving meaningless tasks/unpleasant jobs/belittling a person's ability.<br>▪ Withholding information deliberately/concealing information/failing to return calls or pass on messages.<br>▪ Undervaluing contribution/no credit where due/taking credit for work that is not their own.<br>▪ Constant criticism. |

The management standards for work-related stress, and the underpinning processes that support them, are designed to help simplify and carry out stress risk assessments, help all parties to work together to address work-related stress, and provide the means by which companies can gauge their performance in tackling the main causes of stress.

In addition management competencies have been developed that describe the behaviours managers need to show in order to prevent and reduce stress in their teams. They map across to the areas identified as being the primary sources of stress at work.

The HSE describes the benefits of implementing these standards as shown below.

- Being able to demonstrate good practice through a step-by-step risk assessment approach.
- Enabling assessment of the current situation using surveys and other techniques.
- Encouraging active discussion and working in partnership with employees to help decide on practical improvements that can be made.
- Helping to simplify risk assessment for work-related stress by:
  - identifying the main risk factors
  - helping employers focus on the underlying causes and their prevention
  - providing a yardstick by which organisations can gauge their performance in tackling the main causes of stress.

www.

**The management standards themselves revolve around a series of activities and map directly across to the main causes of work-related stress. The process of implementing the management standards is described in full on the HSE website.**

There are effectively five discrete processes within the standards, defined below.

1. **Identify the risk factors.** When assessing the risks to which your employees may be exposed it is important to focus on organisational level issues that have the potential to impact on group and possibly large numbers of employees, rather than individual employees.
2. **Who can be harmed and how?** The aim of the data gathering and analysis is to get a measure of where an organisation's current performance is against the management standards. To achieve this aim does not require organisations to perform extensive statistical analysis of their data. It is suggested that organisations, where possible, use existing data to identify the underlying causes. Typically, most organisations have access to data relating to sickness absence, staff surveys, turnover data, and so on.
3. **Evaluate the risks.** The primary aim of this step is to take the output from the previous step, data collection and analysis, discuss the conclusions with a representative sample of employees, and work with them to develop solutions.
4. **Record your findings.** By now you will have consulted your employees, explored areas of concern and taken some initial steps to develop some proposed solutions. It is important that you record your findings – to do this you could produce and disseminate an action plan. An action plan will:
   - help you set **goals** to work towards
   - help you **prioritise**
   - demonstrate that you are **serious** about addressing employees' concerns
   - provide you with something to **evaluate** and review against.
5. **Monitor and review.** You should review any action you take to tackle the sources of excessive workplace pressure. You need to:
   - **monitor** against your action plan to ensure the agreed actions are taking place
   - **evaluate** the effectiveness of the solutions you implement
   - **decide** what further action or data gathering, if any, is needed.

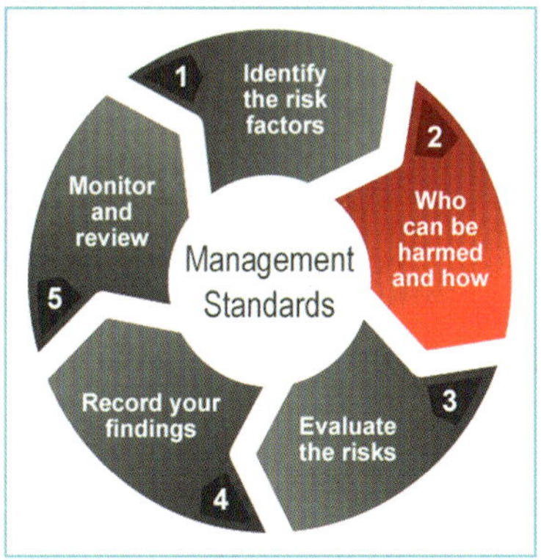


*The management standards demonstrate good practice through a step-by-step risk assessment approach*

## 3.6.1 Line manager competency indicator tool

The line manager competency indicator tool is designed to assess whether the behaviours identified as effective for preventing and reducing stress at work are part of your management repertoire or not. The aim is to help you to reflect upon your own behaviour and management style.

The competencies measured by the tool fall into four main domains, with 12 sub-competencies.

- **Respectful and responsible:**
  - integrity
  - managing emotions
  - considerate approach.
- **Managing and communicating existing and future work:**
  - proactive work management
  - problem solving
  - participative/empowering.

- **Reasoning/managing difficult situations:**
  - managing conflict
  - use of organisation resources
  - taking responsibility for resolving issues.
- **Managing the individual within the team:**
  - personally accessible
  - sociable
  - empathetic engagement.

**The line manager competency indicator tool will enable individuals to compare their own behaviours against the management competencies relevant to the management standards. This can be accessed on the HSE website.**

## 3.7 Occupational health support services

The following services are available to support individuals and employers on matters relating to work-related stress.

- Employment Medical Advisory Service (EMAS).
- Healthy Working Lives.
- Constructing Better Health (CBH).

**For further information on these services refer to Chapter B01 Management of health.**

# 04
# Drugs and alcohol

**Contents**



## Supporting information

**GT 700 Toolbox talks**

## Overview

**The misuse of drugs and alcohol can have a devastating impact on individuals and employers, and can result in social problems, poor health, absenteeism and therefore loss of productivity, as well as contributing to workplace accidents. It is a growing problem in society and construction sites are no exception, so diligence is required to identify and support those who are affected by it.**

**This chapter gives a general overview of the misuse of drugs and alcohol: identification, symptoms, impact and management. It also outlines the legal framework that regulates it.**



## 4.1 Introduction

Identifying, managing and supporting individuals affected by drugs and alcohol are important challenges facing society and the construction industry. Their effects can have huge negative impact on individuals, employers, their businesses and also any occupants of property where work is being undertaken.

Drug and alcohol misuse poses a threat to individuals in terms of their health, safety and welfare, as well as threatening their existing and future livelihood if not controlled. These substances can cause effects (including drowsiness, trembling, lack of concentration and reduced awareness) that can potentially increase the risk of on-site accident and injury to the individual and others working or living alongside them.

It is easy to associate drug and alcohol misuse with individuals who are addicted to them. However, we need to also take into account those who use drugs and alcohol infrequently. In addition, it is important to remember that there can be significant health and safety risks from individuals who have, for example, been heavily drinking the previous evening or those that may have been taking prescription or over-the-counter drugs.

> **According to the HSE, alcohol is estimated to cause 3-5% of all absences from work: about 8-14 million lost working days in the UK each year.**

Successfully identifying, managing and supporting individuals with drug and alcohol problems is beneficial to them, your business and customers. For example, you would save on the cost of recruiting and training new employees to replace those who left work because of untreated misuse.

Offering support to those employees with drug or alcohol-related problems will also help to ensure the following.

- Reduce the risk of accidents caused by impaired judgement.
- Create a more productive environment, and improve employee loyalty and morale.
- Enhance public perception of your organisation as a responsible employer.
- Contribute to society's efforts to combat alcohol and drug misuse.

Raising awareness of managers, supervisors and operatives to ensure that effective identification, management and control measures are always put in place and monitored, are important with helping to reduce the impact of drugs and alcohol on operatives and, where appropriate, occupants. There is a need to comply with legislation, including the Health and Safety at Work Act, the Management of Health and Safety at Work Regulations, the Road Traffic Act and the Transport and Works Act, and a duty to provide safe systems of work and a safe working environment. In appropriate circumstances, employers may also be held liable for the acts of employees under the Misuse of Drugs Act.

> **Drug and alcohol misusers are nearly four times more likely to be involved in workplace accidents, three times more likely to be absent from work for seven consecutive days or more and at least 25% less effective overall.**

## 4.2 Important points

- Managers and supervisors should be aware of the signs and symptoms of drug and alcohol misuse.
- People who misuse drugs and alcohol are likely to be still under the influence when they report for work, so are more likely to endanger themselves and others.
- Drinking coffee, eating stodgy food or sucking peppermints does not minimise the effects of alcohol, as individuals' bodies dispose of alcohol at their own rate, which may differ from individual to individual.
- There is likely to be a negative impact on productivity, enhanced periods of sickness absence and morale generally.
- If people are under the influence of drugs or alcohol at work, decisive action needs to be taken to ensure it does not continue.

- Companies should put into place and communicate an approach to dealing with employees who are unfit for work through drug and/or alcohol misuse.
  - This approach must be reflected in employee handbooks, induction processes and employment contracts. It must cover the right of search and testing, and identify the support in place to assist misusers and the approach to suspension/dismissal from work.
- Unless there is related misconduct, substance misuse should be seen as a treatable illness.
- Anyone facing up to suffering from a drug or alcohol misuse problem should be offered support and rehabilitation in strict confidence – there are many agencies who can offer professional advice and help.
- Drugs testing can be expensive and can introduce more problems than it solves, so the rationale for introducing a testing programme must be thoroughly thought out.
- Alcohol and drugs affect co-ordination, perception and reaction times, so driving, using tools or machinery or working in hazardous environments should be avoided.
- Driving a motor vehicle on a public road whilst under the influence of alcohol is a criminal offence.
- Driving on site under the influence of alcohol is equally, if not more, dangerous than driving on a public road, and employers may consider it appropriate to develop a written policy on the matter. Employers may also need to consider what their policy would be if an employee whose duties included driving (either on or off site) was convicted of drink driving.
- After drinking two pints of beer or half a bottle of wine at lunchtime, alcohol will remain in the bloodstream for approximately three hours.
- Drug and alcohol misuse causes absenteeism and lack of awareness, focus and productivity, as well as harm to the short and long-term health and wellbeing of individuals.
- Approximately 8-10% of adults have used one or more illicit drug within the last year, and around 3% have used Class A drugs.
- Approximately 20% of young adults have used one or more illicit drug in the last year, and around 7% have used Class A drugs.
- According to the Office for National Statistics, in 2011 there were 8,748 alcohol related deaths in the UK and over 66% of these were among males.

**Contrary to popular belief, the majority of people who have a drinking problem are in work.**

## 4.3 Legislative requirements

Under the **Health and Safety at Work etc. Act** (HSWA) all employers have a duty to ensure, as far as it is reasonably practicable, the health, safety and welfare of their employees. There is also a duty under the **Management of Health and Safety at Work Regulations** to assess the risks to the health and safety of their employees.

If an employer knowingly allows an employee to work under the influence of a drug in the workplace, and their behaviour places the employee or others at risk, the employer could be prosecuted. In accordance with the HSWA employees are required to take reasonable care of themselves and others who could be affected by their acts of omissions at work.

### 4.3.1 Transport and Works Act

- It is a criminal offence for workers to be unfit through drugs and/or alcohol while working on railways, tramways and other guided transport systems.
- The operators of the transport system would be guilty of an offence unless they had shown all due diligence in trying to prevent such an offence being committed.

### 4.3.2 Road Traffic Act

- Any person who, when driving or attempting to drive a motor vehicle on a road or other public place, is unfit to drive, through alcohol or drugs, shall be guilty of an offence.
- An offence is also committed if a person unfit through alcohol or drugs is in charge of a motor vehicle in the same circumstances. A person shall be deemed not to have been in charge of a mechanically propelled vehicle if they prove that at that time the circumstances were such that there was no likelihood of their driving it, as long as they remained unfit to drive through alcohol or drugs.
- Courts, in determining whether there was such a likelihood of driving, may disregard any injury to individuals and any damage to the vehicle.
- A person shall be taken to be unfit to drive if their ability to drive properly is, for the time being, impaired.

  ***Note:*** *this also applies to prescription or over-the-counter medicines, so you should always read the labelling and, if you're not sure, consult your pharmacist.*
- Anyone caught driving whilst over the legal alcohol limit or under the influence of drugs will be banned from driving for at least 12 months, fined up to £5,000 and/or be sent to prison for up to six months. Imprisonment, disqualification and the size of the fine depend on the seriousness of the offence.

### 4.3.3 Misuse of Drugs Act

The Misuse of Drugs Act is the principal legislation in the UK for controlling the misuse of drugs. The Act makes the production, supply and possession of these controlled drugs unlawful except when they have been prescribed by a doctor. The Act lists the drugs that are subject to control and classifies them in three categories, according to their relative harmfulness when misused.

- **Class A.** Includes ecstasy, cocaine, heroin, LSD, mescaline, methadone, morphine, opium and injectable forms of Class B drugs.
- **Class B.** Includes oral preparations of amphetamines, barbiturates, cannabis, cannabis resin, codeine and methaqualone (Mandrax).
- **Class C.** Includes most benzodiazepines (such as Temazepam and Valium), other less harmful drugs of the amphetamine group, and anabolic steroids.

The penalties for offences involving controlled drugs depend on the classification of the drug. Penalties for misuse of Class A drugs are more severe than those for Class B drugs, which are more severe than the penalties for Class C drugs. It is possible that in certain circumstances charges may be brought against an employer or an employee under either this Act or the Health and Safety at Work etc. Act, or both. It would be up to the courts to decide on the circumstances of each case.

B 04

## 4.4 Definitions

**Alcohol.** A colourless, volatile, flammable liquid that forms the intoxicating element in beer, spirits and wine.

**Alcoholic.** A person suffering from alcoholism.

**Drug(s) or substance(s).** Deemed to refer to all banned substances, pharmaceutical drugs, alcohol and solvents, unless otherwise stated.

**Drug misuse.** The intermittent or continual use of drugs (as defined above) that, when used for non-medical reasons, are detrimental to the employee's health, safety and work performance.

**Substance abuse or misuse.** The continued misuse of any mind-altering substance that severely affects a person's physical and mental health, social situation and responsibilities.

**Company premises.** All property owned, operated, leased by or otherwise under the control of the company, in whole or in part. This includes building and construction sites as well as company offices on or off site.

**Under the influence.** When there is a sufficient amount of the substance in a person's system to produce a positive result from a medical test or breathalyser and/or when the person shows behaviour likely to pose a risk to themselves or others or to interfere with their job performance. *(For further information refer to 4.7 Driving under the influence.)*

www.

**A document detailing drug misuse and statistics can be found on the Information Centre website.**

**For information on drug misuse at work refer to the HSE Employers' guide.**

## 4.5 Common drugs, effects and symptoms

With so many different drugs available and so much misinformation, it is difficult to find the right information about and help with drug abuse and drug addiction. As it is important for site managers or supervisors to identify, manage and support individuals with misuse, they should be aware of some of the common drugs, effects and symptoms.

### 4.5.1 Class A drugs

#### 4.5.1.1 Ecstasy

A Class A drug also known as MDMA, 'e', doves, mitsubishis, apples, rhubarb and custards or callies. It affects individuals with a buzz and intense pleasure, but also causes dizziness, disorientation, breathlessness and sickness. It increases the pulse-rate and can leave you feeling flushed, restless, anxious and maybe paranoid. Your jaw muscles tighten, pupils get bigger, energy increases and you may lose your appetite and desire to sleep. It enhances affection and energy but can make music and light seem even more intense. A penalty for its use or supply can range from a fine to life imprisonment and it is detectable in urine for two to four days.

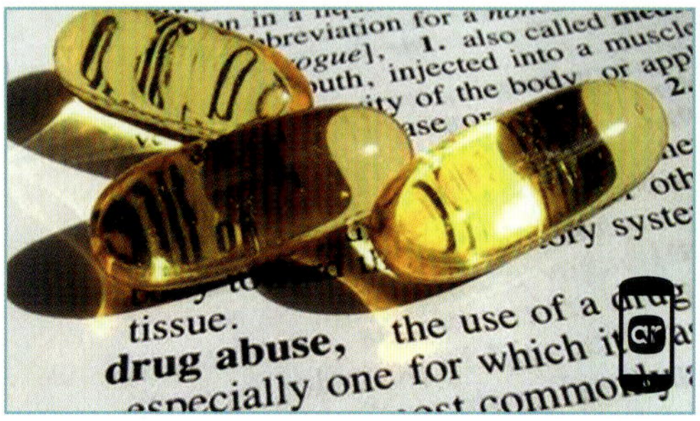

- A few people are sensitive or allergic to ecstasy, which can cause illness or death.
- If you have a heart condition, you could have a seizure.
- It can cause heat stroke, especially if you're in a hot club and dancing a lot, which can cause death as your internal organs stop working.
- Drinking too much water can also be dangerous as fluid can build up on your brain leading to unconsciousness, coma and even death.
- If you have an existing condition (such as epilepsy), ecstasy could trigger it.
- You may develop long-term mental health problems and depression.
- You could do permanent damage to your internal organs (liver, kidneys, heart and brain).

### 4.5.1.2 Cocaine and crack

A Class A drug also known as coke, charlie, gear, banger, snow, crack, rock, bones, stones or freebase. It is a powerful stimulant that speeds up your central nervous system, your heart rate and blood pressure increases and your pupils get bigger. It makes you feel really powerful, as though you can do anything, and it gives you more energy and awareness. The effects of crack are even more intense than coke and you get a much quicker hit, but the effects last for only a short time. A penalty for its use or supply can range from a fine to life imprisonment and it is detectable in urine from 12 hours to four days.

- ☑ You can very easily get hooked – developing a real craving for it, but feeling rough when it wears off.
- ☑ It can cause death, mainly from heart failure or internal bleeding.
- ☑ Regular crack users will almost certainly get breathing problems, because of damage to their lungs.
- ☑ If you snort cocaine regularly you can end up with a perforated septum (the wall between your nostrils).
- ☑ Even if you use cocaine only occasionally you could suffer from disrupted sleep patterns, appetite loss, fatigue, restlessness, anxiety and paranoia.
- ☑ It destroys some of the chemicals in your brain that control your mood, which can make you depressed and even suicidal.
- ☑ It increases adrenaline and this can cause restlessness, extreme paranoia and aggression.
- ☑ Mixing it with alcohol increases the risk of heart and liver damage.

### 4.5.1.3 Heroin

A Class A drug also known as smack, brown, H, gear, skag, harry, horse or jack. It is an analgesic, which makes you feel relaxed and acts as a powerful painkiller. It creates a sense of extreme pleasure and feeling good. Heavy use makes you sleepy, sedated and slurry. Many people are sick the first time they use it. A penalty for its use or supply can range from a fine to life imprisonment and it is detectable in urine for one to two days.

- ☑ There is a high risk of death from overdose, especially if you've been drinking alcohol or taking other depressants (certain types of drugs, like tranquiliser pills prescribed by doctors).
- ☑ Regular use often means you stop looking after yourself and stop caring about the way you look.
- ☑ Injecting increases the risk of dangerous infections and abscesses.
- ☑ Your cough reflex can be reduced for long periods, so you're more likely to get chest infections.
- ☑ Regular users commonly suffer from constipation.
- ☑ You can become tolerant quickly, so you need more heroin to get the same hit or stop getting withdrawal symptoms.
- ☑ If you stop taking heroin for a while your tolerance drops, which means that if you start again and take your normal dose, there is a greater risk of overdosing.
- ☑ Heroin is very physically addictive and though withdrawal is not fatal it is extremely unpleasant.

### 4.5.1.4 LSD

A Class A drug also known as tabs, trips, microdots, strawbs, blotter or acid. It takes between 30 and 60 minutes to take affect and the effects can last from eight to 12 hours. Trips are unpredictable and vary hugely from person to person. The drug works on the brain causing changes to thoughts, senses and perceptions. It can cause visual disturbance, hallucinations, anxiety, dizziness or disorientation. A penalty for its use or supply can range from a fine to life imprisonment and it is detectable in urine for two to three days.

LSD

- ☑ The most common health risk is short or long-term psychological damage.
- ☑ It can trigger a range of mental problems and frequent long-term use can leave you feeling disorientated for quite a long time.
- ☑ Use of LSD can cause permanent eye damage.
- ☑ There is a risk that you could injure yourself when you've taken LSD, by doing something dangerous.
- ☑ You may experience flashbacks (re-living a few seconds or minutes of a trip) weeks, months or even years after taking it.
- ☑ It doesn't mix well with alcohol and cannabis, increasing the side effects (for example, sickness and anxiety).

#### 4.5.1.5 Methadone

A Class A drug, only legal if it's prescribed, and also known as meth, linctus, green, juice and amps. It has similar effects to heroin, though longer acting (24 hours) and less intense. Some users experience an intense allergy-like itchiness. When prescribed for heroin users it can stop withdrawal symptoms for 24 hours, to allow them to gain control of their lives. A penalty for its use or supply can range from a fine to life imprisonment and it is detectable in urine for three to five days.

- ☑ Methadone is physically addictive and withdrawal can be longer and even more unpleasant than heroin.
- ☑ If you mix methadone with alcohol you are at more risk of passing out and, like heroin, your cough reflex is reduced, which means you could choke if you're sick.
- ☑ Overdose is common in users who are not used to the drug or have lost their tolerance.
- ☑ Injecting it or using undiluted 50 mg ampoules can lead to vein damage, and injecting crushed tablets carries serious risk of vein blocking and abscesses.
- ☑ Methadone is extremely poisonous to children.

### 4.5.2 Class B drugs

#### 4.5.2.1 Amphetamines

These are Class B drugs, but are Class A if prepared for injection. They are also known as speed, whizz, billy, crank, meth, pink champagne or amphet. They are stimulants, so they increase your heart rate and blood pressure and you feel more alert, talkative and have more energy. A penalty for its use or supply can range from a fine to seven years' imprisonment and it is detectable in urine for two to four days.

- ☑ Overuse can cause anxiety, panic attacks, irritability and aggressive behaviour, as well as weight loss and illness, because of eating poorly and generally not looking after yourself.
- ☑ Regular use can bring on a state of intense paranoia (feeling terrified of things around you).
- ☑ If you have a heart condition, there is a particular risk of death from heart problems.
- ☑ Depending on how you take it, an amphetamine can damage your nasal lining, gums or stomach. If you inject it, it can cause permanent damage to your body.
- ☑ It can also make your jaw feel tight, which can make you grind your teeth and chew constantly.
- ☑ Amphetamines can reduce your sexual sensitivity and performance.
- ☑ The comedown can cause aches and pains, hunger, tiredness, depression and loss of self-esteem.
- ☑ If you snort drugs, the lining of your nose often breaks and bleeds, and you can easily get an infection.
- ☑ Injecting amphetamines is especially dangerous. It can badly damage your veins and there is the added risk of catching a dangerous disease if you share equipment.

#### 4.5.2.2 Cannabis

A Class B drug also known as marijuana, hash, pot, weed, blow, gear, black, draw, herb, skunk or soap. It is a stimulant, depressant and hallucinogen. It can make you relaxed, giggly, hungry, and appreciate sound and colour more. You may feel anxious and paranoid and the effects can be unpredictable. A penalty for its use or supply can range from a fine to 14 years' imprisonment and it is detectable in urine for two to three days.

*(Photo credit to U.S. Fish and Wildlife Service)*

- ☑ Smoking cannabis, especially with tobacco, can cause lung damage, with an increased risk of lung and throat cancers.
- ☑ Regular use can cause short-term memory loss and make you feel demotivated and listless.
- ☑ There is an increased risk of mental health problems (such as anxiety and paranoia), which can last into adult life.
- ☑ It interferes with learning, so you'll find it harder to study and work.
- ☑ Side effects (such as nausea, palpitations and anxiety) are sometimes made worse by alcohol.
- ☑ If you become dependent you'll find stopping difficult, due to symptoms including sleep disturbance, vivid dreaming, mood swings, irritability and possible aggression, headache and tiredness.
- ☑ Cannabis can stay in your body for up to 30 days and so can show up positive in drug tests for some time after your last use.

### 4.5.2.3 Mephedrone

A Class B drug also known as M-Cat, MMCAT, MC, mieow, meow, 4MMC and plant fertiliser. It is a stimulant (increasing alertness and energy) with similar effects to cocaine, amphetamine and ecstasy. The effects can come on in a head rush and be overpowering, which can make you feel sick (more likely if you've been drinking alcohol or smoking cannabis). The effects of a single dose can last for at least an hour, although some people report it going on for much longer. A penalty for its use or supply can range from a fine to life imprisonment and it is detectable in urine for up to four days.

- ☑ Taking it carries some serious risks so should be treated with caution. These risks are greater if you use large doses, take it for extended periods of time, or combine it with other drugs.
- ☑ The biggest risk is heart failure, so if you have an existing heart problem or high blood pressure, you should especially avoid using it.
- ☑ Some prescribed medication can react badly with it.
- ☑ Drugs (such as mephedrone and ecstasy) can occasionally cause death because of a direct toxic effect on the body.
- ☑ Like other stimulants, it can cause jaw clenching and teeth grinding, which can damage your teeth.
- ☑ The comedown can make you feel exhausted, depressed, confused and disorientated, with a sore head. You won't be able to sleep properly after taking it.



## 4.5.3 Class C drugs

### 4.5.3.1 Ketamine

A Class C drug also known as K, special K, kettle or kit kat. It can make you feel disoriented, with a sense of numbness and a lack of co-ordination. Low doses can create a sense of extreme pleasure and mild hallucinations (K-holing – a feeling of travelling outside the body towards a tunnel of light). Effects shouldn't last for more than about three hours. A penalty for its use or supply can range from a fine to 14-years' imprisonment and it is detectable in urine for up to 14 days.

- ☑ Ketamine is an anaesthetic, which numbs pain, so you may injure yourself without realising it until the effects have worn off.
- ☑ There's a risk of mental health problems from the drug's disorientating experiences.
- ☑ It can cause sickness, headaches and diarrhoea, and may even paralyse you temporarily.
- ☑ If you drink alcohol or take other depressants (certain types of drugs, like tranquiliser pills prescribed by doctors), you increase the risk of heart failure, unconsciousness, vomiting and choking.
- ☑ Serious and permanent bladder problems can develop.
- ☑ If you inject ketamine there are the usual risks of dangerous infections through using needles.

### 4.5.3.2 Benzodiazepine

A Class C drug but legal if you have a prescription for them and also known as nitrazepam, mogadon, lorazepam, ativan, flurazepam, clonazepam, rohypnol, roofies, temazepam, temazzies, librium, diazepam and valium. It relaxes you and reduces anxiety, your muscles feel less tense and it can also help you sleep. A penalty for its use or supply can range from a fine to two to 14 years' imprisonment and it is detectable in urine for one to two days.

- ☑ You may lose co-ordination, become forgetful and vague.
- ☑ You can become tolerant quickly, so after a few weeks the dose stops being effective.
- ☑ It can cause sleeplessness and anxiety if you take it for longer than a few weeks.
- ☑ It can cause vertigo, hypotension, loss of libido, urinary retention and blood disorders.
- ☑ If you are taking other depressants as well, there's a higher risk of overdose.
- ☑ If you crush and inject tablets, you're at risk of abscess-blocked veins as well as the usual risks of intravenous drug use.

## 4.5.4 Legal highs

Legal highs are substances that produce the same, or similar, effects to drugs such as cocaine and ecstasy, but are not controlled under the Misuse of Drugs Act. It is legal for these to be sold, purchased and advertised for human consumption. It is likely that drugs sold as a legal high may actually contain one or more substances that are actually illegal to possess.

**Just because a drug is legal doesn't mean that it is safe.**

- ☑ Legal highs can still cause harm and have similar health risks to illegal drugs (for example, paranoia, coma, seizures and death).
- ☑ Risks are increased if used with alcohol or other drugs.
- ☑ There has been little research into the effects of short to long-term use of legal highs.

- There are a large number of legal highs, which can be known by:
  - their brand or product name (for example, Benzo Fury)
  - a chemical name (for example, Dimethocaine)
  - a slang name (for example, in some areas 'Bubble' is a generic name for any synthetic powder that has temporary bans for legal highs).

The Government can place a temporary ban on any potentially harmful substance, while they await a recommendation from the Advisory Council on the Misuse of Drugs (ACMD) (an independent group of experts), on whether it should be permanently controlled under the Misuse of Drugs Act. When used, the temporary ban will come into immediate effect, but it will have to be agreed by Parliament within 40 days. The drug will not be Class A, B or C, but called a temporary class drug.

### 4.5.5 Over-the-counter drugs

Over-the-counter drugs come in three different types.

- **Stimulants**, such as cough and cold treatments and decongestants, especially non-drowsy (for example, Actifed Expectorant, Sinutab and Sudafed).
- **Depressants**, such as cough and cold linctuses, painkiller analgesic capsules and diarrhoea preparations (for example, Nurofen Plus, Paracodol, Feminax and Syndol).
- **Sedatives**, such as anti-histamines, cough and cold treatments and some night-time sleep aids (for example, Piriton, Night Nurse, Benylin and Contac 400).



Stimulants can make you excited, alert, agitated and anxious, increase your heart rate and blood pressure. Depressants can cause mild euphoria, relaxation, detachment, decreased heart rate and blood pressure, increased effects of alcohol and physical addiction. Sedatives can make you sleepy or drowsy, even at normal dosages, and increase the effects of alcohol.

- Misuse of these products often mimics the classic symptoms of a clinical drug addiction, with physical and psychological effects.
- Dependence doesn't always mean you're regularly taking large daily quantities of a drug. You can become dependent by having to take a daily amount, under the maximum recommended dosage, over many years.
- You can become unintentionally addicted to an over-the-counter drug. You may have simply bought it to treat a physical complaint, without being aware that it could be addictive.

## 4.6 Alcohol

Alcohol is a positive part of life for many people and most of the time drinking alcohol doesn't cause many problems. However, drinking too much at the wrong time can be harmful.

The Department of Health recommends that alcohol intake is limited to 21 units per week (three to four units per day) for men, and 14 units per week (two to three units per day) for women, with at least one day in the week that is alcohol-free.

The usual advice that one glass of wine or one half pint of beer is equal to one unit is misleading and can lead to misunderstanding and accidental over-consumption.

> **e.g.** **Formula for calculating alcohol units**
>
> The number of alcohol units is worked out by the formula:
>
> *Strength (ABV) x Volume (ml) ÷ 1,000 = units*
>
> where: ABV = percentage alcohol content of the drink.
>
> If a person drinks one 200 ml glass of wine with 13% alcohol content:
>
> **13(%) x 200(ml) ÷ 1,000 = 2.6 units.**

**www.** **Refer to the NHS website for an alcohol unit calculator.**

Excessive and continued intake of alcohol can result in serious ill health, including scarring of the liver tissue, which then affects its function. Approximately 30% of people diagnosed with the condition of cirrhosis of the liver only survive five years after diagnosis.

Furthermore, 3% of all cancer is directly caused by alcohol consumption.

**www.** **For an employers' guide to alcohol at work refer to the HSE website.**

## 4.7 Driving under the influence

### 4.7.1 Alcohol

Driving a motor vehicle on a public road whilst under the influence of alcohol is a criminal offence, with penalties that range from a fine, with or without disqualification, to a term of imprisonment. The current legal limit is 80 mg of alcohol per 100 ml of blood. In most other European countries the unit is less, usually 50 mg per 100 ml of blood.

There is no safe limit of alcohol that you can consume and then drive. Each person's body reacts differently to alcohol. The speed at which alcohol is absorbed into your system (and how quickly your system gets rid of it) depends on a large number of factors, including your sex, weight, metabolism, age, current stress levels, health and when you last ate.

It is impossible to know how long it will take to sober up after drinking. Drinking coffee, eating, sleeping and showering **do not** help you to sober up any faster.

Too many people are killed or seriously injured on our roads in drink-driving crashes. Overall, 250 fatal drink-drive accidents occurred in 2012, and a further 6,680 drink-driving accidents.

### 4.7.2 Drugs

It is an offence to drive whilst unfit through drugs. Many people think that if they drive under the influence of drugs a vehicle search and a potential charge of possession is all they have to be worried about, but the following should also be considered.

- ☑ Taking drugs will impair driving skills. Driving whilst under the influence of drugs is extremely dangerous and can affect driving in numerous ways.
- ☑ Drugged drivers can suffer from slower reaction times, erratic and aggressive behaviour, an inability to concentrate properly, nausea, hallucinations, panic attacks, paranoia, tremors (or 'the shakes'), dizziness and fatigue. In such a condition, it is a bad idea to be behind the wheel of a car, for the driver and their passengers.
- ☑ Whilst the effects of drugs are wearing off, the taker may feel fatigued, which will affect their concentration whilst driving.



## 4.8 Managing work-related substance misuse

Workplace problems can be caused through drug and alcohol consumption, both inside and outside of work, as the effects can be long-lasting. The following points should be taken into account when considering the scale of the drug or alcohol problem within a company.

- ☑ The risk of accidents due to impaired performance through drugs or alcohol.
- ☑ Inept and poor decision making.
- ☑ Lower standards of work.
- ☑ Low productivity caused by employees' inability to cope with workplace situations.
- ☑ Disruption and ill discipline by employees under the influence of substances.
- ☑ Time lost from the workplace due to absenteeism, lateness or habitual sick leave.
- ☑ Long-term health of the workforce.
- ☑ Stress factors on employees due to home circumstances.
- ☑ Financial stress on employees of feeding any habits or addiction.
- ☑ Impact on customers.
- ☑ Impact on company reputation.
- ☑ Security concerns.
- ☑ Potential compensation claims against the employer.
- ☑ Poor staff retention rates.

Successfully tackling alcohol and drug misuse can benefit both your business and your employees. For example, you would save on the cost of recruiting and training new employees to replace those who left work because of untreated misuse.

Offering support to those employees who declare a drug-related problem will also help in the following situations.

- ☑ Reducing the risk of accidents.
- ☑ Creating a more productive environment and improving employee loyalty and morale.
- ☑ Enhancing company reputation as a responsible employer.
- ☑ Contributing to society's efforts to combat alcohol and drug misuse.

## 4.8.1 Identifying misuse

Alcohol, drug or solvent misuse by employees may come to light in a variety of ways. The following actions may indicate that a problem exists.

- ☑ Absenteeism without notice.
- ☑ Poor time-keeping.
- ☑ High accident levels and clumsiness.
- ☑ Confusion and disorientation.
- ☑ Poor performance and workmanship.
- ☑ Irritability, aggression and argumentativeness.
- ☑ Misconduct.
- ☑ Failure to remember, or failure to comply with, common instructions.
- ☑ A sudden need for increased supervision.
- ☑ Leaving site either without permission or at lunchtimes to visit licensed premises.
- ☑ Finding empty beer cans, bottles or drug-related paraphernalia.

Physical symptoms of substance misuse may include the following.

- ☑ Rapid loss of weight.
- ☑ Gaunt appearance.
- ☑ Tremors or sweating.
- ☑ Constant tiredness.
- ☑ Trackmarks, severe bruising or abscesses on arms.
- ☑ Over-dilated or very small pupils.
- ☑ Cravings (for example, ice cream, nicotine, sweet foodstuffs).

Behavioural symptoms may include the following.

- ☑ Degenerating personal appearance.
- ☑ Excessive care about personal appearance.
- ☑ Hyperactivity.
- ☑ Severe mood swings.
- ☑ Avoidance of authority or supervision.
- ☑ Deteriorating relations with other staff.
- ☑ Swings in morale.
- ☑ Minimum involvement with other staff.
- ☑ Obsessive or compulsive behaviour.

Communicating with and educating employees, supported by an effective workplace policy and community-based treatment, will improve the chances of the early detection of problems.

Employees need to feel secure in asking for help and made aware of the benefits this provides to all parties in supporting them.

Supervisors and managers may require training and supporting information to enable them to identify problems and then manage and support individuals in line with company policy and legal requirements.

## 4.8.2 Addressing misuse

Known or suspected misuse should lead to consultation between the company, employees and representatives. To agree a way forward is essential if it is to be addressed adequately.

www.

**Employer associations, solicitors and professional bodies (such as Alcohol Concern, Norcas or Drugscope) can advise and help develop a workplace alcohol and drugs policy.**

### 4.8.2.1 Developing and implementing workplace policies

A substance misuse policy that applies to all staff can be of benefit and may form part of a company's overall health and safety policy.

The substance misuse policy that is adopted will need to take account of the particular needs of the company and the practical situations, including those brought about by working on building and construction sites. However, there are a number of minimum requirements (shown below) for such a policy.

- ☑ Contain a clear statement of the behaviour that is expected of employees.
- ☑ Apply equally to all employees, including managers and supervisors, in the workplace.
- ☑ Result from full consultation with employees and, if appropriate, their representatives (such as recognised trades unions) before it is adopted.
- ☑ Be made known to all employees.
- ☑ Be an integrated part of an overall health and safety policy.

- Include clear statements on the roles and responsibilities of all employees in relation to the policy (for example, site-based operatives, HR Department, Occupational Health Department, site managers).
- Address issues in the work environment that are likely to increase the use of alcohol or drugs.
- Encourage those with a problem to come forward under a promise of strict confidentiality and future support.
- To the greatest possible degree, be non-punitive.
- State the conduct likely to result in action being taken under the policy.
- Provide for appropriate treatment and rehabilitation for those with problems.
- Be evaluated after implementation and amended, if necessary, in line with the outcome of the evaluation.

The potential for the policy to interfere in an employee's private life must be lawful and proportionate. The policy is likely to be lawful and proportionate in the following situations.

- When it is instituted to protect and promote employee safety.
- If employees are aware of the policy.
- When the process of collecting, transporting and testing samples can be proven to be independent and beyond reproach.
- Where employees know what the employer will do with the test results.
- If the employer has no other reasonable alternative way of obtaining the same result.



**For a template on developing a drug and alcohol abuse policy refer to Appendix A.**

Implementing a substance misuse policy has four essential components.

- The education and information of all levels of management, employees and their representatives.
- The organisational support shown by the company.
- The addressing of issues in the work environment.
- The prevention and rehabilitation support offered by the company to its employees.

Information about a substance misuse policy, covering alcohol and drugs, must be provided to all employees, and be included as part of any induction training for new recruits. The policy must be supported by education about the harmful effects of alcohol and drugs, the rehabilitation services available and the means by which employers will help individuals to access these services.

It is important that management demonstrates its full support for the policy by ensuring observance by all staff, at whatever level, and endorsing changes to the working environment to facilitate the full and proper implementation of the policy.

The provision of treatment and/or referral services is an important component of implementing the policy. If problems are detected early, before serious physical and social effects occur, a brief intervention may be all that is needed.

Confidentiality for employees undergoing treatment and rehabilitation must be guaranteed. Equally, employees should not be disadvantaged in terms of promotion or seniority because they have sought or are accepting help. Treatment and rehabilitation should be covered by adequate leave entitlements.

However, as with all workplace health and safety matters, consultation with employees and the provision of education and information at an early stage, may prevent the onset of alcohol and drug problems at work.

### 4.8.2.2 Temporary and sub-contracted staff

The company substance misuse policy should also address the employment of sub-contractors and other temporary staff. Sub-contractors are normally obliged to work within the main contractor's policies and this condition could form part of any contract.

### 4.8.2.3 Misuse outside of the workplace

Generally, an employee's conduct outside of the workplace is not within the employer's control. However, if drug or alcohol misuse during recreational times creates a risk to their health and safety or to that of others who may be affected by the employee's actions during working hours, consideration must be given to the situation and to what action should or can be taken.

A company's substance misuse policy may also need to consider situations where an employee's behaviour outside the workplace results in a conviction for a criminal offence, and the effect that this would have on the company's image and reputation.

**If a driver is convicted of a drink-driving or drug-driving offence and they drive for work, the employer will see the conviction when they produce their licence.**

### 4.8.3 Disciplinary procedures

The majority of employers will have a disciplinary procedure in place. It may be appropriate to ensure the procedure covers the consumption of alcohol or drugs in the workplace. You may also wish for the policy to contain a provision that possession, dealing or trafficking in drugs will be reported to the police.

For a drug and alcohol policy to be effective, it is essential that it is consistent with disciplinary procedure.

Employees with a substance misuse problem or those suspected of misusing alcohol or drugs should have the same rights to confidentiality and support (or to any other company procedure, including those agreed with the recognised trades unions) as they would if they had any other medical condition, or if any other disciplinary matter were involved.

It can be very difficult for employees to discuss or openly admit to having an alcohol or drug problem, because of the stigma or fear of reprisals, or the difficulty they have facing up to the issue.

It should also be considered that HSE inspectors may, in appropriate circumstances, issue improvement and prohibition notices and, if they were to find an employee under the influence of alcohol or drugs on site, they would have the option to take appropriate actions against the employer.



**For further information on improvement and prohibition notices refer to Chapter A02 The Health and Safety at Work Act.**

## 4.9 Drug or alcohol screening and testing

Introducing drug testing in the workplace is a difficult and potentially expensive initiative. It is essential to be completely clear on the reasons for doing so, or not. Testing is far from the whole answer and has inherent limitations.

Before any decision is taken by an employer to implement an alcohol or drug testing regime, care must be taken to ensure that an alcohol and drugs policy is fully established, communicated to all employees and, where appropriate, accepted by their representatives.

It is legitimate for employers to take an interest in drug and alcohol use in their workforce. The independent inquiry into drug testing at work concludes that these circumstances are when:

- employees are engaging in illegal activity in the workplace
- employees are actually intoxicated during working hours
- drug or alcohol use is having an impact on work performance that goes beyond a threshold of acceptability
- the nature of the work is such that the public is entitled to expect a higher than average standard of behaviour from employees and/or there is a risk of corruption.

There remains an open question as to whether introducing testing for employees constitutes a solution to any of these circumstances. As yet, there is no clear evidence that this is so, but broadly speaking there are valid arguments for and against.

**Supporters of drug testing** claim the following.

- There are benefits for safety.
- The company is more efficient.
- There is a positive effect on the organisation's external reputation.
- It sends a strong message to employees that drug use is not acceptable.

**Opponents of drug testing** claim the following.

- Tests are unreliable for many reasons, chiefly that they do not necessarily prove impairment, dependence or current use.
- There is no clear evidence of any benefit in terms of deterring use, reducing accidents or improving efficiency.
- It is excessively invasive and a potential infringement of human rights.
- It is damaging to work relations and can hamper recruitment.
- It is very costly, complicated and time-consuming.
- It is possible to cheat drug tests.

### 4.9.1 The legal position

The extent to which employers can require employees to undertake random drug or alcohol testing is limited, even where there is a right to test the employee in their contract of employment.

An unreasonable request to take a test will result in a breach of the implied duty of mutual trust and confidence. This could lead to an employee successfully claiming unfair constructive dismissal. Obtaining samples without consent could, in addition, constitute the criminal offences of assault or battery.

In the absence of factors indicating that the employee is using, or is affected by, alcohol or drugs at work, the employer will have to ensure it can justify any testing it wishes to carry out.

There is no legal requirement to test employees in any industry, and no specific legislation relating to drug testing in the workplace. Consequently, there is a lack of clarity surrounding the legal issues. Case law is also relatively scarce. Important legal decisions hinge on an interpretation of a range of legal implications, the main ones are shown below.

- ☑ Health and safety at work.
- ☑ Data protection.
- ☑ Human rights.
- ☑ Disability discrimination.

It is clear, however, that no-one can be tested against their will. It is important to be aware that any attempt to test employees without their express individual consent would constitute a criminal offence.

## 4.9.2 Why test?

Drug testing might be introduced for a number of reasons. Other than where there is a clear clinical imperative (that is rehabilitation testing), the effectiveness of each approach has not been proven.

**Recruitment screening** usually refers to testing or assessing the health of potential employees during the recruitment process. Testing of this kind presents far fewer legal and logistical problems than introducing testing for existing employees.

**Routine testing** is done at specified times, and gives a clear message that it is not acceptable to be affected by alcohol when working. It might be used in situations where employees are in safety-critical posts (such as operating or driving construction plant on a public road, or operating machinery).

**Random testing** or unannounced testing is used as a deterrent to identify previously undetected drug or alcohol misusers. As with routine testing, any use in situations that are not safety critical may cause feelings of resentment amongst the workforce.

**Reason or 'with cause' testing** might be used if a manager has reason to believe that an employee has been using drugs or drinking alcohol. This might be because of their behaviour or by physical signs (such as smelling alcohol). It may also form part of a post-incident or accident investigation.

**Rehabilitation testing** may be used where an employee has agreed to treatment and the treatment provider is testing to ensure compliance with a prescription (for example, urine testing to ensure that an individual who has been prescribed methadone is not using heroin as well as the prescribed dose). Similarly, testing may be introduced as part of a return to work agreement between employee and employer.

## 4.9.3 Is testing necessary?

In the past drug and alcohol testing has been considered a controversial and complex issue that has scientific, ethical, legal, social, industrial and economic ramifications. However, many major contracts successfully implement such testing programmes.

It is reasonable to expect employees to be unimpaired by drugs or alcohol whilst at work.

Whether testing is appropriate or necessary should be carefully considered, as the damage to employer-employee relations can potentially outweigh the benefits. However, it may also be a client requirement, which should be explained to the employee at induction.

Whilst acknowledging there may be some circumstances where there is a role for testing employees, *The independent inquiry into drug testing in the workplace* concluded:

> **There is no justification for drug tests as a way of policing the behaviour of the workforce, nor is it an appropriate tool for dealing with most performance issues.**

Whether you decide to introduce testing or not, it must be emphasised that it is not an end in itself. Drug testing is no substitute for good management practice and should never be introduced without the following.

- ☑ Full co-operation from employees.
- ☑ A programme of education for managers and employees.
- ☑ Robust systems for referral to adequately trained health professionals.

### Before considering the introduction of a testing programme, employers should be able to fully answer the following questions

- ☑ Why do we want to test? (What do we hope to achieve by it?)
- ☑ What substances will we test for?
- ☑ Which employees will we test?
- ☑ How will we select them?
- ☑ When will we test them (for example, routinely, randomly, pre-employment)?
- ☑ How often will we test?
- ☑ How will we test (for example, by what method)?
- ☑ Who is best placed to conduct the test (for example, independent company/laboratory, Occupational Health Department)?
- ☑ What will we do with a positive result?
- ☑ What training will be necessary and for whom?
- ☑ What will be the financial costs?
- ☑ What may be the other costs (for example, staff morale)?
- ☑ How will we involve the workforce and gain their consent?
- ☑ What will be our safeguards? (How do we ensure that test results are accurate and legally defensible?)

The conclusions that are drawn from these questions should guide you to a well thought-out and rational decision.

## 4.9.4 Methods of testing

The variety of methods can be confusing for employers, and each testing company will advocate the advantages of their particular approach. It is vital that those wishing to introduce a testing programme are clear about the requirements of each, and consider logistical issues (such as those listed above).

- ☑ Gaining employee consent.
- ☑ Clear explanations of the process to employees.
- ☑ Collection of samples.
- ☑ Second sampling.
- ☑ Legal safeguards (chain of custody).
- ☑ Employee confidentiality.
- ☑ Appropriate privacy.

There is a variety in both the methods used for employee testing and in the standards of service offered by drug-testing companies. As yet there is no universally accepted accreditation scheme or quality standard.

It should also be clearly understood that there is a significant difference between testing for alcohol and testing for other drugs.

Alcohol testing indicates whether an individual is under the influence **at that time**. Drug testing shows traces of drugs used in the past, but does not necessarily confirm impairment at the time of testing.

**Alcohol use** can be tested in two ways.

- ☑ **Breath testing** – a breathalyser measures the level of alcohol in the breath. This is convenient and inexpensive. Employees may be tested prior to commencing a shift, or immediately following an incident.
- ☑ **Blood testing** – this is the most accurate measure of alcohol in the body, although it is more invasive than a breath test. It is often inappropriate in a workplace setting due to lack of staff suitably trained to take samples.

**Drug use** may involve the use of illegal drugs, or prescribed and over-the-counter medicines. These can be detected by gaining samples.

- ☑ **Oral fluid** – not as invasive as other methods but a relatively new technology so may be expensive or inaccurate.
- ☑ **Hair** – not accurate for recent use, but depending on hair length the sample may reflect the individual's drug use pattern over a course of months.
- ☑ **Blood** – very invasive, but can be more accurate than sampling.
- ☑ **Urine** – potentially invasive, but a well-established science.
- ☑ **Skin wipe** – simple and quick to use. Drug metabolites (small molecules) are deposited on the skin by perspiration and remain when sweat evaporates.

# Appendix A – Sample template for developing a drug and alcohol abuse policy

## Drug and alcohol abuse policy

### Introduction

<Company> recognises that alcohol and drug abuse related problems are an area of health and social concern. It also recognises that a member of staff with such problems needs help and support from their employer.

The Company also recognises that alcohol and drug abuse problems can have a detrimental effect on work performance and behaviour. The Company has a responsibility to its employees and customers to ensure that this risk is minimised.

Accordingly, Company policy involves two approaches.

Providing reasonable assistance to the member of staff with an alcohol or drug abuse problem, who is willing to co-operate in treatment for that problem.

Disciplinary rules, enforced through disciplinary procedures, where the use of alcohol or drugs (other than on prescription) affects performance or behaviour at work, and where either (1) an alcohol or drug dependency problem does not exist or (2) where treatment is not possible or has not succeeded.

The Company does not have the internal resources to provide or arrange treatment or other forms of specialist assistance. Such services are provided by GPs, hospitals and other agencies. Through this policy the Company will seek both to assist a member of staff in obtaining such specialist help, and to protect their employment.



### Assistance for a member of staff

The Company will, where possible, provide the following assistance to a member of staff:

- ☑ help the member of staff to recognise the nature of the problem, through referral to a qualified diagnostic or counselling service
- ☑ support them during a period of treatment. This may include a period of sick leave or approved other leave, continuation in post or transfer to other work, depending upon what is appropriate in terms of the staff member's condition and needs of the Company
- ☑ the opportunity to remain or return to work following the completion of a course of treatment, as far as is practicable, in either the employee's own post or an alternative post.

The Company's assistance will depend upon the following conditions being met:

- ☑ the Occupational Health Service/Company-approved doctor diagnoses an alcohol or drug dependency related problem
- ☑ the member of staff recognises that they are suffering from an alcohol or drug abuse problem and is prepared to co-operate fully in referral and treatment from appropriate sources.

The Company and its employees must recognise the following limits, regarding what assistance the Company can provide.

- ☑ Where a member of staff fails to co-operate in referral or treatment arrangements, no special assistance will be given and any failure in work performance and behaviour will be dealt with through the disciplinary procedure.
- ☑ If the process of referral and treatment is completed but is not successful, and failure in work performance or behaviour occurs, these will be dealt with through the disciplinary procedure.
- ☑ A member of staff's continuation in their post or an alternative post during or after treatment will depend upon the needs of the Company at that time.

### Disciplinary action

In line with the Company's disciplinary procedure, the following will be regarded as serious misconduct:

- ☑ attending work and/or carrying our duties under the influence of alcohol or drugs
- ☑ consumption of alcohol or drugs whilst on duty (other than where prescribed or approval has been given).

Breach of these rules will normally result in summary dismissal, and only in exceptional cases will either notice or the reduced disciplinary action of a final written warning be applied.

Where a breach of these rules occurs, but it is established that an alcohol or drug abuse related problem exists, and the member of staff is willing to co-operate in referral to an appropriate service and subsequent treatment, the Company will **suspend** application of the disciplinary procedure and provide assistance as described above.

Staff who do not comply with the treatment suggested or continue to abuse alcohol or drugs will be subjected to the application of the disciplinary policy.

# Drug and alcohol abuse policy *continued*

## Procedures

### Nature of the procedures

The procedures define management responsibilities and provide guidelines on:

- ☑ where assistance to a member of staff should be provided and the nature of and limits to such assistance
- ☑ the application of the Company's disciplinary procedure.

Through the Occupational Health Service/Company-approved doctor, the Company will provide advice and support to managers on:

- ☑ whether an alcohol or drug related problem exists
- ☑ progress in treatment
- ☑ re-establishment or continuation at work of a member of staff or other appropriate arrangements
- ☑ assistance to members of staff with alcohol or drug abuse related problems.

This does not include directly providing treatment or specialist help, which is the responsibility of GPs, hospitals and other agencies working in the field. The Occupational Health Service/Company-approved doctor, in close liaison with these persons and agencies, will assist staff referred in the following ways:

- ☑ through counselling, encouraging them to come to a better understanding of their problem and the benefits of seeking treatment or help
- ☑ providing advice and direction regarding obtaining treatment and specialist help
- ☑ assisting in continuing at or achieving a return to work.

Alcohol or drug abuse related problems can come to the notice of management through:

- ☑ failures in work performance or behaviour necessitating use of the disciplinary procedure. In such situations the procedure described above should be followed
- ☑ other means, whereby a member of staff seeks or agrees to accept assistance on a voluntary basis. In such situations, the procedures described above should be followed.

### Situations where use of the disciplinary procedure is appropriate

#### Recognising the existence of a possible alcohol or drug abuse problem

Abuse of alcohol or drugs can affect performance and behaviour at work. This could be either through serious misconduct at work (where there is a direct and demonstrable breach of the disciplinary rules regarding alcohol or drug abuse at work), or where there is a falling off of standards of work performance or behaviour, and abuse of alcohol or drugs is a possible cause.

The immediate line manager will be responsible for responding to such situations, carrying out either counselling or disciplinary investigations and interviews, supported as appropriate by a more senior manager.

In such interviews the possible existence of an alcohol or drug abuse problem should be explored. The line manager is not required to diagnose the existence of an alcohol or drug abuse problem, merely to assess whether such abuse is a possible factor.

Any requirements of the disciplinary procedure regarding allowing the member of staff representation will be observed.

#### Diagnosing the existence of an alcohol or drug abuse problem

Should the interviews lead to the conclusion that an alcohol or drug abuse problem might exist and the member of staff accepts referral, the manager should refer the matter to the Occupational Health Service/Company-approved doctor, who will be responsible for establishing whether or not a diagnosis of alcoholism or drug dependence can be made.

Disciplinary action should be suspended until diagnostic advice is obtained. Where appropriate, suspension arrangements in the disciplinary procedure should be followed.

If the interview fails to lead to the conclusion that an alcohol or drug abuse problem exists, or the member of staff rejects or fails to co-operate in referral, disciplinary action should be continued, where and as the situation justifies.

#### Confirming that an alcohol or drug abuse problem exists and arranging treatment

If a positive diagnosis of an alcohol or drug abuse problem is made, and the member of staff agrees to co-operate in treatment, treatment arrangements should commence.

## Drug and alcohol abuse policy *continued*

Where necessary, the Occupational Health Service/Company-approved doctor will advise the member of staff regarding treatment and will be responsible for monitoring progress and advising the manager concerned. This advice should be available at least monthly following commencement of treatment and thereafter as appropriate. (Disciplinary action should be discontinued unless the member of staff fails to co-operate with the treatment arranged.) Should a diagnosis of alcoholism or drug dependence not be confirmed, or should the member of staff refuse to co-operate in treatment, disciplinary action should be continued.

The Occupational Health Service/Company-approved doctor will advise on whether there is a lack of progress with treatment or lack of co-operation by the member of staff. Managers must then review the facts and consider whether or not there should be a return to the use of disciplinary procedures.

Where medical certificates are submitted, sick leave should be given. Should the employee continue to be fit for work during the period of treatment, they should be permitted to continue in their post (or alternative work), unless such an arrangement would have an adverse effect on Company services. In such circumstances, annual or unpaid leave should be approved or, exceptionally, suspension arranged.

If a member of staff has been off work during the period of treatment, before returning to duty, they will be seen by the Occupational Health Service/Company-approved doctor who will advise management regarding capability for continuation in their own post and whether any special supervision or other arrangements are required.

Every effort should be made to comply with the advice provided by the Occupational Health Service/Company-approved doctor. If it is not reasonably practicable to do so, and as a result the member of staff is not able to resume duty, employment may be terminated on the grounds of incapacity (ill health).

If a member of staff is again involved in disciplinary situations resulting from alcohol or drug abuse related problems, a second referral to the Occupational Health Service/Company-approved doctor and suspension of the disciplinary procedure may be appropriate. If they advise positively on the possibilities of further treatment or help and the willingness of the member of staff to co-operate, the disciplinary procedure may be suspended again to permit treatment and help to be undertaken. This second referral will not apply if the further disciplinary problems involve serious misconduct. Third and subsequent referrals are not permissible.

### Situations where a disciplinary situation does not exist

There may be situations where the possible existence of alcohol or drug abuse problems affecting a member of staff come to a manager's attention, although there is, or has been, no discernible effect on work performance or behaviour. This could arise if a member of staff confides in their manager about an alcohol or drug abuse problem, or a manager sees a need to approach a member of staff after observing possible indicators of an alcohol or drug abuse problem (such as an absence pattern or information provided by the member of staff's colleagues).

In such situations, the Company would wish staff to feel they could seek help from their employer (in complete confidence) without worry that their job security would be in jeopardy. Accordingly, if managers should be faced with a situation of this type they should:

- ☑ seek the advice of the Occupational Health Service/Company-approved doctor regarding whether and how the matter could be dealt with
- ☑ counsel the member of staff and, if appropriate, arrange for the member of staff to be interviewed by the Occupational Health Service/Company-approved doctor.

As in the procedure described above, the Occupational Health Service/Company-approved doctor will play a facilitating role; seeking to establish whether a problem exists, and advising and directing the member of staff towards appropriate forms of treatment and help.

These steps cannot be taken without the co-operation of the member of staff. If the member of staff does not wish to co-operate, no further action should be taken.

Should a member of staff take up the opportunity of assistance on this voluntary basis there need be no further formal involvement of management in terms of action or the right to learn of progress with treatment. It may be, however, that the member of staff would wish, or agree to, further involvement of management as a means of assisting progress with treatment.

Use of the disciplinary procedures and/or the application of the approach described above would only be appropriate if, subsequently, the member of staff is involved in a breach of disciplinary rules.

Should the problems of the member of staff develop to an extent that their continuation in post or employment became impossible, it may be necessary to identify alternative work or arrange for termination, on the same basis as the Company operates for staff with problems of incapacity due to ill health.

## Drug and alcohol abuse policy *continued*

**<OPTIONAL SECTION>**

## Drug and alcohol testing

<Company> will ensure that all its employees work within the laws of the land. The UK laws on use of drugs and alcohol are clear:

- it is a criminal offence for certain workers (such as drivers or operators of public transport systems) to be unfit for their work due to taking drugs or alcohol
- it is a criminal offence to be unfit to drive, attempt to drive or be in charge of a motor vehicle when under the influence of drugs or alcohol
- the possession, supply or production of controlled drugs is unlawful except for in special circumstances (such as when they have been prescribed by a doctor).

Employees are also legally required to take reasonable care of themselves and to behave in a way that does not pose risks to the health and safety of themselves or others in the workplace. This includes consideration of the effects that intoxication through taking alcohol or drugs may have.

In order to ensure compliance with the law, <Company> will undertake drug and alcohol testing for certain jobs within the Company. These will be carried out pre-employment, as part of a random testing scheme or as a result of an incident. These jobs are:

- <Insert jobs in Company that will be subject to testing – usually posts where safety is vital (such as driving or machine operating posts)>. The Company reserves the right to add to or amend this list as appropriate.

Individuals in these posts will be asked to agree to testing as part of their contract of employment.

To ensure the testing is legal and safe the following arrangements will apply:

- testing will only be carried out as part of this policy, and only by trained staff who will carry out the test in a non-invasive way (usually by urine sample or exhalation)
- samples to be collected under supervised conditions but respecting human dignity (two identical samples are taken, either on site or split in the test laboratory)
- samples to be kept under chain of custody at all times
- screening test for alcohol or common drugs to be carried out on one sample with either positive or negative results
- any positive results from screening to be confirmed by approved scientific techniques
- results to be reviewed by an expert and reported back
- second sample to be kept for further analysis as part of any appeal by the employee
- confidentiality will be maintained at all times.

<Company> believes that effective workplace drug and alcohol policies are a better way of achieving results than drug and alcohol testing and that providing an environment where employees can discuss any drug and alcohol problems they have, with the prospect of gaining help and support, will be more effective than a testing regime. Therefore, the undertaking of drug and alcohol testing in the workplace will be minimal and used only where the Company has a reasonable belief that abuse is taking place.

# 05

# First aid

**Contents**



## Supporting information

**G: Checklists and forms**



**GT 700 Toolbox talks**

## Overview

**In the event of injury or sudden illness, failure to provide first aid could result in a casualty's death. The employer should ensure that an employee who is injured or taken ill at work receives immediate attention.**

**In these scenarios the Health and Safety (First Aid) Regulations require employers to provide adequate and appropriate equipment, facilities and personnel to ensure their employees receive immediate attention. These regulations apply to all workplaces, including those with less than five employees and to the self-employed.**

## 5.1 Introduction

The aim of first aid is to reduce the effects of injury or illness suffered at work, whether caused by the work itself or not.

First aid at work is covered by the **Health and Safety (First Aid) Regulations**, together with approved Health and Safety Executive (HSE) guidance that provides further information on such matters as first-aid equipment and training. The regulations provide a flexible framework within which employers can develop effective first-aid arrangements appropriate to their workplace and the size of their workforce.

Under the regulations, duties are placed on employers to:

- ☑ provide adequate first-aid equipment and facilities appropriate to the type of work or operations undertaken
- ☑ appoint a sufficient number of suitable and trained people to render first aid to employees who are injured or become ill at work
- ☑ appoint a sufficient number of suitable people who, in the temporary absence of the first aider, will be capable of dealing with an injured or ill employee needing help from a medical practitioner or nurse, and who are able to take charge of first-aid equipment and facilities
- ☑ inform employees of the first-aid arrangements, including the location of equipment and personnel. This will require that notices be posted and signs displayed. Provision should be made for employees with language or reading difficulties.

The guidance sets out what employers and the self-employed need to do to address first-aid provision in the workplace. It provides guidance on the following points.

- ☑ Requirements and training for first aiders.
- ☑ Requirements for appointed persons.
- ☑ Managing the provision of first aid (for example, first-aid kit, equipment and room).
- ☑ Making employees aware of first aid arrangements.
- ☑ First aid and the self-employed.
- ☑ Cases where the Health and Safety (First Aid) Regulations do not apply.

**An employer shall inform their employees of the arrangements that have been made in connection with the provision of first aid, including the location of equipment, facilities and personnel.**

It is recommended that first-aid notices are displayed as an effective means of informing the workforce of the employer's arrangement for first aid. Signs should comply with the (Health and Safety) Signs and Signals Regulations.

## 5.2 Important points

- ☑ Trained first-aid staff and first-aid equipment must be available on site.
- ☑ The level of provision of trained staff and first-aid equipment will depend upon the findings of a needs assessment.
- ☑ Everyone working on site should know where the first aiders and the first-aid kits can be found.
- ☑ All accidents causing injury must be recorded in an accident book.
- ☑ In an emergency, assess the situation but do not put yourself in danger.
- ☑ Don't move casualties who are obviously injured unless it is necessary to do so – summon the first aider and dial 999.
- ☑ Cover severe bleeding with a clean pad and apply direct pressure.
- ☑ First aiders have the potential to save lives.

## Adequate and appropriate

The definition of *adequate* and *appropriate* will depend on the circumstances in the workplace. This includes whether trained first aiders are needed, what should be included in a first-aid container and if a first-aid room is required. Employers should carry out an assessment of first aid needs to determine what to provide.

## 5.3 Definition of first aid

First aid is defined in the regulations as:

- in cases where a person will need help from a doctor or a nurse, treatment for the purpose of preserving life and minimising the consequences of injury or illness until such help is obtained
- treatment of minor injuries, which would otherwise receive no treatment or which do not need treatment by a doctor or nurse.

It should be noted that the definition covers any illness at work and not just accidents. You must, therefore, plan for times when someone has a heart attack or collapses.

Emergency first aiders can give a restricted range of first-aid treatment to someone who is injured or becomes ill at work. Fully trained first aiders can do the above, plus apply first aid to a range of specific injuries and illnesses.



## 5.4 Assessing first-aid needs

An employer should make an assessment of first aid needs, appropriate to the hazards and risks of each workplace.

In assessing their needs employers should consider the nature of the work and workplace hazards and risks, as well as the work pattern and size of the organisation. Some of the factors that should be considered are:

- the type of work or operations being carried out
- whether or not employees work alone or in scattered and isolated locations
- whether there are special or unusual hazards
- whether or not there is shift work (first aid cover will be required at all times that work is being carried out)
- the maximum number of people likely to be on site at any one time
- the remoteness of emergency medical services
- cover for first aiders' holidays and sickness absence (first aid cover will be required at all times that work is being carried out)
- the presence of work-placement trainees
- the organisation's history of accidents.

Unless arrangements have been made for the sharing of first aid cover and facilities, all contractors on the site must make their own provisions for their own employees.

On sites where special or unusual hazards are present, a proportionately larger number of first aiders, having regard to the factors already mentioned, will be needed. Good practice should encourage all the contractor's site personnel to be trained in basic emergency first aid.

On major construction projects where there is a site nurse and/or a doctor on call, their advice in connection with first aid should be followed.

**A summary of considerations for assessing first-aid needs has been provided at Appendix B.**

### 5.4.1 Ambulance

The local ambulance service should be informed about large sites and of any particularly hazardous operations being undertaken. It is helpful to supply a map locating the site and its entrances and, where appropriate, the first-aid room.

**Provide 'tear and go' printed map/directions to the nearest Accident and Emergency Department, including phone number and sat-nav postcode.**

### 5.4.2 Induction

Induction training for employees and other persons joining the site should include details of the location of first-aid kits, qualified first-aid personnel and actions to be taken in cases of injury or illness.

### 5.4.3 Responsibility for visitors and other non-employees

The regulations require employers to make first-aid provision for their own employees. However, there is also a general duty upon employers in respect of their premises or work with regard to people who are not their employees, and first-aid arrangements should extend to cover visitors and other non-employees.

### 5.4.4 Shared facilities

Where employees of more than one employer are working together, arrangements may be made for one of the employers to take responsibility for providing first-aid cover. All employers should agree the arrangements and the employees should be kept informed. A written agreement between the employers is recommended.

In such circumstances, it is the responsibility of each employer to ensure that the agreed facilities are actually provided, and that all their employees are aware of these arrangements.



### 5.4.5 Self-employed persons

Self-employed persons must provide adequate first-aid provisions for themselves. However, if they are working from home and the risk is low, normal household first-aid requirements are sufficient. Where the use of potentially dangerous tools and machinery present a hazard, an appropriate first-aid provision should be made. If a self-employed person is working under an employer or with another self-employed person, joint arrangements can be made.

### 5.4.6 Trained and suitable personnel

First aiders must have received training and hold a current first-aid certificate. They must remain competent and so they should undergo refresher training and re-examination as necessary. The employer must keep a written record of such training.

First aid at work certificates, which have been issued by, or in, another country, are not valid in mainland Britain.

### 5.4.7 First aiders

A first aider is someone who has undertaken training and attained a recognised qualification.

They must hold a valid certificate in either:

- first aid at work (FAW)
- emergency first aid at work (EFAW).

Where 25 people are employed at least one first aider should be provided. The needs assessment will help the employer decide how many first aiders are required, dependent on the size of undertaking, the hazards present and the number of people employed.

www.

**The checklist in the HSE guidance (L74) serves as a general guide on the number of first aiders and appointed persons required.**

**The *First aid at work* assessment tool helps employers determine the type and number of first-aid personnel required.**

### 5.4.8 Appointed persons

An appointed person is someone who has been nominated by the employer to take charge of first-aid arrangements, including looking after equipment and facilities and calling the emergency services.

They will act in the absence of the trained first aider or in situations where it is deemed that a first aider is not required (such as in a small, non-hazardous working area) and where there is easy access to professional medical assistance (such as a hospital Accident and Emergency Department).

Appointed persons do not need first-aid training. However, emergency first-aid training could be considered for all appointed persons.

Appointed persons must not be regarded as an alternative to qualified first aiders but they can provide cover when the first aider is absent (excluding annual leave). They must not, however, be required to render first aid.

## 5.5 Equipment and facilities

Based upon the findings of an assessment, the employer must:

- provide and keep stocked suitable first-aid containers and other appropriate equipment (such as eyewash stations and burns kit), as determined by a first aid needs assessment, in places that can easily be accessed by all employees
- display notices giving the identity of first aiders and the location of first-aid equipment.

The needs assessment may indicate that additional materials and equipment are required (for example, disposable aprons). These may be stored in the first-aid container, if there is room, or stored separately.

Personal protective eqiupment (PPE) (such as foil blankets) that is identified as being required (for example, if the first aider has to enter a dangerous atmosphere), should be kept securely near the first-aid container, room or hazardous area, as appropriate.

A suitable first-aid room(s) should be provided where the first-aid needs assessment identifies it as necessary. It is essential that all employees should have quick and easy access to the first-aid facilities on site.

Where employees are working in large numbers and in close proximity, facilities should be centralised in that area. When employees are spread over a wider area, it is necessary to distribute first aiders and equipment accordingly. Sometimes, a combination of these arrangements may be appropriate.

All employees must be aware of the location of first-aid facilities and the arrangements for providing treatment. The location of first-aid facilities should be clearly marked with the appropriate symbol.



### 5.5.1 First-aid containers

Depending on the findings of the first-aid needs assessment more than one first-aid container might be required. They should be strategically placed, easy to get to and clearly marked with a white cross on a green background in accordance with the **Health and Safety (Safety Signs and Signals) Regulations**.

The first-aid container should hold first-aid equipment and nothing else, and should protect the contents from dust and damp. The recommended content of a first-aid kit is contained in the HSE publication *First aid at work*. Generally, medicines, pressure bandages and home remedies should **not** be kept in first-aid kits. If workers require access to prescribed medication it is recommended that they carry their own. A first aider may assist the individual to take their own prescribed medication, but they must not administer it themselves.

#### Medicine legislation restricts the administration of injectable medicines

Unless self-administered, injectable medicines may only be administered by or in accordance with the instructions of a doctor (for example, by a nurse).

Adrenaline is an exemption to this restriction. In an emergency a layperson is permitted to administer adrenaline by injection for the purpose of saving a life. Using an EpiPen to treat anaphylactic shock falls into this category. Therefore, first aiders may administer an EpiPen if they are dealing with a life-threatening emergency, involving a casualty who has been prescribed and is in possession of an EpiPen, and where the first aider is trained to use it. *(Source HSE.)*

It is essential that the contents of first-aid kits are replenished after use and checked frequently by the first aider or appointed person. Some of the items are prone to deterioration after a certain period of time.

**The minimum recommended contents of first-aid kits are listed in Appendix A, which should be adjusted following an assessment of the first aid needs of a specific site.**

### 5.5.2 Travelling first-aid kits

Special or small travelling first-aid kits should be provided to those employees (based on the assessment of their first aid needs):

- who are working alone or in small groups in isolated locations (such as maintenance gangs)
- whose work involves travel in remote areas
- who use potentially dangerous tools or machinery.

Organisations with employees who work in remote areas should consider issuing personal communication devices and also providing additional training.

### 5.5.3 Carrying equipment

Where first aiders are employed, stretchers or appropriate carrying equipment (such as a carrying chair or wheelchair) should be provided in an easy to access location, clearly identified by a sign. If a site covers a large area, or contains a number of distinct working areas, it will be necessary to provide such equipment at a number of suitable locations. However, it is recommended that, in most incidents, casualties are moved as little as possible before the emergency services arrive.

### 5.5.4 Water for eye irrigation

If mains tap water is not readily available for eye irrigation, at least one litre of sterile water or sterile normal saline (0.9% w/v), in sealed, disposable containers, should be provided.

### 5.5.5 First-aid rooms

A suitable first-aid room(s) should be provided where the first-aid needs assessment identifies it as necessary. The assessment will consider the number of persons on the site, the type of work and whether a hospital or other emergency facilities are close to hand.

The first-aid room will normally be under the control of the first aider who should be nearby or on call, with access to the room when employees are at work. The name of this person should be displayed, together with the names and locations of all other first aiders and appointed persons. On some larger sites, the first-aid room will be staffed by a qualified nurse.

The room should be clearly identified, available at all times and used only for rendering first aid. It should be of sufficient size to contain a couch, with adequate space around it to allow people to work, and have an access door to allow the passage of a stretcher or other carrying equipment. Pillows and blankets should be provided and be frequently cleaned.

The room itself should be cleaned each working day, have smooth-topped, impermeable working surfaces and provision for privacy and refuse disposal.

Heating, lighting and ventilation should be effective. In addition to the required first-aid materials, which should be stored in a suitable cabinet, the following could also be provided.

- ☑ A sink with running hot and cold water.
- ☑ Drinking water with disposable cups.
- ☑ Soap, nail brush and paper towels.
- ☑ A chair.
- ☑ A suitable container for disposal of clinical waste (yellow bags).
- ☑ A telephone, where possible, or other communication equipment (such as a siren or klaxon) to alert personnel on call.
- ☑ An accident recording book, for which the first aider or appointed person is responsible.

In first-aid rooms that are supervised by the site nurse, other items may be provided on their advice.

If the first-aid room cannot be reserved exclusively for first aid, employers need to make sure that the first-aid facilities can be made available quickly, if necessary.

Consideration should be given as to whether:

- ☑ the furnishings and equipment can be moved easily and quickly
- ☑ the activities carried out in the room can be stopped immediately
- ☑ there is a storage room for first-aid equipment.

## 5.6 Training and qualifications

The employer is responsible for ensuring that those people who have been selected as fully qualified first aiders have undergone training and possess a recognised qualification. In order to be able to demonstrate compliance with the regulations, employers must keep written records of all training that has been given to employees, along with results of that training. Additional training may be necessary to cope with any special hazards in a particular working environment.

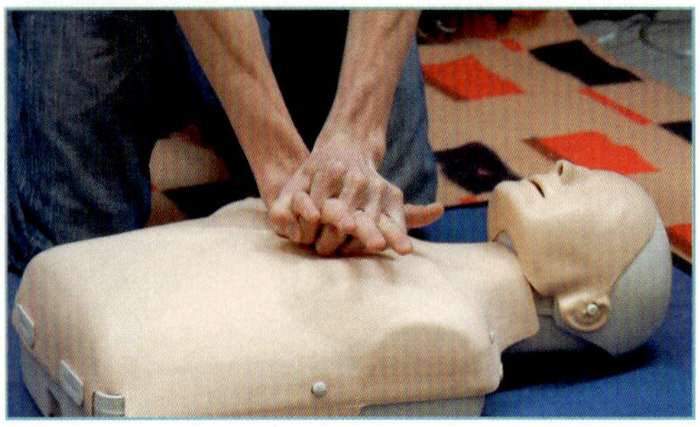

The training of emergency first aiders at work (EFAW) must meet the requirements of the Health and Safety (First Aid) Regulations.

First aiders will hold a valid certificate of competence in either EFAW or FAW.

EFAW training enables a first aider to give emergency first aid to someone who becomes injured or ill while they are at work.

FAW includes EFAW and also equips first aiders to apply first aid to a range of specific injuries and illnesses.

Instruction in emergency first aid (such as resuscitation, control of bleeding and treatment of unconsciousness) is desirable for all staff.

**For guidance on actions to take in an emergency refer to Appendix C.**

## 5.6.1 Initial selection of first aiders

Whilst it is desirable to appoint staff who have already received first-aid training and utilise their skills, in many instances this may not be an option. On most new sites it is unlikely that a trained first aider will be available, and it will be necessary to arrange training for a suitable member of staff.

In selecting people for this role, consideration should be given as to whether they:

- have a friendly, reassuring disposition
- are acceptable to male and female staff
- can cope with stressful and physically demanding emergency procedures
- are able to remain calm in an emergency
- are employed on a task that they can leave immediately in order to go to the scene of an emergency
- are capable of acquiring the knowledge and qualifications required.

## 5.6.2 Training organisations

Training organisations should use training material in accordance with:

- current guidelines published by the Resuscitation Council (UK)
- the latest first-aid manual of Voluntary Aid Societies (St Johns Ambulance, British Red Cross and St Andrew's First Aid)
- other published guidelines, which are in line with the points above, or are supported by a responsible body of medical opinion.

www.

**The HSE provides guidance to assist employers in selecting a competent first-aid training provider.**

**First-aid training providers should demonstrate how they meet the criteria set out by the *Assessment principles for first-aid qualifications*.**

## 5.6.3 Fully qualified first aiders

It may be necessary to provide specialised instruction in the use of protective equipment or rescue techniques, where these are important in the trainee's workplace or if special hazards exist there.

An FAW training course will involve at least 18 hours of training and will run over a minimum of three days. Where an alternative qualification is identified, in place of FAW or EFAW, the employer will need to seek assurance that the standard of training received, and the competence of the organisation that delivered the training, met the criteria outlined in the guidance.

## 5.6.4 First aiders for special or unusual situations

First aiders should have completed training in the subjects described for first aiders, and been given any specialised training related to the particular requirements of their workplace and its hazards. It is the duty of the employer to let the training organisation know if there are any particular hazards at their workplace, so that training can be tailored appropriately.

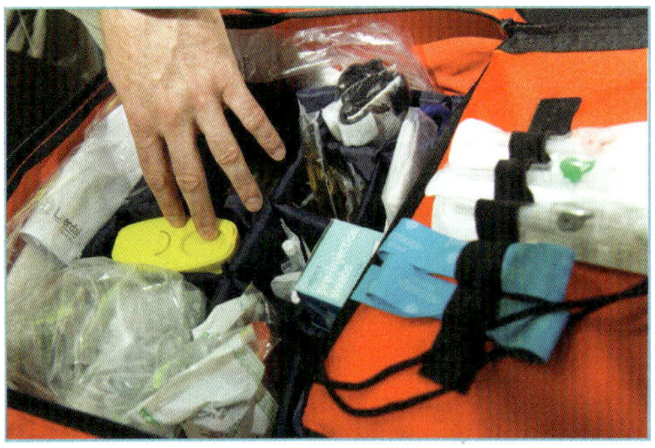

Some workers carry their own medication (such as inhalers for asthma) or Epipens, which contain injectable adrenaline for the treatment of severe allergic (anaphylactic) reactions (for example, to peanuts). These medications are prescribed by a doctor. If an individual needs to take their own prescribed medication, the first aider's role is limited to helping them do so and contacting the emergency services as appropriate.

## 5.6.5 Emergency first aiders

Emergency first aiders must undertake an EFAW course, which involves at least six hours of training and should be run over a minimum of one day. The certificate will be valid for three years. As with fully qualified first aiders, the HSE recommends that emergency first aiders undertake annual refresher training during any three year certification.

### 5.6.6 Appointed persons

To fulfil their role, appointed persons do not need first-aid training, although they may benefit from an EFAW course (or other suitable alternative).

### 5.6.7 Expiry of certificates

All first-aid certificates, whether FAW or EFAW, are valid for three years. Re-qualification training, with re-examination, will be required before re-certification.

First aiders can undertake re-qualification training before the expiry of their current first-aid certificate. The FAW re-qualification course lasts for two days and the EFAW re-qualification course should be of the same duration and content as the initial EFAW course. The new certificate will be dated to run on from the expiry date of the previous one. Ideally, employers will take advantage of this period. Where this is not possible or practical, re-qualification training can be taken at any time after the expiry date. However, if a considerable period has elapsed (for example, more than a month) it would be advisable to complete the three-day FAW course.

It is up to the employer to decide what is the most appropriate training course to re-qualify an individual as a first aider.

### 5.6.8 Annual refresher course

The HSE strongly recommends that first aiders undertake annual refresher training. The suggested content of the annual refresher course includes administering first aid to a casualty who is unconscious, wounded and bleeding, or suffering from shock.

B
05

## 5.7 Accident records

First-aid treatment should be recorded. If the accident book does not allow enough detail to be gathered an additional treatment book may be necessary.

Employers are required to keep accident records under the requirements of the **Social Security (Claims and Payments) Regulations**.

Records can be stored in any medium, including electronic, providing that printable copies are readily available if required.

Records must include the following details.

- ☑ Date, time and place of accident.
- ☑ Full name, address and job of injured or ill person.
- ☑ Details of injury/illness and what first aid was given.
- ☑ What happened to the person immediately afterwards (for example, went home, to hospital, back to work).
- ☑ Name and signature of the first aider or person dealing with the incident.

Details of an accident should be recorded by the injured person, but can be completed by any employee. However, some employers insist that records are completed by first aiders, which requires a first aider to be available at all times. This is a company operating procedure and is not strictly necessary.

Completion of an accident record does not meet the employer's obligation to report specific accidents and dangerous occurrences to the HSE or Local Authority.

This information can help identify accident trends and possible areas for improvement in the control of health and safety risks.

All accident records have had to comply with the **Data Protection Act** to ensure the confidentiality of entries. Accident Book BL510 enables each accident record to be detached and stored separately when complete, thus maintaining the confidentiality of the injured person's details. All personal information must be kept in confidence, and in a secure location (such as a lockable cabinet).

www. **For further information on the Accident Book BL510 refer to the HSE website.**

Accident books designed and produced in-house may still be used, provided that:

- ☑ all details required by BL510 are recorded
- ☑ the requirements of the Data Protection Act are met
- ☑ information recorded electronically can be made readily available in hard copy.

## 5.8 Reporting of Injuries, Diseases and Dangerous Occurrences Regulations

People covered by the regulations include employees, the self-employed and non-workers who have been injured (such as members of the public).

**Trainees are not specifically mentioned within these regulations, but other regulations require that all trainees, including non-employed trainees, must be treated as employees for all health and safety purposes.**

Employers, and others in control of premises, must report and keep the following records.

- Work-related accidents that cause death.
- Work-related accidents that cause certain serious injuries.
- Diagnosed cases of certain individual diseases.
- Certain dangerous occurrences.

RIDDOR applies to all work activities but not all incidents are reportable.

**For further details on RIDDOR refer to Section A: *Legal and management*.**

**For examples of accident report templates and investigations refer to Section G: *Checklists and forms*.**

## Appendix A – Recommended contents of first-aid kits

There is no mandatory list of items that should be included in a first-aid container, but the findings of the first aid needs assessment will influence the contents. As a guide, for low hazard environments, a minimum stock is provided below.

| Item | Quantity in first-aid kits | Quantity in travelling first-aid kits |
|---|---|---|
| First aid guidance card | 1 | 1 |
| Individually wrapped sterile adhesive dressings (assorted sizes) | 20 | 6 |
| Sterile eye pads, with attachment | 2 | Nil |
| Individually wrapped triangular bandages | 2 | 2 |
| Safety pins | 6 | 2 |
| Medium-sized, individually wrapped, sterile, unmedicated wound dressings (approximately 12 cm x 12 cm) | 6 | Nil |
| Large, sterile, individually wrapped, unmedicated wound dressings (approximately 18 cm x 18 cm) | 2 | 1 |
| Individually wrapped, moist cleaning wipes (pack of 10) | Nil | 1 |
| Disposable gloves (pair) | 3 | 2 |

Where tap water is not readily available for eye irrigation, sterile water or sterile normal saline (0.9%) in sealed disposable containers should be provided.

**BS 8599 provides further information on the contents of workplace first-aid kits, but contents should reflect the outcome of the first-aid needs assessment.**

### Travelling first-aid kits

Small, travelling first-aid kits are designed for use where the workforce is dispersed widely (possibly with hazardous tools), for self-employed persons, and for employees working away from their employer's establishment.

**First-aid kits purchased from major chemists or suppliers can vary in size to cater for the numbers of people employed.**

B
05

# Appendix B – Considerations for assessing first-aid needs

## First-aid provision

- ☑ How many employees are involved?
- ☑ How is the workforce distributed/grouped (is it widely dispersed)?
- ☑ Are remote locations involved?
- ☑ Are shifts worked?
- ☑ What is the nature of the work?
- ☑ Does it involve special operations?
- ☑ Can particular hazards be identified (such as falls, electric shock, dangerous substances)?
- ☑ How many first aiders are needed (consider holiday and sickness cover)?

## Training

- ☑ Which personnel require first-aid training?
- ☑ Does the training offered meet foreseeable needs?
- ☑ Is there a system to trigger a warning to management when a first aider is within three months of their certificate expiring?
- ☑ Are training records kept?
- ☑ Are individuals, who are working in isolated locations, trained to cope with emergencies?
- ☑ Where appointed persons are in charge, do they understand their duties?
- ☑ Does induction training cover first-aid arrangements?

## Equipment

- ☑ Is first-aid equipment placed in locations where it is likely to be needed?
- ☑ Does it meet foreseeable needs and special hazards?
- ☑ Are travelling first-aid kits available when required?
- ☑ Is a first-aid room needed, or available, and suitably equipped?
- ☑ Are information signs provided?
- ☑ Are first-aid containers and kits properly stocked and maintained?

## General

- ☑ Has responsibility for first-aid provision and organisation been assigned to an individual?
- ☑ Are there established procedures for reviewing:
  - training and equipment needs
  - new work processes
  - special operations
  - changes in work patterns
  - site locations
  - size of labour force
  - arrangements with contractors?

## Appendix C – What to do in an emergency

General first-aid guidance is given in the HSE publication *Basic advice on first aid at work*. The information in this leaflet, which is reproduced below, is not intended as a substitute for effective training.

### Priorities

- ☑ Assess the situation – do not put yourself in danger.
- ☑ Make the area safe.
- ☑ Assess all casualties and attend first to any unconscious casualties.
- ☑ **Send for help – do not delay.**

Follow the advice given below.



### Check for a response

If there is no response to gentle shaking of the shoulders and shouting, the casualty may be unconscious. Your priorities are to:

- ☑ shout for help
- ☑ open the airway
- ☑ check for normal breathing
- ☑ take appropriate action.

The priority is to check the **A**irway, **B**reathing and **C**irculation. This is the **ABC** of resuscitation.

**A – A**irway

To open the airway:

- ☑ place one hand on the casualty's forehead and gently tilt the head back
- ☑ lift their chin with two fingertips.

**B – B**reathing

Look along the chest, and listen and feel at the mouth for signs of normal breathing, for no more than 10 seconds.

If the casualty **is** breathing:

- ☑ place in the recovery position and ensure the airway remains open
- ☑ get help
- ☑ monitor that the casualty continues to breathe until help arrives.

If the casualty **is not** breathing:

- ☑ get help
- ☑ start chest compressions (see CPR below).

**C – C**PR

To start chest compressions:

- ☑ lean over the casualty and, with your arms straight, press down (5-6 cm) on the centre of the breastbone, and then release
- ☑ repeat at a rate of about 100-120 times a minute (more than one compression per second!)
- ☑ after 30 compressions, open the airway again
- ☑ pinch the casualty's nose closed and allow the mouth to open
- ☑ take a normal breath and place your mouth around the casualty's mouth, making a good seal
- ☑ blow steadily into the mouth while watching for the chest rising
- ☑ remove your mouth from the casualty and watch for the chest falling
- ☑ give a second breath and then start 30 compressions again without delay
- ☑ continue with chest compressions and rescue breaths in a ratio of 30:2 until qualified help takes over or the casualty starts to breathe normally.

## Bleeding

In the case of severe bleeding:

- apply direct pressure to the wound
- raise and support the injured part (unless broken)
- apply a dressing and bandage firmly in place.

## Broken bones and spinal injuries

If a broken bone or spinal injury is suspected, **obtain expert help**. **Do not move casualties** unless they are in immediate danger.

## Burns

Burns can be serious so, if in doubt, **seek medical help**. Cool the part of the body affected with cold water until pain is relieved. Thorough cooling may take 10 minutes or more, but this must not delay taking the casualty to hospital.

Certain chemicals may seriously irritate or damage the skin. Avoid contaminating yourself with the chemical. Treat in the same way as for other burns but flood the affected area with water for 20 minutes. Continue treatment even on the way to hospital, if necessary. Remove any contaminated clothing that is not stuck to the skin.

## Eye injuries

All eye injuries are potentially serious. If there is something in the eye, wash it out with clean water or sterile fluid from a sealed container to remove loose material. **Do not attempt to remove anything that is embedded in the eye.**

If chemicals are involved, flush the eye with water or sterile fluid for at least 10 minutes, whilst gently holding the eyelids open. Ask the casualty to hold a pad over the injured eye and send them to hospital.

## Record keeping

It is good practice to use a book to record any incidents involving injury or illness that you have attended. Include the following information in your entry.

- The date, time and place of the incident.
- The name and job of the injured or ill person.
- Details of the injury or illness and any first aid given.
- What happened to the casualty immediately afterwards (for example, went back to work, went home, went to hospital).
- The name and signature of the person dealing with the incident.

This information can help identify accident trends and possible areas for improvement in the control of health and safety risks.

# 06

# Personal protective equipment

**Contents**



## Supporting information

**G: Checklists and forms**



**GT 700 Toolbox talks**

## Overview

**During the course of their work, building and construction workers will have to wear some items of personal protective equipment (PPE), such as safety helmets, high-visibility (hi-vis) vests, gloves, light eye protection and safety footwear, as a matter of course.**

**Other PPE will have to be provided and worn as required, as indicated by the findings of a risk assessment or safe system of work. PPE should always be considered as a last resort; over reliance is sometimes placed on the need to wear PPE, as opposed to eliminating the risk at source.**

## 6.1 Introduction

Personal protective equipment (PPE) is any item of equipment or clothing that is used or worn by a person to protect them from any identified risk to their health or safety. A sub-group of that, designed to protect the wearer against respiratory (breathing) hazards (such as the inhalation of dust and fumes), is known as respiratory protective equipment (RPE).

Within the construction industry PPE is commonly thought of as equipment that is used to protect the head, ears, eyes, respiratory (breathing) system, skin, hands and feet.

However it must be appreciated that PPE is also commonly used for the following reasons during construction work.

- ☑ To prevent or arrest falls (for example, harnesses and lanyards).
- ☑ To enable a person in distress to be rescued from a confined space (for example, a rescue harness or escape RPE).
- ☑ To enable someone who has fallen into water to stay afloat and be rescued (for example, a lifejacket).



If it is found necessary for employees to wear PPE, its selection and use must comply with the Personal Protective Equipment at Work Regulations, to ensure that it will effectively protect the user against the hazard for which it has been selected.

All PPE must bear the CE mark to show conformity with European Standards. When employers are deciding how best to protect employees from a risk to their health and safety at work, the decision to issue PPE may only be made where it is found that the risk cannot be adequately controlled by other means that are equally or more effective. In effect, the issue and use of PPE is the last resort in terms of risk control.

PPE must be selected by a competent person who, if necessary in conjunction with the suppliers, can identify the PPE that will be effective against the hazards present in the workplace. An example of this is the selection of the correct type of respirator or filter to protect the user against the various types of airborne substances, either particles or gases.

It must be remembered that failure of an item of PPE, or the wrong type of PPE being used, could expose an employee to the possibility of occupational ill health, serious injury or death.

## 6.2 Important points

- ☑ The correct use of PPE is essential in many cases to protect the wearer from harm.
- ☑ Given the nature of most construction sites, the use of some mandatory items of PPE (such as safety helmets and safety footwear) is a daily occurrence.
- ☑ However, it must be remembered that the use of PPE as a means of protecting against risks to health or safety is the last resort; it only protects the wearer and only then if it is:
  - the right PPE for the job
  - in good working order
  - being used properly.
- ☑ Employers have a legal duty to investigate the use of other protective measures before resorting to the issue of PPE.
- ☑ Employees must look after the PPE that has been issued to them and inform their employer if it becomes defective, damaged or is lost.
- ☑ Employees have a legal duty to be supplied the necessary PPE free of charge.
- ☑ RPE is a sub-group of PPE.
- ☑ Managers and supervisors must set an example and wear PPE if needed.

## 6.3 Personal Protective Equipment at Work Regulations

The Personal Protective Equipment at Work Regulations cover the general provision and use of PPE. However, specific PPE, specified by a risk assessment (for example, hearing protection or RPE) are covered by other regulations.

### The following regulations have alternative requirements

- The Ionising Radiation Regulations.
- The Control of Lead at Work Regulations.
- The Control of Asbestos Regulations.
- The Control of Substances Hazardous to Health Regulations.
- The Control of Noise at Work Regulations.

However, this does not mean that PPE need not be provided where it is required when carrying out work under the above regulations.

Where work is carried out under any of the above regulations, any PPE required must be provided to comply with the respective set of regulations. For example, hearing protection **must be** provided to meet the requirements of the Control of Noise at Work Regulations, not the Personal Protective Equipment at Work Regulations.

The Personal Protective Equipment at Work Regulations require that where a risk has been identified by a risk assessment and it cannot be adequately controlled by other means, which are equally or more effective, then the employer must provide **suitable** PPE and ensure that it is correctly used and cared for by employees.

Detailed requirements of any such risk assessment are specified in the regulations and require the problem to be thought through in a structured manner and the right equipment chosen for the right reasons.

A vital factor is the competence of the person carrying out the assessments. If they do not get it right, the consequences for the health and safety of employees could be very serious.

In essence, PPE may only be used as a last resort after all other means of eliminating or controlling the risk have been considered.

In deciding which type to issue, the employer must take into account the hazard that the PPE is being used to protect against and ensure that the PPE will fit the wearer and allow them to work safely. If more than one item of PPE is being used at any one time, the employer must make sure that individual items of PPE are compatible and do not adversely affect the performance of each other.

This is of particular importance in the building and construction industry since operatives often need to simultaneously wear a combination of PPE (such as safety helmets, eye protection, ear protection or respiratory protection).

Employers are responsible for providing, replacing and paying for PPE for their employees. It is an offence to charge an employee for any item of PPE that the employer is required to provide under any legislation.

However, some employers come to an agreement with their employees whereby PPE (for example, safety boots) are purchased by the employee and then subsidised by the employer, or provided under other schemes or conditions.

Further complications can arise as to whether the employer is responsible for the safety of labour-only employees and some other categories of site-based staff. It is suggested that this is agreed at the start of the contract, and documented in the health and safety plan.

Whenever PPE is to be issued, the employer must ensure that employees have been given adequate and appropriate information, instruction and training to enable the employees to understand the risks being protected against, the purpose of the PPE and the manner in which it is to be used.

Whilst the employer must ensure that PPE is supplied and used, the employee has the following duties.

- Properly use the PPE provided, in accordance with the information, instruction and training that they have been given.
- Return PPE to its storage facility, where provided, after use.
- Know the procedures for reporting loss of any PPE or defects in it to their employer.

### 6.3.1 Supplying suitable PPE

Employers must provide **suitable** PPE to employees, and the self-employed must ensure that they are provided with **suitable** PPE.

Where a risk cannot be adequately controlled in some other manner that is equally or more effective, PPE will only be deemed to be **suitable** in the following situations.

- If it is appropriate for the risks involved and the conditions of exposure.
- When it takes account of the ergonomic requirements and state of health of the user.
- When it can fit the wearer properly, if necessary after adjustment.
- As far as is practicable, when it effectively prevents or adequately controls exposure to risk without increasing the overall risk.
- When it complies with any relevant European Community directive.

**The Health and Safety at Work Act requires that employers provide PPE free of charge.**

Also supplying one-size-fits-all PPE (such as gloves) or one size of hi-vis vests (for example, XXL) may not offer everyone the same level of protection and could introduce other risks (such as entanglement or snagging).

Employers must ensure the compatibility of PPE when more than one item of PPE must be worn at any one time, so that one item does not reduce the protection offered by another.

## 6.3.2 Assessing suitability

Employers must carry out assessments of the suitability of PPE regarding the nature of the risk, before selecting it. The assessment must consider the following points.

- ☑ The risks to health and safety that have not been controlled by other means.
- ☑ The nature of the risks to health and safety, against which the PPE is to protect the user.
- ☑ A comparison of the nature of the risks and the performance capabilities of the PPE.
- ☑ The compatibility of the PPE under consideration and any other PPE that will be worn at the same time.

## 6.3.3 Reviewing the assessment

Employers must ensure that the following points are adhered to.

- ☑ Review such assessments if it is thought that they are no longer valid or if there has been a significant change in the matters to which it relates.
- ☑ Incorporate any changes that are indicated by the review.



## 6.3.4 Maintenance and storage

Employers must ensure that PPE that has been provided to employees is maintained (which includes replacement or cleaning) in an efficient state, efficient working order and good repair. The same duty is on **self-employed** persons with regard to any PPE provided to them.

Employers and self-employed persons must provide suitable storage facilities for PPE that has been issued, for when it is not in use.

## 6.3.5 Information, instruction and training

Employers who have provided employees with PPE must also provide **adequate and appropriate** information, instruction and training to enable employees to know the following.

- ☑ The risk(s) for which the PPE has been provided.
- ☑ The purpose for which, and the manner in which, the PPE is to be used.
- ☑ Any actions that they (the users) must take to keep the PPE in the correct condition.
- ☑ Any information that should be available to them.

To be adequate and appropriate, the information must be understandable by the persons receiving it.

Training can be theoretical and/or practical. Where appropriate the employer should, at appropriate intervals, arrange suitable demonstrations in the correct wearing of PPE.

## 6.3.6 Usage and defects

Legal duties are required of the following people.

- ☑ Employers to take reasonable steps to ensure that the PPE provided to employees is used correctly.
- ☑ Employees to use the PPE provided in accordance with any instruction and training provided.
- ☑ Self-employed persons to make full and proper use of PPE.
- ☑ Employees and the self-employed to take reasonable steps to return PPE to any storage facilities provided.
- ☑ Employees to report any defect in the PPE issued, or the loss of it, to the employer as soon as possible.

# 6.4 Using personal protective equipment

After carrying out a risk assessment, in accordance with the Management of Health and Safety at Work Regulations, the employer or self-employed person must then implement measures to control the risks identified. This may involve the identification and issue of appropriate PPE. However, PPE must only be selected as a means of controlling risks as a last resort.

All other methods of controlling the risks arising from the work activity must have been considered and found not to be reasonably practicable before the decision is taken to use PPE as a means of reducing the risk.

Construction industry workers will need to wear or use PPE on many occasions. They will wear or use it for one of two reasons.

- ☑ They have been told to (site rules).
- ☑ It makes sense.

The more often that it is done for the second reason, the better. In circumstances when wearing or using PPE is necessary it must become second nature for those workers who are at risk. However, at present this is still often not the case. For example:

- ☑ cases of occupational asthma and dermatitis show that PPE that protects the skin and respiratory system are not being used where they should; the problem is not being taken seriously either by employers, supervisors or employees
- ☑ deaths have occurred through falls, either because a harness and lanyard were not being worn or because they were worn but the free end of the lanyard was not clipped onto a suitable anchorage point.

There is the temptation to ignore the need to wear PPE and the protection it gives because 'the job will only take a minute' … and that 'minute' may be all the time that the job needs to kill or injure someone.

It must be remembered that, for PPE to be fully effective, the user must have received adequate training and instruction in its use and it must:

- ☑ have been designed to protect the user against the type of hazard that will be present
- ☑ be available at all times that it is needed
- ☑ be adjusted properly where necessary
- ☑ fit the wearer properly and be compatible with other PPE worn at the same time
- ☑ be worn/used during the period(s) of risk
- ☑ be treated with care and returned to its storage after use, where this is necessary
- ☑ be inspected and maintained as necessary
- ☑ be replaced if it becomes defective.



Failure of an item of PPE, or using the incorrect type of PPE, could expose an employee to the possibility of serious injury, ill health or even death.

Employers are likely to be far more successful in persuading employees to wear the PPE provided if the employees themselves are involved in the process of selecting the PPE purchased.

PPE can be cumbersome and uncomfortable and the cheapest may not be the most suitable for the wearer. In such circumstances the likelihood is that it will not be worn, at least not for long, leaving the worker unprotected against the hazard.

It is much better to purchase PPE that fits comfortably and will be used willingly.

The PPE selected must offer the level of protection required for the hazard(s) that have been identified. For example, whether the job involves the following.

- ☑ The use of substances that have the potential to create hazardous dust or fumes.
- ☑ The use of substances that could irritate or burn the skin.
- ☑ Creating airborne dust through cutting, grinding, and so on.
- ☑ Creating fumes from hot-work processes.
- ☑ Any process that could result in eye injuries.
- ☑ Working at height in circumstances where the wearing of a harness and lanyard is the only practical fall protection measure.

**As well as assessing PPE for the task you must also assess any additional PPE requirements for the surrounding site conditions or additional hazards (such as noise, dust, fumes, falling objects and so on).**

Manufacturers and suppliers have a statutory duty to provide information regarding the performance characteristics of the PPE products that they manufacture or sell. If necessary, they should be consulted.

For some basic PPE (such as a pair of general safety spectacles) the exact fit may not be an issue. However, in selecting some PPE (such as in the examples below), achieving a satisfactory fit is essential.

- ☑ When a respirator is to be used, the effectiveness of the device is dependent upon the face fit, which in turn will require that the head-harness straps be adjusted to suit the wearer and their facial features.
- ☑ Adjusting the head-harness of a safety helmet to suit the wearer will ensure that it is comfortable and secure.
- ☑ Gloves should be a close fit to protect from chemical ingress, entanglement and to maximise dexterity (buying gloves in only one size should be avoided).
- ☑ Adjusting the fit of a safety harness, which could at worst have to take the shock loading of an arrested fall, is essential if the harness is to be fully effective.

Where a satisfactory fit is not, or cannot, be achieved, the wearer is likely to suffer discomfort and is much more likely to stop using the PPE and also lose concentration regarding the job in hand.

The employee's co-operation must be established in the selection of comfortable and acceptable PPE.

e.g.

**Consider the potential wearers' physical needs. If they wear glasses and have to wear a mask, goggles or safety glasses, they may require a special type. If they have a beard and have to wear respiratory equipment, can they obtain an airtight seal? These are crucial considerations.**

Supervisors must ensure that employees understand 'why', 'what', 'who', 'how' and 'when' there is a need for PPE.

- ☑ **Why** is the PPE needed?
- ☑ **What** will be the implications of not wearing it?
- ☑ **Who** is going to provide the PPE along with all necessary information, instruction, training and supervision?
- ☑ **How** is it fitted, worn or adjusted?
- ☑ **When** must it be worn?

!

**Protection is available for the hazard that you are about to work with. Find it and use it.**



## 6.4.1 Combinations of personal protective equipment

In many circumstances it will be necessary for operatives to simultaneously wear more than one item of PPE.

*Wearing a combination of PPE*

Whilst this is entirely acceptable, attention should be given to ensuring that the different types of PPE are compatible with each other, to avoid the possibility of a dangerous situation.

For example, hearing protectors that are fitted directly to a safety helmet will not be effective if the safety helmet is poorly fitted and, by moving around on the head, does not allow the hearing protectors to form an effective seal around the ears.

## 6.4.2 Counterfeit personal protective equipment

The British Safety Industry Federation (BSIF) is a trade body which, amongst other things, represents the interests of the manufacturers of PPE within the United Kingdom.

In recent years the BSIF has become aware of the emergence of counterfeit PPE which, in many cases, looks identical to genuine PPE produced by reputable manufacturers. Much of the counterfeit PPE comes into the UK from abroad.

www.

**The BSIF has issued a safety flash highlighting dangerous counterfeit safety helmets, which is available online.**

It is likely that the people within companies who are responsible for purchasing and issuing PPE will be unable to distinguish counterfeit and non-conforming items from the genuine article. Frequently these products are incorrectly (fraudulently) CE marked and do not perform to the required standard. The wearer or user of the PPE will almost certainly be unaware of any problems until it is too late.

It is recommended that PPE is only purchased from reputable suppliers and offers of unduly cheap PPE are resisted.

## 6.5 Hearing protection

Many types of building and construction activity and equipment generate excessive noise, which can cause permanent hearing damage in those exposed to it, unless appropriate control measures are put into place.

Excessive noise can also cause annoyance, fatigue, loss of concentration and disrupted communication, and may lead directly or indirectly to an increased risk of accidents. Whilst the law requires that the use of PPE as a control measure is only considered as the last resort, the practicalities of working in a construction site environment mean that hearing protection is often the only way of controlling personal exposure to noise.

There are two basic types of hearing protection.

- ☑ Earplugs (either disposable or reusable).
- ☑ Ear defenders.

Hearing protection helps block out hazardous noise. The amount of noise blocked out or reduced is known as attenuation.

To achieve the stated attenuation levels of hearing protection it is vital that it is worn correctly.

### 6.5.1 Earplugs

#### 6.5.1.1 Disposable earplugs

These are made of very fine mineral fibre, sometimes ready shaped. They must be inserted correctly and, if taken out, should not be reused. They should only be handled with clean hands.

When it comes to protection from hazardous noise, earplugs are designed to be a safe distance from the sensitive eardrum, even when deeply inserted.

Employees need to be instructed on how to insert disposable earplugs correctly. Disposable earplugs are frequently worn incorrectly, by users not inserting them deeply enough.

A poorly fitted foam earplug actually offers little or no protection from noise.



#### 6.5.1.2 Reusable earplugs

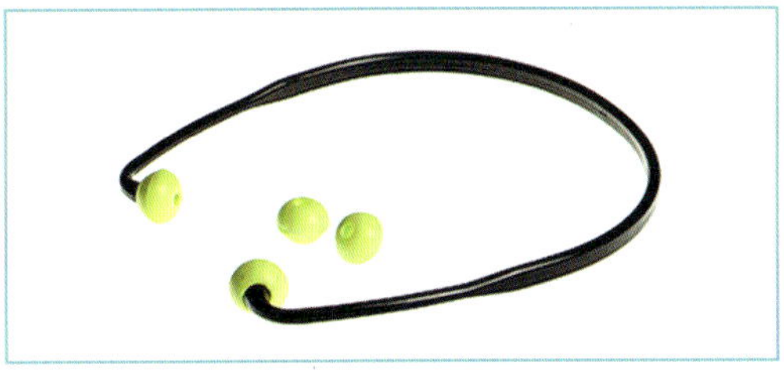

These are made of rubber or plastic, and need regular and careful washing. They must be a good fit. A competent person should be responsible for instructing employees in their correct fitting and use. Different sizes may be required for each ear.

Reusable earplugs, like disposable ones, must be fitted with clean hands, as any contamination by dirt, grease or swarf may cause ear irritation.

#### 6.5.1.3 Moulded earplugs

These are individual moulded earplugs, which are moulded to the shape of the ear. Even though these are initially more expensive, they can offer a longer life span and potential cost savings. It is believed that moulded earplugs offer an improved level of hearing protection and comfort, compared to other earplugs and defenders.

### 6.5.2 Ear defenders

Ear defenders, sometimes referred to as earmuffs, completely cover the ear, and are sealed to the head with a foam or liquid-filled seal. Badly designed or badly produced ear defenders may give little or no protection against the noise.

Ear defenders can be worn over safety glasses but the determining factor is the width of the eyeglass frame where it meets the earmuff cushion. Thin frames (thickness of 2 mm or less) cause very little obstruction to the seal, resulting in no measurable change in attenuation of the earmuff. Thicker frames (typically seen on safety glasses with adjustable sidebars) can reduce attenuation by 10 decibels. If workers must wear earmuffs over safety glasses, thin frames should be chosen for best attenuation. Alternatively, earmuffs can be fitted to certain types of safety helmets, and this might be a better solution for a worker who wears glasses.

**For further information refer to Chapter B13 Noise.**

## 6.6 Eye protection

- ☑ Many eye injuries occur to people at work each year because eye protection is not being worn.
- ☑ These accidents are easily preventable simply by wearing the correct type of eye protection.
- ☑ The loss of sight, even in one eye, will have a profound effect on the sufferer and is likely to affect future job prospects and earning power.
- ☑ Given the nature of most construction sites, in many cases protection of the eyes will be achieved by the issue and wearing of appropriate PPE.
- ☑ In common with other types of PPE, employers must:
  - identify the correct type of eye protection necessary
  - provide it at no charge to employees who need it
  - provide adequate information, instruction and training in its use
  - make sure that it is worn.
- ☑ Users of eye protection must:
  - wear it when there is a risk of eye injury as indicated by a risk assessment
  - look after it, particularly with regard to protecting the lenses or face shield
  - return it to any accommodation allocated to it when not in use
  - report to the employer any defect (such as scratched or crazed lenses) and obtain a replacement
  - report to the employer if it is lost and seek a replacement.

*Wear eye protection*

The Control of Artificial Optical Radiation at Work Regulations (AOR) came into effect in 2010 and apply to a limited number of construction industry activities.



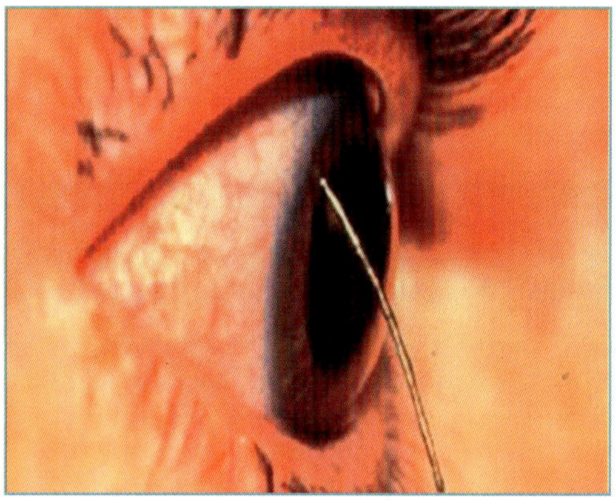

*Eye injury sustained as a result of not wearing eye protection*

There are, on average, 1,000 injuries to people's eyes every working day. Some injuries are so severe that they cause partial or even total blindness. A person's eyes are very vulnerable and an accident or injury can completely change that person's way of life.

Analysis of injuries to people's eyes shows that damage is caused:

- ☑ 75% by impact
- ☑ 10% by abrasion following ingress of dust or other foreign body
- ☑ 15% by burns or chemical contamination.

The majority of these injuries would have been prevented if the correct eye protection had been worn.

The Personal Protective Equipment at Work Regulations make provision for the protection of the eyes of employees at work, and also persons not employed, who may be at risk.

The protection provided must conform to the approved specifications and includes goggles, visors, spectacles, face screens and fixed shields, either free standing or attached to machinery or plant.

Construction personnel involved in a wide range of work (for example, grinding, welding, cutting, hammering and handling chemicals) run the risk of eye injury. Some risks are listed below.

- ☑ Impact of solids.
- ☑ Ingress of liquid, dust or gas.
- ☑ Splashes of hot metal.
- ☑ Exposure to glare.

All types of eye protection must meet the following requirements.

- ☑ Comply with European Standard specifications.
- ☑ Suit the type of work or risk involved, including resistance to impact, heat, dust and chemical penetration.
- ☑ Suit the user to ensure minimum discomfort and ease of movement whilst working.
- ☑ Be marked to identify their type and suitability.
- ☑ Be kept clean and disinfected.

## 6.6.1 Types of eye protector

There are several types of eye protector and it is important to select and issue the correct type to give the required protection.

**For eye protector types and their markings refer to Appendix B.**

*General purpose safety spectacle*

*Face shield*



### Eye protection safety

- Have operations requiring eye protection been identified?
- Has the work activity been assessed to determine what, if any, hazards exist?
- Are appropriate types of eye protection available for the various work to be carried out?
- Does all eye protection comply with the relevant standard?
- Is the eye protection supplied on a personal basis to employees?
- Are there sufficient quantities of eye protectors available for occasional users?
- Is the use of eye protection satisfactorily monitored?
- Have employees been informed of work activities requiring eye protection?
- Have employees been trained in the correct use and maintenance of eye protection?
- Are employees aware of their responsibilities with regard to the care and reporting of loss or defective eye protectors?
- Are appropriate safety signs displayed?

All eye protectors and shields provided must comply with British and European Standard specifications and meet the following requirements.

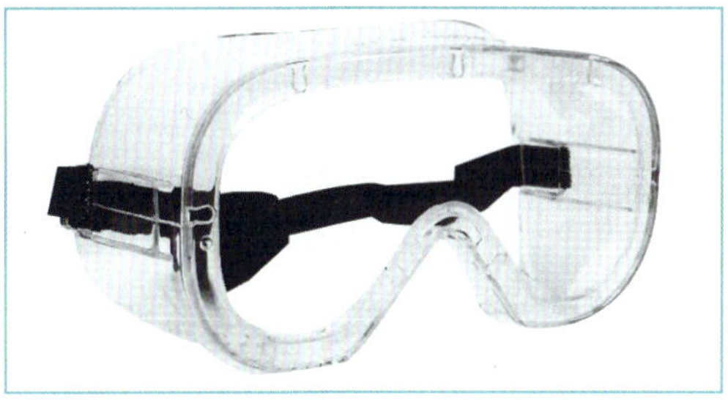

*Safety goggles*

- Be suitable for the type of work or risk involved.
- Be suitable for the user to give them minimum discomfort and ease of movement whilst working.
- Be marked to identify their type and suitability.
- Be maintained, kept clean and disinfected.

The following requirements are specific for **eye protectors.**

- Should be issued on a personal basis to the person at risk.
- Sufficient numbers should be maintained and readily available for persons occasionally employed.
- Sufficient numbers should be kept available so if any become lost, destroyed or defective they can be replaced.

The following requirements are specific for **fixed shields**.

- Must conform to the relevant European Standard specification.
- Must be cleaned regularly, disinfected and properly maintained.
- Must be constructed and kept in position so that they protect the eyes.

### 6.6.2 Identifying the type of hazard

Only when the employer has carried out a risk assessment to determine the hazards can the correct type of eye protector be supplied.

Some of the types of hazard detailed require eye protectors to have sufficiently strong lenses or shield to withstand the impact of particles or fragments striking them.

The effectiveness of the seal made between the eye protectors and the operator's skin is very important in affording protection against the type of hazard where irritant or corrosive materials are involved.

The ability to withstand high temperatures or reduce strong light and glare is a main requirement for the other types of eye protector.

**For further information concerning specific requirements or combinations of different kinds of protection, manufacturers' literature should be consulted.**

### 6.6.3 Lasers

- Full training and information must be given to persons using lasers.
- There should be no unauthorised access to any laser equipment.
- All personnel must be aware of the hazards when working with lasers, the safe working procedures and accident reporting procedures.
- Any necessary eye protection equipment, hazard signs or barriers, for example, must be available and in use as necessary.
- Any eye protectors used in conjunction with lasers must be suited to the wavelength of the laser in use. General purpose safety glasses offer no protection whatsoever against lasers and should not be used.
- All hazard areas must be clearly defined with signs and barriers.
- The laser beam should only be directed at non-reflecting surfaces. Any adjacent reflective surfaces must be covered; otherwise the beam will diverge and could affect other areas and people not directly involved in the job.
- Extra care must be taken when working near reflective surfaces (for example, water, dust and spray) that cannot be marked or covered.
- Special precautions must be taken when working near roads, airfields and other public areas, where a stray beam could cause a hazard.
- When work requires the use of high-powered lasers, the work should, when possible, be undertaken when the site is vacated (such as evenings or weekends). If this is not possible, special precautions will be necessary to ensure that unauthorised persons do not enter the work area or any designated area.

Items of equipment producing light amplification by the stimulated emission of radiation, more normally known as lasers, are widely used on construction sites, mainly for alignment and levelling in civil engineering. Most are of the helium or neon continuous wave type and emit visible light, but some lasers emit in the invisible infrared region of the electromagnetic spectrum, and these require extra caution.

The Health and Safety Executive (HSE) says that it receives few reports of ill health or injury arising from the use of lasers. However, those that are reported arise from misuse of the equipment. The optical radiation produced by a laser is absorbed by the first few centimetres of the body and so the skin and eyes are the tissues most at risk of damage.

All lasers should comply with BS EN 60825. This standard groups laser products into five classes (with some sub-classes), based on acceptable emission levels, and is intended to ensure that the manufacturer and user of laser products comply with current requirements. It should be noted that if users modify instruments (for example, by adding lenses) they take on the responsibilities of a manufacturer for the class of laser.

The use of Class 1 and 2 products is preferred on construction sites because these represent the lowest risk of eye injury. However, even these lower power lasers can cause eye damage if they are misused (for example, staring directly into the beam or viewing the beam through any magnifying device).

Class 3R and 3B lasers, which may sometimes be in use, can involve hazards to both the user and other personnel. Those who maintain, operate and supervise the use of these products must be fully trained, competent and capable of implementing the necessary safety and hazard control procedures.

Where lower power lasers are used, the human blink reflex will offer some protection. However, this should not be relied upon and is unlikely to offer any protection from higher power laser.

*Laser beam*

**For a table showing laser health risks and control refer to Appendix A.**

## Laser eye injury

In the event of an eye injury, caused by a laser, ensure the following.

- ✓ No medication is applied to the eye.
- ✓ The eye involved should be covered with a clean, dry material.
- ✓ Immediate medical attention should be sought.

A thorough ophthalmic examination should be carried out within 24 hours, with a full biophysical investigation.

## Laser safety

- ✓ Has a risk assessment been carried out?
- ✓ Are only competent and trained people allowed to operate laser equipment?
- ✓ Has the hazard area been defined and clearly marked?
- ✓ Has an exclusion zone been created if the more powerful classes of laser are being used?
- ✓ When work with lasers is taking place, are only authorised people allowed in the area?
- ✓ Is correct eye protection in use during all laser operations?
- ✓ Is there no danger to any other person(s) resulting from stray reflections or from any activity involving the use of lasers?
- ✓ Where necessary, is the source and direction of the laser beam clearly identified?
- ✓ Is the laser beam only directed at a non-reflecting surface?
- ✓ Are any other reflective surfaces covered?
- ✓ Does all laser equipment comply with BS EN 60825?
- ✓ Are beam attenuators and any other safety devices in use when using Class 3R and 3B products?

## 6.7 Respiratory protective equipment

### 6.7.1 Hazards

Dust has long been known as hazardous to the health of construction workers, especially when inhaled for long periods. While the health issues associated with asbestos are well recognised, the greater part of the dust problem in the industry currently relates to more common substances (for example, cement, plaster, wood, MDF, stone, silica, fillers and plastics). High-speed cutting of most materials can produce sufficient dust to cause a health hazard.

Dust that is visible in the air is generally accepted as being hazardous. However, dust that is too fine to be seen by the naked eye also causes many health problems, the symptoms of which may take many years to manifest themselves. Small dust particles of any material entering the lungs can be absorbed into the body and can cause scarring and sometimes cancer within the lungs.

Skin irritation, dermatitis and ulceration can be caused by contact with some dusts, and eating food with dirty or dust-covered hands can cause stomach disorders.

Fumes from certain substances (such as solvents, paints and adhesives) can have serious health implications. When used in poorly ventilated or confined spaces, it is not uncommon for fatalities to occur.

Such problems are unlikely to arise if occupational exposure limits and the Control of Substances Hazardous to Health Regulations (COSHH) are observed and safe systems of work maintained.

Whenever RPE is to be used for work in circumstances where the COSHH, lead or asbestos regulations apply, then, in line with the supporting Approved Codes of Practice, face-fit testing for employees should be carried out. This test checks that a facepiece (the respirator) matches the person's facial features and seals adequately to the wearer's face. It will also ensure that incorrectly fitting facepieces are not selected for use. This test must be carried out by a competent person.

Research indicates that up to 50% of all RPE used does not offer the level of protection assumed.

**The presence of facial hair in the region of the face seal will significantly reduce the protection provided.**

**The British Safety Industry Federation (BSIF) has introduced a scheme for facepiece fit testers, which may help you decide whether a fit tester is competent.**

The training of employees in the correct use of RPE is essential before first use and should be repeated at suitable intervals. It is essential that training is carried out by a competent person and it covers the following.

- Why the RPE is necessary.
- The hazards, the risks and the effects of exposure.
- What RPE is to be provided.
- How the RPE works.
- Why face-fit testing might be necessary.
- How to wear and check the RPE correctly.
- What maintenance is required and when.
- Where and how to clean the RPE and store it.
- How to report defects in the RPE or any other problem with it.
- The employer's responsibilities and those of employees.
- Use and misuse of RPE.

## 6.7.2 Selecting respiratory protective equipment

When selecting suitable RPE it may be necessary to seek expert advice from manufacturers or suppliers. Training in the types and use of respiratory equipment must be given. RPE must reduce exposure to as low as reasonably practicable, which must be below any workplace exposure of control limits.

**Guidance and recommendations are provided in the HSE publication *Respiratory protective equipment at work: a practical guide*.**



The provision and use of RPE must only be considered when equally or more effective protective control measures cannot be used. The failure of RPE could have serious consequences.

The importance of the correct type of RPE being provided and used cannot be overstated as it must be assumed that the user will be working in a hostile environment. However, there are several potential problems arising from the selection and/or use of RPE.

- The **failure** of an item of RPE where, for whatever reason (such as lack of routine maintenance), it fails to provide the necessary level of protection.
- The **misuse** of RPE (such as it being mistreated or not used in accordance with the manufacturer's instructions or the training given).
- It being the **wrong type** of RPE (for example there would be no protection from a filtering respirator designed solely to capture airborne dust if being used where the workplace hazard is in fact a toxic gas).
- The effectiveness of the **face fit**. Many types of RPE depend upon a good seal between the facepiece and the skin of the user at all times, including where physical activity and exertion are required. Factors such as facial hair or the shape of the face can interfere with a good fit.

Where the wearing of RPE is inevitable, European Standard BS EN 529 recommends that employers and the self-employed define and document a policy covering the selection, use and maintenance of RPE, which is communicated to, and understood by, all levels of the organisation.

Each type of RPE is assigned a filter protection factor, which gives the user some idea of the level of protection that the device will provide. For example, a filtering half-mask marked:

- **FFP1** is a low efficiency device offering a protection factor of four
- **FFP2** is a medium efficiency device offering a protection factor of 10
- **FFP3** is a high efficiency device offering a protection factor of 20.

A protection factor of 10 means that in controlled conditions, for every 10 units of contaminant outside the mask, only one unit will get inside the mask, or for every 20 units outside the mask there will be two units inside, and so on. It is important, therefore, that the correct filter is selected for the type and level of contaminant in the air.

**It is recognised good practice to use RPE with an FFP3-rating to protect against dust (such as silica) that is created when mechanically cutting concrete, bricks, slabs and so on – even when wet cutting, which only removes about 75% of airborne particles.**

There are many types of RPE. Some examples are listed below.

- ☑ Disposable face-mask respirators.
- ☑ Half-mask dust respirators.
- ☑ High efficiency dust respirators.
- ☑ Positive, pressure-powered respirators.
- ☑ Ventilator visor or helmet respirators.
- ☑ Compressed, air-line breathing apparatus.
- ☑ Self-contained breathing apparatus.

**It should be noted that nuisance dust masks (cup-shaped filters often held in place by a single strap) are not classed as PPE or RPE. They do not meet any current standards or legislative requirements and offer very little or no protection to the wearer.**

*High efficiency dust respirator*

*Ventilated visor and ventilated helmet respirator*

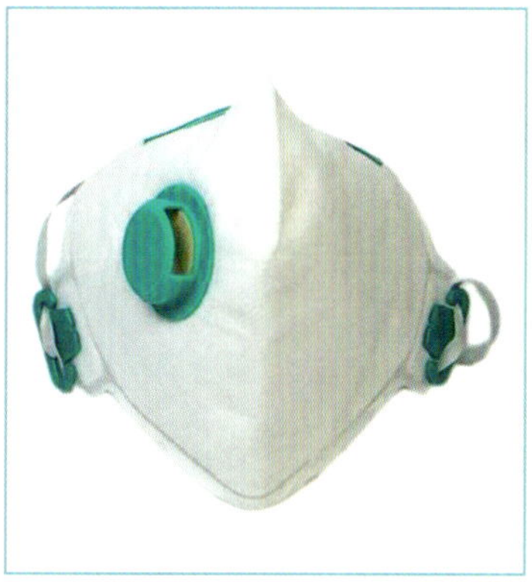

*Disposable face-mask respirator*

B 06

Under the Personal Protective Equipment at Work Regulations, the employer must carry out an assessment to determine **when** RPE is required and **what type** is appropriate for controlling exposure to the hazardous material. Selecting RPE that is both suitable for the user and the job must be carried out by a competent person, because the choice will depend on a number of interacting factors.

- ☑ The nature of the hazards and materials.
- ☑ The measured dust concentrations.
- ☑ The period of exposure.
- ☑ If working outdoors, the prevailing weather conditions.
- ☑ Suitability for each user (field of vision, provision for communication and the need to move in cramped or difficult working places, such as confined spaces).

**The HSE has launched a new, easy-to-follow pocket card aimed at workers. It covers the key points about wearing a face mask to make sure it is effective. Download a copy from the HSE website.**

## 6.7.3 Using and maintaining respiratory protective equipment

Both the employer and the employee have a duty to ensure that all RPE provided is used correctly and that it is stored correctly after use.

Employers must also ensure that non-disposable RPE is thoroughly examined and tested at appropriate intervals. The Approved Code of Practice, which supports the Personal Protective Equipment at Work Regulations, specifies that such examinations and tests are carried out at least every month, and more frequently where conditions are particularly severe. Longer intervals may be more appropriate in the case of certain RPE (for example, half-mask respirators used infrequently for short spells against air contaminants of relatively low toxicity). However, the longest interval between examinations and tests should not exceed three months.

Disposable RPE, provided it is only used for one working day or shift then disposed of, does not require any examination or tests.

## RPE – Common failings

Research undertaken by the HSE targeted workplace RPE inspections. Their findings are shown below.

- A perception that using RPE was simple or obvious.
- Managers and supervisors had knowledge gaps on critical aspects of RPE.
- There was limited use of external information sources (for example, manufacturer's literature and websites).
- There was an assumption that workers know how to put on and use RPE.
- RPE misuse is common – but it is generally blamed on the workers.
- Limited management input and involvement.
- Little information was provided to the worker.
- Poor standards of training, hazard awareness and RPE use.
- Little supervision and enforcement.
- Deficiencies in provisions for RPE storage and maintenance regimes.
- RPE pre-use checks were unlikely.

In addition other failings include the following.

- Inadequate face-fit testing.
- Wearers having more than one day's stubble growth, which substantially reduces the RPE's seal around the face and thus reduces the protection factor.
- Mask straps not being adjusted, tightened or straps in the wrong position on the head.



**For further information refer to Chapter B10 Dust and fumes.**

## 6.8 Skin protection

Protective clothing and other PPE provides one of the most practical ways of limiting contact between the skin and other substances. To be effective, all protective clothing must be the right size, fit for the purpose, maintained in good condition, cleaned regularly and stored carefully when not in use.

Protective clothing may include gloves, overalls, eye protectors (such as goggles and face shields), aprons, boots and leggings, depending on the work being undertaken. Legislation requires the provision and wearing of protective clothing for specific processes and operations. The protective equipment provided must be suited to the requirements of the job.

Regular inspections must be made to ensure it remains sound and adequate.

British Standards cover many types of protective glove but care is needed in selecting the right type for a particular hazard. For example, a glove suitable for handling abrasive materials may offer no protection against chemicals, while the appropriate glove to protect the skin against contact with diesel oil may offer no protection against some solvents.

All manufacturers offer advice on the most suitable gloves for specific types of hazard, some of which are summarised in the following table.

**For guidance on the selection of gloves refer to Appendix C.**

### 6.8.1 Industrial dermatitis

Industrial dermatitis is caused by contact between the skin (usually the hands) and irritant substances. It is essential that a risk assessment identifies the properties of the hazardous substance so that the correct type of gloves can be provided.

Dermatitis, an inflammatory skin disease, accounts for over half of all working days lost through industrial sickness. There are two general types.

- **Contact or irritant dermatitis** – usually where the skin comes into contact with an irritant substance.
- **Allergic or sensitive dermatitis** – where a person develops an allergic reaction to a substance.

With different people, some substances are known to have the effect of either an irritant or a sensitiser (such as turpentine).

In the course of their work, many construction workers are likely to come into contact with one or more possible skin irritants, such as those shown below.

- Cement, lime and plaster.
- Certain types of wood, resins, fungicides and pesticides.
- Paint.
- Tar, pitch and bitumen.
- Solvents, thinners and degreasers.
- Mineral oils and grease.

**For further information refer to Chapter B08 Skin protection.**

## 6.8.2 Cuts and abrasions

Many people working in the construction industry will carry out manual work that will render them susceptible to cuts and abrasions if the correct type of gloves are not provided and worn.

Again, gloves designed to protect the hands against cuts and abrasions are freely available.

Generally, rigger gloves offer adequate protection for most work, although for some work (such as handling sheet glass) specialist Kevlar-impregnated gloves will be necessary.

**38% of construction injuries in Europe are to the hands.**

## 6.8.3 Hot works

Work such as welding and grinding will require that the hands, forearms and face are protected against high temperatures and welding fumes or grinding sparks. To achieve this level of protection it may be necessary for those who carry out such work to wear specialist PPE made for the purpose (for example, welders should wear welding gauntlets that extend up to the elbow and a face shield).

## 6.8.4 Acid and alkali burns

Some substances that are in common use in the construction industry have sufficiently strong acid or alkali properties that can cause burns to the skin.

Gloves are available to protect the users of such substances from chemical burns.

## 6.8.5 Vibration

Some retro-fit products are available that are designed to protect operators from vibration. Only those approved by the machine manufacturers should be used.

The wearing of anti-vibration gloves is not recommended as problems can include the following.

- Reduced flexibility at the hands resulting in higher grip and push forces and loss of precise tool control.
- The possibility of gloves amplifying the tool vibration in some cases (these cases are very difficult to predict).
- They are only tested in one direction and vibration occurs in three directions.
- Field trials of gloves have shown that the vibration isolation materials are not always durable.

One benefit from gloves is that they keep the hands warm and offer other protection.

If an employer intends to provide items of PPE as part of their strategy to reduce the risks from vibration in the workplace, it is important that the correct PPE is selected.

As with all PPE for use at work, gloves or anti-vibration protection should be selected by a competent person who can ensure, in discussion with the supplier, that they carry the CE mark and meet the appropriate standards. Most leading manufacturers and suppliers will offer advice on the selection of different types of gloves and other PPE. All PPE produced or imported by reputable companies is manufactured to British and European Standards.

**For further information refer to Chapter B14 Vibration.**

| Hazard | Recommended type |
|---|---|
| Acids, concrete, brickwork, stain removers, solvents and alkalis. | Neoprene, nitrile, PVC or rubber. |
| Esters, ethers, ketones (mastic, sealers), aldehyde and petroleum-based products. | Medium and heavyweight rubber, neoprene, nitrile or PVC. |
| High and low temperatures. | Nitrile, PVC or medium and heavyweight rubber. |
| Abrasion, unloading bricks and blocks and general materials handling. | Rubber, nitrile, PVC, neoprene or chrome-leather with reinforced palm. |
| Bitumen and hot work. | Asbestos substitute or Nomex. |

It should be noted that industrial safety gloves are rated from 1-4 for their resistance to abrasion, tear and puncture, and 1-5 for blade cut. Those specifying and purchasing work gloves must ensure that the correct grade is obtained, if necessary by speaking to the manufacturers or suppliers.

## 6.9 Head and foot protection

### 6.9.1 Head protection



From 6 April 2013 the PPE Regulations apply to the provision and use of hard hats on construction sites.

Employers must provide hard hats to employees and ensure they are worn when there is a risk of head injury. Self-employed workers should also obtain and wear hard hats.

Therefore, it is a requirement to wear suitable head protection on all building and construction sites, unless there is no risk of head injury, either from falling objects or by banging the head.

Established good practice is to ensure that head protection is always worn by everyone on site, except when in designated safe areas (such as the site office or canteen).

There are many makes of safety helmet available that are constructed to British Standards, and it is the duty of the employer to provide safety helmets that are suitable for the job and the wearer. Each safety helmet has a kite mark and a date of production. They should be replaced if they become damaged or show signs of wear and tear.

Employees, for their part, must follow their employers' instructions. They must wear the safety helmets at all times, when instructed to do so, and report any damage or loss to their employer.

Safety helmets are designed to offer a pre-determined level of impact resistance if they are correctly worn. **The practice of wearing them back-to-front must not be tolerated.**

It has been established that the solvents in some paint, adhesives and indelible markers can reduce the strength of the plastic from which helmets are manufactured. Employees must be discouraged from marking or decorating their safety helmets, other than applying official stickers (such as first aider) or confirmation of site induction.

A safety helmet that has fallen from height onto a hard surface may have suffered damage that will affect its strength even though no cracks are visible. In most circumstances, a replacement helmet should be obtained.

Where the work involves leaning over exposed edges, or similar, chinstraps must be fitted and worn. Many safety helmets have in-built features that enable compatible ear defenders or a face shield to be securely attached.

**Bump caps** could be used where the risk assessment has identified that the worker needs to be protected against low level risks only. They protect the worker from bumping their head (for example, when walking into a fixed object). However, they do not offer adequate protection where there is a risk of falling objects, or moving or suspended loads.

Under Regulation 11 of the Employment Act, construction workers who are practising members of the **Sikh faith** are exempt from wearing a safety helmet whilst wearing a turban. No other workers are covered by this exemption. Sikhs who are not wearing turbans are not exempt from the regulations and, therefore, are required to wear the same head protection as other operatives.

**For more detailed information on the requirements and application, refer to the regulations themselves.**

### 6.9.2 Foot protection

Accidents arising from the manual handling of articles and substances are common causes of injury to feet, as well as to hands.

Foot protection comes in many types and styles, such as safety trainers, safety shoes or boots, safety wellington boots and rigger boots. Properly manufactured and selected foot protection with steel toecaps and mid-soles can protect the feet against dropped objects and penetration of the sole of the foot by upward-pointing nails or glass. They can also be oil and slip resistant.

- ☑ **Safety trainers** offer good grip on sloping or slippery surfaces and offer more comfort. They are more suitable to trades (such as floor layers) who repeatedly kneel and bend their feet.
- ☑ **Safety wellington boots** are essential in preventing burns when operatives have to stand in wet concrete. The cement content, when mixed with water, becomes highly corrosive and will cause severe burns to body tissue.
- ☑ **Safety boots,** as commonly worn by construction workers, provide the required level of protection with steel toecaps and a steel plate moulded into the mid-sole, protecting the wearer against dropped objects and penetration through the sole by sharp objects.

The ankle support provided by some styles of safety boot is important in the prevention of injuries resulting from walking on uneven surfaces and some industries insist on this type (for example, the rail industry).

As with hand protection, manufacturers offer advice on the most suitable footwear for specific types of hazard.

It is essential that protective footwear is worn when people are on site, both from an employer's point of view, in being able to provide a safe place and a safe method of working, and from an employee's position where safety footwear has a benefit in preventing injuries.



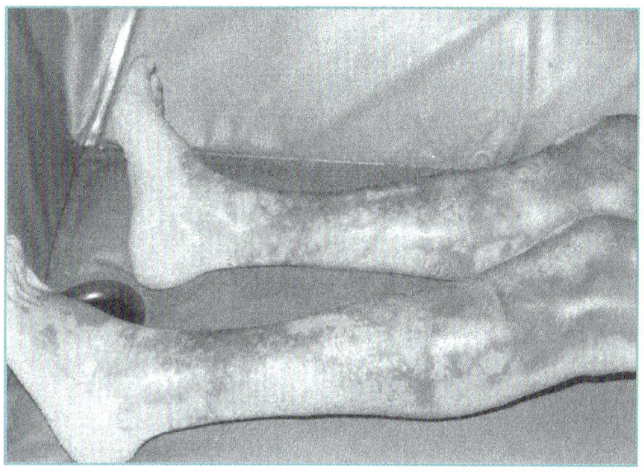

Wellington boots are essential in preventing burns to persons standing in wet cement or concrete. The cement content, when mixed with water, becomes highly corrosive and will cause severe burns to body tissue. It quickly burns and kills nerve endings and can continue to burn deeply without the person feeling much immediate pain.

This picture shows the severely burnt legs of a man who was unaware of the dangers of wet cement, the effect it can have on skin, and the need to wear wellington boots to protect the legs.

## 6.10 Protection against additional hazards

### 6.10.1 High-visibility clothing

High-visibility (hi-vis) clothing that protects the wearer against any risk to their health or safety is classified as PPE whereas clothing (such as uniforms), when the primary purpose is to promote a corporate image, is not.

There are wide ranges of hi-vis clothing and accessories (including vests, coats, fleeces, polo-shirts, trousers and overalls). Risk assessment or policy will determine the level of visibility required but all hi-vis clothing should comply with BS EN 471.

There are three classes of hi-vis clothing.

- ☑ **Class 1 – low visibility.**
- ☑ **Class 2 – medium visibility** required when working on or near A and B class roads or sites with vehicle or plant movements.
- ☑ **Class 3 – high visibility**, required when working on or near dual carriageways, with a speed of 50 mph or above, or motorways. It can also be a requirement when working in high-risk areas (such as airports, highways maintenance and railways).

## 6.10.2 Weather appropriate clothing

Clothing that is designed to protect the wearer against cold and/or wet weather (as per the examples below) is also classified as PPE and must therefore be provided at no charge by the employer.

- ☑ Padded and/or waterproof jackets (either hi-vis or not), equipped with a hood that can accommodate a safety helmet where necessary.
- ☑ Padded and/or waterproof leggings.
- ☑ Suitable footwear.
- ☑ Thermally protective gloves and socks.

## 6.10.3 Fall protection

Items of equipment that are used by a person to prevent that person falling from height (as per the examples below) are also classified as PPE.

- ☑ Safety harness.
- ☑ Fall-arrest or restraint lanyard.
- ☑ Inertia reel fall-arrest block.

All the employers' and employees' duties that apply to other types of PPE apply to this type of equipment also.

A major additional consideration regarding the use of this type of PPE is the prompt rescue of anyone who has fallen and is suspended in a harness. A medical condition known as suspension trauma, which at worst can result in the death of the suspended person, can occur if rescue is not carried out within 10 minutes.



**For further information refer to Chapter D05 Fall arrest and suspension equipment.**

## 6.10.4 Lifejackets

Another category of PPE is that which enables the user to keep afloat should they fall into water or other liquids. These are broadly divided into lifejackets and buoyancy aids.

**For further information refer to Chapter F05 Working over or near to water.**

## Appendix A – Laser health risks and control

| Class of laser | Health risks | Control measures |
|---|---|---|
| **Class 1M** | Potentially harmful to the eye but only if deliberately viewed through an optical magnifying device (such as binoculars). | No-one must be allowed to deliberately look at the beam or to direct the beam into another person's eyes.<br>Magnifying devices (such as binoculars) must not be used by any person who may be exposed to a laser beam whilst using them. |
| **Class 2** | May be harmful to the eyes if deliberately misused (for example, if someone stares directly into the beam). | As above. |
| **Class 2M** | Harmful to the eyes if viewed through a magnifying optical device. | As above. |
| **Class 3R (formerly Class 3A)** | These are higher power lasers that can cause eye injuries; generally exposure is no more hazardous than to a Class 2 device because of the human blink reflex. | BS EN 60825 specifies minimum training requirements for the users of Class 3 and Class 4 lasers. This will include information on the risks from the beam and the advice against misuse. |
| **Class 3B and Class 4** | A higher power laser that can cause eye injury, either directly from viewing the beam or from reflections. | Appropriate eye protection (PPE) must be worn whenever Class 3R or more powerful lasers are used. Particular training on these classes of laser is required. The human blink reflex is not likely to offer any protection to anyone accidentally exposed to the beam. |

# Appendix B – Eye protection selection

## The standards of eye protection

| Hazard description | Standard | Symbol | |
|---|---|---|---|
| | | Frames | Lenses |
| **Optical class*** | | | |
| Refractive power +/- 0.06 | BS EN 166 | | 1 |
| Refractive power +/- 0.12 | BS EN 166 | | 2 |
| Refractive power + 0.12 | BS EN 166 | | 3 |
| Refractive power - 0.25 | BS EN 166 | | 3 |
| **Mechanical strength**** | | | |
| Increased robustness (12 m/s). | BS EN 166 | – | S |
| Low energy impact (45 m/s). | BS EN 166 | -F | F |
| Medium energy impact (120 m/s). | BS EN 166 | -B | B |
| High energy impact (190 m/s). | BS EN 166 | -A | A |
| **Field of use** | | | |
| Droplets and splashes of liquid. | BS EN 166 | 3 | – |
| Large dust particles. | BS EN 166 | 4 | – |
| Gas and fine dust particles. | BS EN 166 | 5 | – |
| Short-circuit electric arc. | BS EN 166 | 8 | – |
| Molten metal and hot solids. | BS EN 166 | 9 | 9 |
| **Other** | | | |
| Non-mist (resistance to fogging). | BS EN 166 | – | N |
| Welding work equipment. | BS EN 175 | – | – |
| Sun glare filters | BS EN 172 | – | – |
| Infrared filters | BS EN 171 | – | – |
| Ultraviolet filters | BS EN 170 | – | – |
| Welding filters | BS EN 169 and 379 | – | – |

* *1, 2 or 3 indicates the optical quality of the ocular, with Class 1 being the best.*

** *S and F is for any type of eye protection*
*B is for goggles and face shields only*
*A is for face shields only*

### Notes

1. Eye protectors manufactured to the British and European Standard are subjected to a number of tests (including temperature, robustness and optical quality) before approval.
2. In the test of robustness, for example, general purpose goggles to EN 166.1.S must withstand the impact of a 6 mm steel ball travelling at 12 m/s (27 mph). Impact goggles to EN 166.1.F must withstand the impact at 45 m/s (100 mph) and for EN 166.1.B they must withstand an impact at 120 m/s (270 mph).
3. Safety goggles are marked with a combination of letters and numbers to indicate the standard of protection provided, for example:
   – BS EN 166.1.F is impact-resistant to a low energy projectile
   – BS EN 166.1.B.3.4 is impact-resistant to medium energy projectiles, droplets, splashes of liquid and large dust particles
   – BS EN 166.1.A.9 is impact-resistant to high energy projectiles, molten metal and hot solids.

**Safety glasses, commonly referred to as light eye protection, are either low or medium energy impact rated. They are not high energy rated and must never be used as a substitute for safety goggles during high impact work (such as using grinders, petrol cut-off saws, cartridge guns, gas-powered nail guns and breaking out).**

## Selection

Eye protection must be selected in the light of the work activity to be undertaken and the assessed level of risk. A suitable and sufficient risk assessment will identify hazards and indicate the control measures required to minimise the likelihood and severity of potential risks.

**For further information on the selection of eye protection refer to the appropriate British Standard.**

# Appendix C – Glove selection guidance

## Choosing the right glove for the right job

| **BS EN 420** – General requirements for gloves |
|---|
| ▪ Mark identifying the manufacturer.<br>▪ Product identifying mark.<br>▪ Size designation (normally in range **6** to **11**).<br>▪ Date of obsolescence (if appropriate).<br>▪ Dexterity performance in range **1** (lowest) to **5** (highest), if required.<br>▪ Markings specific to individual risks, including pictograms where appropriate. |

### Mechanical hazard

Mechanical hazards are associated with the handling of rough or sharp objects that could abrade, cut or pierce the skin (such as glass, thin metal sheet and masonry blocks). A mechanical hazard is not associated with moving machinery, in fact it can be extremely dangerous to wear gloves that could catch in moving parts or serrated blades.

**Gloves should not be used when working with serrated blades – *use guards.***

| | | |
|---|---|---|
| <br>**4. 1. 4. 1.**<br>**BS EN 388** | ▪ 4 = Abrasion. Performance index 0 to 4.<br>▪ 1 = Blade Cut. Performance index 0 to 5.<br>▪ 4 = Tear. Performance index 0 to 4.<br>▪ 1 = Puncture. Performance index 0 to 4. | Highest number equals greatest resistance. |

### Chemical hazard

Whether total immersion or merely splash is involved, any substance that would irritate, inflame or burn the skin is classed as a chemical hazard. In order that a more informed and relevant glove selection can be made, there is a list of 12 chemicals, identified by the letters A to L. Refer to the manufacturer for details of the specific chemicals.

| | |
|---|---|
| <br>**BS EN 374 2003 ABC** | To gain approval as a chemical resistant glove, a breakthrough time greater than 30 minutes has to be achieved. The glove can carry a revised pictogram, together with the identification letters (A to L) of the three chemicals against which it was tested. |
| <br>**BS EN 374 2003** | If a glove fails to achieve 30 minutes' breakthrough time it can still be classified as a low chemical resistant glove and is identified by a different pictogram, this time without the identification letters. |
|  | The micro-organism pictogram can be used where the glove performs to at least the Level 2 for the permeation test (greater than 30 minutes). |

### Thermal hazards hot and cold

| | |
|---|---|
| <br>**BS EN 407** | Thermal hazards come in many forms, denominated with six digits in a horizontal line, each graded X or 1 to 4. Heat can be radiated and conducted, or it may be actual flames. |
| <br>**BS EN 511** | Cold can be anything from cold water to frozen gases. It is important to know the type of hazard and the temperature involved in order to recommend suitable protection. |

*(Table reproduced with the permission of Arco Ltd.)*

B 06

# 07

# Control of substances hazardous to health

## Contents



## Supporting information

### G: Checklists and forms



### GT 700 Toolbox talks

## Overview

**Since they were introduced, the Control of Substances Hazardous to Health (COSHH) Regulations have probably been among the most poorly understood pieces of legislation.**

**However, the regulations are based on very simple principles. The intention of the regulations is to protect human health from exposure to hazardous substances by either totally preventing exposure or, where that is not reasonably practicable, controlling the level of exposure to safe values, by appropriate means.**

**Two dangerous substances, asbestos and lead, are commonly encountered during construction work, particularly the refurbishment of older buildings, but are not covered by the COSHH Regulations because they have their own regulations.**

## 7.1 Introduction

Much has been written about the poor safety performance of the construction industry in recent years and generally, having put in considerable effort, the industry has raised its game. Sadly, in many cases, exposure to occupational health hazards has not received the same degree of attention.

Whereas the results of accidents are immediately obvious and often dramatic, the onset of occupational health problems are often subtler, slower to develop and therefore easier to miss or ignore.

The COSHH Regulations deal with harmful substances in relation to their health effects. However, the regulations do not cover any flammable or explosive properties that the substances might also possess.



## 7.2 Important points

- ☑ Many of the substances **used or created** during work processes have the potential to cause harm to the health of anyone exposed to them.
- ☑ In construction many COSHH issues relate to substances created (such as dust or fumes), as opposed to chemicals that have been bought in.
- ☑ Hazardous substances that are already present on site when it is first occupied can also pose hazards to health.
- ☑ All purchased products that are hazardous to health must carry an appropriate warning symbol on the packaging. However, hazardous substances that are created by the work process or are already present on site will carry no such health warning.
- ☑ Employers have legal duties to establish the health risks to their employees, and others who may come into contact with hazardous substances, by carrying out an appropriate assessment and putting in place adequate control measures.
- ☑ The assessment should take into account how the substance is used and should not merely be a copy of the supplier's information.
- ☑ Ideally, exposure to any hazardous substance would be rendered impossible by eliminating the use of that substance (for example, by changing the way that the job is carried out so that the substance is not necessary). Alternatively, risk can be reduced by:
  - the substitution of safer substances (for example, replacing solvent-based paint with water-based paint)
  - modifying the method of its use (for example, total enclosure of the process).
- ☑ In many cases, none of these measures are practical in a construction site environment: If the prevention of exposure is not possible, the level of exposure must be controlled. This can be through engineering controls, safe systems of work and personal protective equipment (PPE).
- ☑ Using PPE to control exposure must only be considered as a last resort, after other methods have been explored and found not to be reasonably practicable.
- ☑ In some cases employees exposed to hazardous substances must be offered health surveillance.

## 7.3 COSHH Regulations

www.

**The regulations can be downloaded from the HSE or Government legislation websites.**

The regulations place duties on both employers and the self-employed. These duties cover people actually working with substances and other people (such as the public or other contractors) who might be affected.

If five or more people are employed, the significant findings of the COSHH assessment and the actions that will be taken to control exposures must be written down.

The main requirements of the regulations are shown below.

- ☑ To assess the health risks to employees or other people created by work that involves substances hazardous to health.
- ☑ To implement suitable control measures to effectively protect employees and others from exposure.
- ☑ To review the assessment if there have been any changes that may invalidate it, such as:
  - a change in the way the work is carried out, or
  - the results of monitoring indicating that existing control measures are not effective.

The emphasis under COSHH is to avoid exposure to hazardous substances unless it is not reasonably practicable to do so, in which case adequate control measures must be put in place to control exposure to a safe level.

The regulations require the following thought process in relation to control.

- ☑ Can the work be carried out by a less hazardous method that does not require the use of hazardous substances?
- ☑ If not, can the substance be changed (substituted)?

If the answer to both of these questions is 'no' then the introduction of measures to control exposure will be necessary.

Engineering controls should be the first controls to be considered (such as pouring devices to stop splashes, the use of dust extraction, increasing ventilation and so on). PPE should not be considered as a control, until engineering control options have been exhausted, because of the following reasons.

- ☑ It can be expensive.
- ☑ It can be unpleasant to wear.
- ☑ It only protects the wearer and then only if it is being used and maintained correctly.
- ☑ It often requires considerable management effort to ensure that it is used correctly.

Removing the need to buy and use it makes good occupational health and business sense.

The regulations apply to all industries and while some fixed workplaces (such as factories and warehouses) may find it practical to introduce effective engineering controls, the nature of construction sites and work conditions mean that it will often be difficult to do anything other than use PPE. It is, however, becoming easier to introduce engineering controls as newer equipment is designed to overcome exposure problems (for example, powered hand tools can be fitted with dust extraction and collection attachments). Similarly, a number of UK hire companies stock air movers to enable ventilation to be improved.

The requirements of the regulations are very thorough and one of those requirements is to ensure that the control measures that have been identified as suitable are properly used.

To ensure that the control measures are effective, the regulations require the following.

- ☑ Extract ventilation systems must be thoroughly examined periodically.
- ☑ If using substances that are known to damage health, part of the assessment is likely to identify that health surveillance is necessary.
- ☑ Any records must be kept for 40 years and made available to the people who have been exposed to the hazard.
- ☑ There is a duty to communicate the information and provide relevant training to people who may be exposed.
- ☑ Emergency arrangements are put in place and, where required, practised.

## 7.3.1 Summary of the COSHH Regulations

Employers must carry out a risk assessment of health risks created by work involving substances hazardous to health. Each assessment must take account of the following.

- ☑ The hazardous properties of the substance.
- ☑ Information provided by the supplier on the potential harmful effects.
- ☑ The type, level and duration of exposure.
- ☑ The way in which the job will be carried out, including the amount of the substance used (or present in the case of substances created by a work process).
- ☑ Work (such as maintenance) where there is the potential for high levels of exposure.
- ☑ Any published WEL for the substance.
- ☑ The effects of any control measures that are, or will be, in place.
- ☑ The results of any health surveillance and/or exposure monitoring that has been undertaken.
- ☑ The risks where there is exposure to more than one hazardous substance at any one time.
- ☑ Other information that the employer may need or have in order to complete the assessment.

Any assessment must be reviewed regularly if there is reason to suspect that the assessment is no longer valid, or if there has been a significant change in the work to which the assessment relates, or exposure monitoring results indicate it is necessary.

### 7.3.2 Hierarchy of control

The preferable method of prevention or control is to replace the substance or process with a non-hazardous or less hazardous substance or process.

Controls shall be, in order of priority:

- engineering controls
- organisational controls
- providing suitable PPE (as a last resort).

The control measures must:

- ensure the safe handling, storage, transportation and disposal of hazardous substances
- ensure maintenance procedures, which involve exposure to hazardous substances, are suitable
- reduce to a minimum the number of people exposed, the level and duration of exposure and the quantity of hazardous substances present in the workplace
- include control of the working environment, including the provision of adequate ventilation
- include adequate hygiene and washing facilities.

This regulation contains further details of measures that must be taken to control exposure to carcinogens, mutagens and biological agents.

With regard to this regulation, it is considered that control of exposure will be generally adequate if the following are met.

- Work is organised to minimise the release and spread of hazardous substances.
- Account is taken of the routes of exposure (inhalation, skin absorption and ingestion).
- The control measures selected:
  - are proportionate to the degree of health risk
  - are effective in minimising the escape and spread of the substance
  - may, where necessary, include a combination of control measures, including PPE.
- The control measures selected are periodically reviewed for their effectiveness.
- Users of hazardous substances are informed of the hazards and risks and trained in the use of the control measures provided.
- It does not increase the overall risks to health or safety from other sources.

Employers who provide any control measure are required to ensure that they are properly used or applied. All employees must ensure the following.

- They make proper use of any control measure (including PPE) provided.
- All steps are taken to return it to its place of storage after use.
- Any defects are reported in the control measure to their employer.

**The four routes of entry for a hazardous substance into the body are ingestion, absorption, inhalation and injection.**

### 7.3.3 Monitoring controls

Where control measures are provided in accordance with Regulation 7, adequate maintenance, examination and testing of control measures, including any PPE provided, must be undertaken to ensure they are in efficient working order and remain clean.

Where engineering controls are undertaken, the employer must ensure thorough examinations and testing are carried out on a regular basis.

Where indicated as necessary by the COSHH assessment, monitoring of the exposure to hazardous substances must be undertaken using suitable procedures, unless it can be demonstrated by another method of evaluation that exposure is adequately controlled.

Suitable records of any monitoring should be kept for five years, or 40 years if personal exposures occur.

### 7.3.4 Health surveillance

**The HSE has published new online guidance, with guidelines on health surveillance needed where, even after all precautions are taken, there is still a risk that workers may be exposed to chemicals or other hazardous substances.**

Where it is appropriate for protecting employees' health, health surveillance must be carried out and recorded.

Where an employee requires medical surveillance following exposure, and it has been decided that the employee cannot continue in that work, the employer must take steps to ensure the employee adheres to the medical decision unless it has been cancelled.

Upon reasonable notice, an employer must allow the employee to access any medical records applying to them.

### 7.3.5 Information, instruction and training

Information, instruction and training must be provided to employees who may be exposed to substances hazardous to health so that they are aware of the danger of exposure and the precautions that should be taken.

Training must cover the following points.

- ☑ Details of the substances hazardous to health to which the employee is liable to be exposed, including:
  - the names of the substances and the risks that they present to health
  - any relevant occupational exposure standard, maximum exposure limit or similar occupational exposure limit
  - access to any relevant safety data sheet
  - other legislative provisions that concern the hazardous properties of those substances.
- ☑ Significant findings of the risk assessment.
- ☑ Appropriate precautions and actions to be taken by the employee in order to safeguard themselves and other employees at the workplace.
- ☑ Results of any monitoring of exposure and, in particular, in the case of a substance hazardous to health for which a maximum exposure limit has been approved, the employee or their representative shall be informed if the results of the monitoring show that the maximum exposure limit has been exceeded.
- ☑ Collective results of any health surveillance undertaken in a form calculated to prevent those results from being identified as relating to a particular person.

### 7.3.6 Incidents and emergencies

Procedures to deal with accidents, incidents and emergencies involving hazardous substances must be provided. These procedures should include the following.

- ☑ First-aid provisions.
- ☑ The use of safety drills and their regular testing.
- ☑ Identification and details of hazards.
- ☑ Specific hazards that are likely to occur during any accident, incident or emergency, together with warning and communication systems and emergency actions.

These procedures must be made available to accident and emergency services, and be displayed on site.



## 7.4 COSHH responsibilities for duty holders

### 7.4.1 Designers

The chain of responsibilities starts at the design stage of a project. Under the Construction (Design and Management) Regulations (CDM), designers have a duty to consider the risks created for the construction, maintenance, cleaning and use of a structure that could arise out of their designs. This must include consideration of COSHH issues.

It is important to be aware that this may not eliminate all COSHH risks. Consider, for example, the periodic painting of a high level structure. It may be considered preferable to continue to use a solvent-based paint, as opposed to a water-based paint (a less hazardous product) on the grounds that the periods between painting will be longer, thereby reducing the frequency of working at height.

Furthermore, designers must take all reasonable steps to provide sufficient COSHH information about aspects of the design or its construction or maintenance, to adequately assist the client, other designers and contractors to comply with their duties under the regulations.

### 7.4.2 Clients

CDM places a duty on the client to provide pre-construction information to other parties involved in a project to protect the health and safety of anyone carrying out construction work, anyone affected by it or those who will use the structure as a place of work.

This will obviously include providing information on any known existing hazardous substances (such as the presence of hazardous residues in pipework or the existence of contaminated ground). Where necessary, this may involve commissioning surveys or taking samples to enable accurate information to be available for a risk-based control. It is no longer acceptable for the client to say: 'there *may* be the presence of x'.

**The CDM Regulations require lead surveys to be carried out wherever paintwork and other surface coatings are liable to be disturbed. This is a mandatory requirement as part of pre-construction information.**

### 7.4.3 Contractors

The principal contractor and contractor(s) not only has legal obligations to their own employees but also has duties towards contractors under their control, including self-employed people, and others (for example, visitors and members of the public) who may be affected by the work.

Under CDM and other regulations, organisations that share a workplace must:

- co-operate with the principal contractor and help them ensure the work is carried out safely
- have undertaken their own COSHH assessments in relation to the work they are to undertake
- have effective arrangements to ensure that control measures are put in place and are monitored.

Taking account of the above points should assist in compiling the health and safety plan. Some risks are likely to have been highlighted in the information provided by the client and designers.

### 7.4.4 Self-employed

The COSHH Regulations apply to the self-employed. If you have no employees, but hazardous substances are taken to other people's premises, all parts of the COSHH Regulations will apply, except those relating to monitoring and health surveillance.

### 7.4.5 Employees

Under various sets of health and safety regulations, employees' duties are as follows.

- Work with their employer to enable them to comply with the law.
- Make proper use of any control measures provided (including PPE).
- Return any control measure, where provided (mainly PPE), to its accommodation after use.
- Report any defects in the control measures to their employer.
- Attend health surveillance medicals where required (the employer must pay for the medical and it must be in paid work time).



### 7.4.6 Work on another employer's premises

Under CDM the client has a duty to provide pre-construction information to the principal contractor or contractor, including the information necessary for maintenance or other work to be carried out, where this work is being done in an occupied premises. Some examples of such information are shown below.

- Details of the substances contained in pipework or tanks, if for example a pipefitter is to break into a pipe to replace a valve.
- What gases, vapours or fumes may be discharged through a rooftop ventilation duct during the time a roofer has to work next to it.

There is also a requirement for the client to make sure that contractors are aware of emergency procedures that might arise out of the use of any particular substance(s) on the site.

Obviously, this duty is reciprocal. The contractor has a duty to inform the client or the site occupier if the contractor's work poses risks to the client's staff and visitors and to outline how the risks will be controlled.

This is particularly important where the client has out-of-hours security staff. Often, arrangements that are effective during the working day, to ensure that the contractor and client liaise, can become non-effective after normal working hours (for example, by the security staff entering an agreed exclusion zone due to ignorance of the hazards present).

## 7.5 Sources of harm

The regulations cover substances that have chronic or delayed effects, including substances that are carcinogenic (cause cancer), mutagenic (cause mutation of the body) or teratogenic (cause malformation of an embryo).

The purpose is to safeguard the health of people using or coming into contact with any substance that is harmful to health, apart from lead and asbestos.

The regulations apply to those substances that are classified as being very toxic, toxic, harmful, corrosive or irritant under the Classification of Substances and Preparations Dangerous for Supply, in Schedule 1 of the Chemicals (Hazard Information and Packaging for Supply) Regulations, also known as CHIP. The symbols used on the containers of such substances are reproduced later in this chapter *(refer to 7.7.1)*.

Many of the basic substances (products) bought in and used in the construction industry have the potential to harm the health of people using them.

Additionally, many of the essential construction processes can create potentially hazardous substances, and a third group of substances are harmful substances (including micro-organisms) that may already be on site when a project commences.

### 7.5.1 Bought-in products

The first, and easiest, stage is to look at the substances that are bought in. This involves identifying what is used, what is not hazardous to health and how much is used. Most construction processes are relatively simple as they rarely use a large number of substances or involve mixing of substances. Mechanical workshops (for example, where plant is serviced) tend to be more challenging simply because of the amount of chemicals present in the substances that they normally use.

Another consideration is the substances that will be brought onto site by other contractors, how those substances might affect other people and the quality of the contractors' COSHH assessments.

Furthermore, the site office and other accommodation must not be overlooked. For example, it is not unreasonable to suppose that strong cleaning materials will be used in catering and other welfare facilities.

Having made a list of all substances, it is then sensible to identify any products that are obviously not hazardous, so that they can be ruled out.

> **e.g.** **Identification of hazardous and non-hazardous substances**
>
> In the case of cleaning chemicals, washing-up liquid does not have any warning symbols on it and therefore, other than noting its presence, no further action is necessary. However, the information on a container of bleach should provide the basis for determining how it can be used safely. Of the two products that have been considered, one requires no control measures to be identified but the second does.

### 7.5.2 Products created by the work process

The situation becomes more complicated when potentially harmful substances (such as many forms of dust or fumes) are created by work processes. The situation is further complicated if the substance created has a workplace exposure limit (WEL) that must not be exceeded. This may require that exposure levels are measured, unless exposure can be eliminated or controlled to a known safe level. Again, it will be necessary to also consider potentially harmful processes that will be carried out by other contractors.

Depending upon the complexity of the project, it may not be possible to complete this part of the exercise prior to the start of the project unless all work processes and substances that will be created are known. In these circumstances, it will be a case of building up the COSHH information as the job progresses, but this must be achieved in such a way that no-one is exposed to a potentially harmful substance until the assessment of it has been carried out and appropriate controls are in place.



### 7.5.3 Products already present on site

A third category of potentially harmful substances are those substances, including micro-organisms, that may already be present on site.

Any number of hazardous substances might be present in the ground when former industrial (brownfield) sites are redeveloped.

- ☑ Land, heavily contaminated with fuels, oils and other hazardous liquids that have seeped into the ground over many years.
- ☑ Residues of hazardous substances left in pipework, underground tanks and drums.
- ☑ Substances (such as asbestos and polychlorinated biphenyls (PCBs)) that were deliberately buried by the past users of the land.

There could also be the following sources of micro-organisms in contaminated land.

- ☑ Leptospirosis (Weil's disease) from the presence of infected rats or their carcases.
- ☑ Infected syringes, needles and other items associated with drug taking (for example, where a derelict site is being refurbished).
- ☑ Tetanus from infected ground or other materials.
- ☑ A range of respiratory diseases arising from the disturbance of accumulated pigeon or bat droppings.
- ☑ Pipework and sumps containing sewage sludge residue.

### 7.5.4 Types of exposure

Hazardous substances can enter the body in four ways.

1. **Inhalation** (breathed) into the lungs, when the substance is in the form of a gas, vapour, fume, mist, aerosol or dust.
2. **Absorption** through the skin or eyes by contact with a substance that can penetrate unbroken skin, or is absorbed through unprotected cuts or grazes.
3. **Injection** by contact with contaminated sharp objects or high-pressure equipment (such as water jetting).
4. **Ingestion** (eating or drinking) by swallowing particles of a hazardous substance resulting from hand-to-mouth transfer.

## 7.6 Workplace exposure limits

Unsurprisingly, some hazardous substances have legal limits to which people may be exposed. All of these substances have a workplace exposure limit (WEL) that represents a concentration of a substance in the air measured over a specific period of time. The taking of such measurements (workplace monitoring) is a specialist activity that must be carried out by someone who is competent to do so and who possesses the appropriate equipment. Such monitoring must be carried out where a (COSHH) risk assessment indicates that it is necessary.

The following substances, all of which have a WEL, are commonly used in or produced by construction work.

- ☑ General dust.
- ☑ Hardwood dust.
- ☑ Softwood dust.
- ☑ Silica.
- ☑ White spirit.
- ☑ Pulverised fuel ash.
- ☑ Synthetic mineral fibre (rock wool/fibreglass).
- ☑ Asphalt.
- ☑ Welding/cutting fumes.
- ☑ Gypsum.
- ☑ Portland cement.
- ☑ Micro-organisms associated with:
  - blood products
  - Weil's disease
  - tetanus
  - sewage
  - certain black mould species
  - anthrax.

This list is not exhaustive. Employers have a legal duty to establish that an in-use substance has a WEL, and to control exposure to it.

www.

**A list of all WELs is published by the Health and Safety Executive (HSE) in Guidance Note EH40, available in hard copy or to download from its website.**



Those who plan and carry out work that could result in exposure to hazardous substances may have difficulty in appreciating that there is a (real or potential) problem. This is particularly true when a hazardous substance is created by the work process.

e.g.

### Hazardous substances created by the work process

A hardwood plank should not pose any serious health issues in the form that it is delivered to site. However, cutting or sanding it will produce dust that, unless controlled, has the potential to cause irritation of the nasal passages, sensitisation or, on rare occasions, nasal cancer.

Cutting, sawing, grinding or sanding any substance has the potential to liberate harmful dust. Furthermore, many types of hot works will create harmful fumes or gases that may be inhaled unless the process is closely controlled.

!

**Myth: 'Of course it's not a risk to health – we've always done it this way.'**
**Reality: some diseases take years to develop. If exposure is high because the task has always been done that way then the task needs reassessing to protect the workforce.**

## 7.7 Identifying hazardous substances

### 7.7.1 Packaging or labels

The law on chemical classification and labelling has changed. From 2015 the European regulation on classification, labelling and packaging of substances and mixtures (otherwise known as CLP) applies to all EU member states, including the UK.

The CLP Regulation adopts the United Nations' globally harmonised system on classification and labelling of chemicals (GHS).

The new symbols (shown overleaf) have similar images to the previous ones, but are a different colour and shape.

| Globally harmonised pictograms | Previous European hazard (CHIP) symbols |
|---|---|
|  **Toxic**<br>Toxic if swallowed. |  **Very toxic or toxic**<br>Substances that, in very low quantities or low quantities, cause death or acute or chronic damage to health when inhaled, swallowed or absorbed via the skin. |
|  **New pictogram**<br>This replaces the previous CHIP irritant symbol (shown right). Refers to less serious health hazards (such as skin irritancy or sensitisation). May cause an allergic reaction. |  **Irritant**<br>Non-corrosive substances that may cause inflammation, skin irritancy or sensitisation through immediate, prolonged or repeated contact with the skin or mucous membrane. |
|  **Corrosive**<br>Danger – causes severe skin burns and eye damage. |  **Corrosive**<br>Substances that may, on contact with living tissues, destroy them. |
|  **New pictogram**<br>May cause serious longer term health hazards (such as carcinogenicity and respiratory sensitisation). | Image on left is a new symbol (no CHIP alternative). |

www.

**Further information on labelling and packaging can be found on the HSE website.**

## 7.7.2 Material safety data sheets

Before a COSHH assessment is undertaken, it is important to collate information about the substance. Material safety data sheets (MSDS) are available for most substances.

**Material safety data sheets (MSDS) are not COSHH assessments.**

Manufacturers and suppliers have a legal obligation to provide the information. Many suppliers have MSDS on their websites. Nevertheless, it should be possible to go into any builder's merchant or DIY store and obtain sufficient information about the products that are being purchased.

By law, data sheets must contain the following information.

- Identification of the substance or preparation and the company or undertaking providing the substance.
- Composition and information on ingredients.
- Hazard identification.
- First-aid measures.
- Fire-fighting measures.
- Accidental release measures.
- Handling and storage.
- Exposure controls and personal protection.
- Physical and chemical properties.
- Stability and reactivity.
- Toxicological information.
- Ecological information.
- Disposal considerations.
- Transport information.
- Regulatory information.

Other information can be found in HSE guidance material, technical reference sources, through experience, in information gathered from previous use of the substance(s) and from trade associations.

If the substance is a carcinogen or a mutagen (for example, capable of causing cancer or mutation of the body) every possible step should be taken to eliminate the need for its use.

**It is considerably harder to find out information about substances created by the work process.**

## 7.8 COSHH assessments

An assessment is the fundamental requirement of the COSHH regulations, and it is in two parts.

**Part 1.** An employer must not carry out any work that is liable to expose employees to any substance hazardous to health, unless a suitable and sufficient assessment of the risks created by the work has been made.

**Part 2.** If the first part indicates that substances hazardous to health will be used or created, employers must identify the actions to be taken to comply with the remainder of the COSHH regulations.

### Definitions

The meanings of the following words need to be clearly understood.

- **Substance** means any natural or artificial substance, in solid, liquid, gaseous or vapour form, and includes micro-organisms.
- **Hazard** is the potential for the substance to cause harm, illness or damage to health.
- **Risk** is the likelihood that the hazardous potential of the substance will be realised.

### 7.8.1 Who can carry out an assessment?

Employers have the duty to make an assessment, but they can arrange for anyone who is competent to do so to assist with the task, whether from within the company or from outside.

It is the responsibility of the employer to ensure that anyone who carries out any duties under the COSHH Regulations is competent to do so, and has received the necessary information, instruction and training, whether or not the assessor is an employee.

The majority of assessments for small building and construction work can be carried out without the need for the assistance of specialist outside consultants, provided the assessor is competent and meets the following requirements.



- Has access to the safety data sheets for the products concerned.
- Understands, in basic terms, what the COSHH Regulations require to be done.
- Is knowledgeable of the work process being assessed.
- Has the ability to systematically gather relevant information regarding exposures to hazardous substances and the subsequent risks to staff by:
  - observing working practices
  - obtaining information on substances used
  - asking questions in the workplace
  - making informed 'what if' judgements regarding possible divergences from standard working practices.
- Can specify the steps and control measures to be taken to comply with the COSHH Regulations.
- Can appreciate their own limitations; knowing when to call in specialists with certain skills (such as when there is a need to undertake air sampling).
- Has the ability to make valid conclusions, to make a report and communicate findings regarding risks and precautions to the employer and employees.

### 7.8.2 Carrying out an assessment

**The HSE, in collaboration with the TUC and CBI, has developed a COSHH essentials toolkit to help firms comply with the COSHH Regulations.**

#### 7.8.2.1 Know what products and substances you are using

- Compile a list of the hazardous substances that are in use.
- Add to the list any hazardous substances that are created as a by-product of a work process.

#### 7.8.2.2 Assess the health hazards they can cause

- From manufacturer's information and other relevant sources, determine the level of risk to health, the degree of exposure and what action is needed to eliminate or control exposure.
- Carry out a COSHH risk assessment to establish how the hazardous substances might cause harm.
- Record the findings of the risk assessment and the control measures to be taken.
- Review any assessment regularly or whenever the exposure monitoring results indicate that it is necessary.

### 7.8.2.3 Eliminate or minimise the risk of exposure

- ☑ Design a work process that prevents exposure to, or the creation of, hazardous substances (for example, use hydraulic croppers to cut brick pavers, rather than disc cutting them, to reduce exposure to dust, or use hydraulic shears to cut steelwork, rather than burning gear).
- ☑ Substitute or dilute the substance. Designers, managers and specifiers should look towards less hazardous options (for example, lead paint removal by a system that does not heat the paint sufficiently to liberate lead fumes).
- ☑ Use dust or fume extraction. This may be a standalone extractor unit or built-in to some hand tools.
- ☑ Use engineering controls (such as totally enclosing the process – often not feasible in the construction environment) or wet cutting.
- ☑ Issue suitable PPE, including respiratory protective equipment (RPE) and make sure it is worn (only after the use of all other risk control measures have been explored).

#### e.g. Eliminate or minimise the risk of exposure

- ☑ Alter the work method so the process that produces the exposure is no longer necessary (for example, use a demolition shear to cut structural steelwork rather than gas cutting and therefore avoid a process that may produce metal fumes and toxic gases).
- ☑ Change the work method to prevent the production of a hazardous waste product (for example, purchase panels of the correct size, rather than cutting oversize panels on site and producing dust). Given the pressure on reducing waste and manual handling, this is another example where good health and safety is good business.

These examples of controlling the COSHH risk may indicate that some companies are already doing COSHH assessments without realising it.

Some control measures are very simple (for example, damping down the dust on a floor slab before sweeping). Other situations may require a little more thought and ingenuity. However, it is not always possible or reasonably practicable to introduce engineering controls and so the implementation of certain organisational controls may be possible.

### 7.8.2.4 What to establish

- ☑ Who is exposed? Is it just the person using the substance or can it affect other people?
- ☑ What are they going to do with it? The decision to either spray or apply paint by brush may make a significant difference. Spray application will probably mean a much smaller droplet size, creating a more severe respiratory hazard. This assessment needs to be honest and objective. For example, paint removal gels state on the tin that they are only for brush application, although it is physically possible to spray them. However, the controls required to spray without potentially damaging the skin, eyes or lungs are completely different to those required for brush application.
- ☑ How often and how much of a substance is used, and for how long, are also very important factors.

### 7.8.2.5 Personal protective equipment

Obtaining appropriate PPE for hazardous substances that can affect the skin might be as simple as identifying the correct type of gloves. However, where there is need for respiratory protection, selecting the correct type of RPE is critical. For example, a filtering face mask designed to filter out dust will be useless against gases, fumes or vapours.

The need for employees to work in masks or respirators is always the last resort. If RPE is necessary, it must meet the following requirements.

- ☑ Adequately control exposure to the hazardous substance(s) identified.
- ☑ Suit the wearer (comfort and fit).
- ☑ Be appropriate for the job and be used correctly.

Before selecting RPE, proper thought must also be given to the following.

- ☑ The physical condition of the employee (breathing through some types of RPE for extended periods can require effort) and whether facial hair or glasses would make the equipment ineffective.
- ☑ Providing suitable training on the safe use and maintenance of the RPE.

### 7.8.2.6 Information, instruction and training

Before work starts, give information, instruction and training to employees relating to the following.

- ☑ The nature and degree of known risks.
- ☑ The control measures adopted and how they should be put into operation.
- ☑ Reasons for, and the correct use of, PPE.
- ☑ Any exposure monitoring arrangements that are in use.
- ☑ The purpose of, and arrangements for, any health surveillance, if appropriate.

**For an example of a COSHH assessment for the use of diesel refer to Appendix A.**

### 7.8.3 Health surveillance

Regulation 11 requires that employees, who are or are liable to be exposed to substances hazardous to health, must be put under the appropriate health surveillance, provided by the employer.

In many cases, health surveillance must be carried out by an occupational health practitioner and recorded. Employees must have access to medical records that apply to them.

Health surveillance has to be undertaken when an employee is exposed to the following.

- One of the substances and is involved in a process listed in Schedule 6 of the COSHH Regulations, to which reference should be made, although those listed are unlikely to apply to the construction industry.
- A hazardous substance that is linked to an identifiable disease related to the exposure (for example, exposure is known to cause asthma) and there are valid techniques for detecting indications of the disease.

### 7.8.4 Monitoring controls

It is important to monitor the effectiveness of any risk controls. Observation of the task and speaking to the people doing the job is one way to measure the effectiveness of controls. It may also require the regular testing of equipment (such as ventilation), which must be kept in efficient working order.

Organisational controls can be introduced. These are concerned with investigating whether the way in which the job is carried out can be changed so that individual exposure is reduced. For example, by carrying out a job out of normal working hours the number of persons exposed, who would otherwise have to wear PPE, will be significantly reduced. Further examples include:

- job rotation so that no individual person is exposed to a substance above its WEL
- moving a work activity into the open air to prevent the accumulation of vapour or fumes.

In some circumstances the application of control measures will continue after the actual work activity is completed. Some jobs will require the operatives to go through a full decontamination procedure (for example, working with heavily contaminated land). Anyone who has been in the live working area may have to follow a strict procedure about where they take boots and overalls off, or even go through a shower, and it may involve wearing additional gloves to ensure that contaminants are kept off their skin when decontaminating.

Often, simply washing hands with hot soapy water will suffice. Good COSHH practice and the provision of good welfare facilities are very closely linked. This may mean in some circumstances that eating and drinking are not allowed other than in designated clean zones.

In the past, the HSE has targeted a lack of adequate site welfare facilities in relation to occupational health issues. In order to serve a prohibition notice the HSE has to consider whether or not there is imminent risk of harm to health and/or safety. Simply by looking at the substances present and their COSHH assessments may be enough. It is easy to determine, for example, whether a lack of hot water and a hand cleanser has the potential to create a health problem. If there is a lack of such facilities, an HSE inspector may consider there to be an imminent risk to health and therefore justify the serving of a prohibition notice.

### 7.8.5 Records

The COSHH assessment, training, briefings, monitoring arrangements and health surveillance must be recorded. Some records may need to be kept for 40 years. In companies where there are union-appointed safety representatives, or representatives of employee safety, the above information should be available to them.

### 7.8.6 Emergencies

If significant or dangerous accidental releases or leakages of a hazardous substance are possible, despite the control measures that have been implemented, an emergency plan should be drawn up and instigated for achieving suitable control and for safeguarding the health of anyone who may be affected.

This needs to be kept in context – spilling 500 ml of gloss paint is probably more of an environmental and quality issue than a serious occupational health hazard.

The emergency plan should include first-aid provisions and safety drills, including the testing of drills at regular intervals. Any particular hazards that are likely to occur as a result of the emergency must be specified.

The emergency plan should be made available to all people potentially affected and be displayed on site. It should also be made available to the accident and emergency services.

Depending on the substance, a spillage may also be a pollution issue.

Emergency plans must be drawn up and consideration should be given to the following.

- Making appropriate first aid provision.
- Developing and practicing safety drills (for example, site evacuations) as appropriate.
- Identification and details of hazards.
- Making available details of specific hazards that are known to exist.
- Developing warning and communication systems.
- Displaying emergency plans.
- Making relevant information available to the emergency services.

B 07

### 7.8.7 Summary

The assessment is a considered judgement that balances the hazardous properties of the substance, the method by which it will be handled and the environment in which it will be used.

The skill of the COSHH assessor is to:

- sift through the information contained on the MSDS and other sources (such as on the container)
- extract the useful information
- incorporate their knowledge of how, when and where the substance is used
- from the information available, produce a useful and useable COSHH assessment to guide those who will be doing the work.

e.g.

**Insulating roof spaces with synthetic mineral fibre offers a number of challenges**

The material has a WEL for the concentration of fibres in air, and is irritating to the skin. The roof space is an unpleasant working environment as it can be extremely hot in summer and the level of natural ventilation may be low.

The obvious way to reduce exposure is to provide a Type 5 coverall and a disposable mask to CE 149 P3. However, whether this is sufficient must be considered under the requirements of the COSHH Regulations.

For a company that employs people full time to insulate lofts, the answer is probably not; they should be looking at the use of ventilation equipment to drive exposures and possibly the temperature down. However, a small contractor carrying out this type of work five or six times a year can be more selective about when to carry out the work, so it could be argued that by carrying out the work during the cooler months, the lower level controls are sufficient.

The judgement is based on experience and backed up with paperwork to justify decisions.

www.

**The HSE has compiled a set of example COSHH risk assessments for some industries, available on its website.**

**There is also excellent guidance on silica exposure on the HSE website.**

B
07

## 7.9 Control measures

### 7.9.1 Use of control measures

Employers should have procedures in place to ensure that measures provided to control exposure to hazardous substances, including the provision of PPE, are properly used or applied. These procedures should include regular inspections of working practices and a system to ensure that, where remedial action is found to be necessary, it is promptly taken.

Employees' duties are shown below.

- Make full and proper use of any control measures and to properly wear any PPE provided for their use.
- Take all reasonable steps to return the PPE after use to the accommodation provided.
- Notify any defects at once to management.

These are all common sense measures. Working with hazardous substances also dictates that employees make every effort to practise a high standard of personal hygiene, for example, by adhering to the points below.

- Removing any protective clothing (this may be contaminated) and thoroughly washing before eating and drinking.
- Consuming food and drink only in mess rooms or canteens.
- Making full use of shower facilities.
- Using the storage facilities provided and keeping personal protective clothing separate from ordinary clothing, to avoid possible contamination.
- Smoking only in designated areas and thoroughly washing hands before handling cigarettes or tobacco (including rolling cigarettes), otherwise contamination may spread from hands to the mouth and be ingested into the stomach, which can lead, in some circumstances, to serious health problems.

### 7.9.2 Maintenance, examination and test of control measures

Employers are required to ensure that all measures installed to prevent or control exposure to substances hazardous to health under the COSHH Regulations are maintained in efficient working order and in good repair.

Certain engineering controls require thorough examination and tests, as follows.

#### 7.9.2.1 Local exhaust ventilation plant

Local exhaust ventilation plant should be examined and tested at least once every 14 months. This would be expected in, for example, a woodworking shop. Technically, using a vacuum cleaner as an extractor on a power tool is creating a local exhaust ventilation system. However, because this is not a fixed system, it is unlikely that this would be considered for formal testing, but obviously it would need to work effectively.

More frequent testing of local exhaust ventilation is required for those processes listed in Schedule 4 of the regulations, although none of those processes are directly related to construction work.

Any defects in local exhaust ventilation systems must be reported and promptly rectified.

#### 7.9.2.2 Non-disposable respiratory protective equipment (RPE)

Thorough examinations and tests of non-disposable respiratory protective equipment (RPE) should be carried out, where appropriate, at suitable intervals.

The Approved Code of Practice (ACoP) that supports the COSHH Regulations (L5) specifies that such examinations and tests should be carried out at least every month, and more frequently where the conditions of use are particularly severe. Longer intervals may be more appropriate in the case of certain RPE (such as half-mask respirators used infrequently for short spells against air contaminants of relatively low toxicity). However, the longest interval between examinations and tests should not exceed three months.

Face-fit testing by someone who is competent is required for any tight-fitting masks. For full face masks this needs to be quantitative testing using a computerised method.

**For further information on RPE refer to Chapter B06 Personal protective equipment.**

#### 7.9.2.3 Disposable RPE

No examinations or tests are required, provided that the disposable RPE is used for only one working day or shift and then disposed of.

Again, face-fit testing by a competent person is required. This can be qualitative testing using a bitter/sweet solution to check the effectiveness of the fit. (If the wearer can taste or smell the solution then the fit is not correct and the test is a fail.)

#### 7.9.2.4 Records

All examinations, tests and repairs carried out on engineering controls and non-disposable RPE should be suitably recorded in any format provided they are easily retrievable. These records should be kept for at least five years.

**Detailed maintenance arrangements for engineering controls and non-disposable RPE are in the Approved Code of Practice (L5).**

#### 7.9.2.5 Review of assessments

An assessment should be reviewed regularly, and at once in case of the following.

- ☑ There is reason to believe that it is no longer valid (for example, new information on health risks has come to light).
- ☑ The work to which it relates has changed significantly (for example, new substances have been introduced, or the method of working is to change, such as the use of a spray gun to apply paint instead of a brush or roller).
- ☑ Environment and/or health monitoring results indicate it is necessary.

The definition of regularly will depend on a number of factors (such as the nature of the risk). However, the maximum period between reviews should not exceed five years.

Each review should trigger an opportunity to consider whether exposure can now be prevented (for example, by substituting a less hazardous substance or by process changes). Similarly, control measures should be reappraised to see whether they are still adequate or if further improvements are necessary and possible.

## 7.10 Monitoring exposure at the workplace

The Approved Code of Practice (L5) defines monitoring as the use of valid and suitable occupational hygiene techniques, by competent people, to measure the exposure of employees to substances hazardous to health.

There are certain situations, outlined below, in which the monitoring of exposure to a hazardous substance is required. Sometimes, however, it is so obvious that there is a problem that the money may be better spent on solving the problem rather than simply confirming what was already suspected.

Monitoring is required:

- where a serious health hazard could arise because of failure or deterioration of the control measures
- where it is necessary to ensure that a WEL or employer-imposed working standard is not exceeded. Significant exposure to silica dust may require monitoring
- when it is necessary to carry out an additional check on the effectiveness of any control measure
- where work involves the use of any carcinogen or mutagen and any work with substances or processes listed in Schedule 4 of the COSHH Regulations (for example, work involving vinyl chloride monomer or chromium plating).

It is unlikely the competency for carrying out monitoring will be available in-house to many companies. A number of health and safety consultancies can carry out the work. If competent advisors are bought in, it is essential to establish that they have the necessary experience and resource to do it.

**The work would often be considered to be occupational hygiene so it is worthwhile contacting the British Occupational Hygiene Society.**

In some situations, information about typical exposure values is available from trade bodies or HSE guidance. If the job being carried out is typical in all respects then, as a starting point, it would normally be acceptable to take these levels of exposure as being typical of the exposure levels actually experienced. However, there are obvious dangers in relying heavily on typical exposure values, particularly if the way the job is being carried out starts to diverge from the norm.

An example of monitoring, would be the use of a personal sampler to monitor an airborne contaminant in the breathing zone of an employee.

## 7.10.1 Monitoring records

Monitoring records must be kept in a suitable format and be available either as individual records or as a suitable summary for five years. If they are representative of the personal exposures of identifiable employees, the records must be kept for at least 40 years.

## 7.10.2 Health surveillance

The main purpose of health surveillance is to detect problems with the health of employees at the earliest possible stage. The purpose of control measures is to prevent damage to the health of employees; this is something that health surveillance cannot do. However, adverse health surveillance results may indicate that the existing control measures are not working properly.

Health surveillance has to be undertaken when an employee is exposed to:

- one of the substances and is involved in a process listed in Schedule 6 of the COSHH Regulations, to which reference should be made, although those listed are unlikely to apply to the construction industry
- a substance that is hazardous to health and there is an identifiable disease or adverse health effect related to this exposure (which may occur because of the conditions of the work) and there are valid techniques for detecting indications of the disease or effect. For example, isocyanates used in two-pack paints are respiratory irritants and can result in sensitisation and asthma.

Working on contaminated land often requires some form of health surveillance. This may include lung function testing or direct analysis of blood, urine or hair samples. Normally this would occur before, during and after the work. It allows a personal baseline to be established and then simply acts as a check that the control measures are working.

Suitable health surveillance can range from surveillance under the supervision of an employment medical adviser, an appointed doctor or a registered medical practitioner, to enquiries about symptoms, or an examination by an occupational health nurse. At the other end of the scale, health surveillance could simply involve a trained manager or supervisor inspecting an employee's hands and forearms, looking for the early signs of dermatitis.

Where the hazardous properties of a substance indicate, via the COSHH assessment, that health surveillance may be appropriate, advice on how to proceed can be sought from the Employment Medical Advisory Service (EMAS) of the HSE.

Employers are required to keep health records of employees under health surveillance for at least 40 years from the date of the last entry.

## 7.10.3 Information, instruction and training for people who may be exposed to hazardous substances

If an employee is likely to be exposed to substances hazardous to health, the employer must provide sufficient information, instruction and training so that the employee is aware of the health risks and the precautions that should be taken.

It is important that workers do not put themselves at risk due to lack of information, instruction or training. Therefore, they should be knowledgeable of the health risks, the precautions they should take (including the control measures), and be able to use the supplied PPE effectively.

They should also know what procedures to follow in the event of an emergency.

## 7.11 REACH Regulations

REACH is a European Union Regulation, which came into force on 1 June 2007. It concerns the **R**egistration, **E**valuation, **A**uthorisation and restriction of **Ch**emicals.

REACH will operate alongside COSHH and is designed so that better information on the hazards of chemicals and how to use them safely will be passed down the supply chain by chemical manufacturers and importers through improved safety data sheets.

REACH applies to substances manufactured or imported into the EU, in quantities of one tonne or more per year.

The regulations exclude the following.

- ☑ Radioactive substances.
- ☑ Substances under the customer's supervision.
- ☑ The transport of substances.
- ☑ Non-isolated intermediates.
- ☑ Waste.
- ☑ Some naturally occurring low-hazard substances.

Some substances are covered by more specific legislation and have tailored provisions.

### REACH aims

- ☑ To provide a high level of protection, for human health and the environment, from the use of chemicals.
- ☑ To make manufacturers and importers responsible for understanding and managing the risks associated with chemical use.
- ☑ To allow free movement of substances on the EU market.
- ☑ To enhance innovation in, and the competitiveness of, the EU chemical industry.
- ☑ To promote the use of alternative methods for the assessment of the hazardous properties of substances.



**Further information can be found on the HSE website and on the European Chemical Agency website.**

**To check your knowledge of your duties, as required by the COSHH Regulations, attempt the self-assessment quiz in Appendix B.**

## Appendix A – COSHH assessment example

### Diesel fuel

| | |
|---|---|
| **Name of hazardous substance** | Auto diesel. |
| **Substance hazard classification** | Flammable, harmful/irritant. |
| **Trade name(s)** | Any auto fuel production company. |
| **Substance used for** | Motive power for plant and other diesel powered vehicles. |
| **Likely circumstances of exposure** | Refuelling vehicles or filling other containers. |

| Potential hazards | Risk control measures | Emergency procedures |
|---|---|---|
| **Inhalation** can lead to nausea and headaches. | 1. Avoid inhaling vapour or mist; dispense directly into tank using nozzle.<br>2. Refuel vehicles or otherwise decant in the open air. | Remove to fresh air. Seek medical attention if conditions are severe. Remove the victim from exposure. |
| **Skin contact** can be irritating and have a defatting effect.<br>Can cause contact or irritant dermatitis. | 1. Avoid skin contact. Wear PVC gloves. Do not use as a cleaning agent.<br>2. Only refuel vehicles from a dispensing nozzle directly into fuel tanks.<br>3. Use funnel if dispensing into container. | Remove contaminated clothing. Wash skin thoroughly with soap and warm water. |
| **Eye contact** will cause irritation. | 1. Wear eye protection if splashing can occur.<br>2. Ensure refuelling nozzle is fully inserted into fuel tank neck.<br>3. Dispense at a rate that avoids splashes. | Rinse immediately with water until irritation subsides. Seek medical advice. |
| **Ingestion** will irritate mouth, throat, and so on. | 1. Do not eat, drink or smoke when handling.<br>2. Do not attempt to siphon using the mouth. | Do not induce vomiting. Wash mouth with water. Seek immediate medical attention. |
| **Fire:** flammable liquid. Products of combustion are toxic. Vapour/air mixture is explosive. | 1. Do not smoke when handling.<br>2. Store bulk diesel away from heat, sources of ignition and flammable materials.<br>3. Do not allow to come into contact with hot engine parts during refuelling. | Clear the area. Do not inhale vapours or smoke.<br>If trained, use foam or $CO_2$ extinguisher. Call emergency services to large fires. |
| **Spillage:** fumes/vapour likely to collect in low areas. | 1. Do not allow to enter drains. Eliminate ignition sources.<br>2. Ensure good ventilation. | Contain with sand or granules. Remove into a container. Dispose of as hazardous waste. |

**Additional information.** Environmentally damaging.

Are current controls adequate? Yes/No

| | | | | | | | |
|---|---|---|---|---|---|---|---|
| **Assessment date** | | | | **Next review date** | | | |
| **Approved for use by** | | | | | | | |
| **Name** | | **Position** | | **Signature** | | **Date** | |

B 07

## Appendix B – Self-assessment quiz

| Question | Emergency procedures |
|---|---|
| 1. What is the main purpose of the COSHH Regulations? | The main purpose of the COSHH Regulations is to protect the health of employees working with substances hazardous to health. |
| 2. When do you have to start complying with the regulations? | You must start now. The regulations are fully in force. Unless you act promptly, you could be breaking the law. |
| 3. What is a substance hazardous to health? | (a) Substances listed as very toxic, toxic, harmful, corrosive or irritant.<br>(b) Substances listed as having a workplace exposure limit (WEL).<br>(c) Anything else that produces similar effects to any of the things mentioned above. |
| 4. What is said about lead and asbestos? | They are not covered by the COSHH Regulations but, of course, you must comply with the Control of Lead at Work Regulations and the Control of Asbestos Regulations. |
| 5. Are there any other exceptions to the regulations? | Yes, anything that is a hazard because it is radioactive, explosive or flammable is excepted, but only for those reasons: If the substances have other hazardous properties, like giving off a fume (solvents), these are covered by the regulations. |
| 6. What must you make an assessment of? | The risk to employees of working with a substance hazardous to health and the actions needed to comply with the regulations.<br>Substances may be hazardous solely at high or low temperatures or at high or low pressure. |
| 7. If your assessment shows that an employee will be exposed to a substance hazardous to health, what should you do? | Prevent the exposure, if possible. If you cannot, you must adequately control it. |
| 8. What is the main recommendation about control measures? | Control should be exercised without the use of personal protective equipment, if at all possible. |
| 9. Whose responsibility is it to provide or use control measures? | The employer must provide them, and the employee must use them. The employer must also ensure use by properly supervising the workplace and employees. |
| 10. When is monitoring of the workplace necessary? | When it is necessary to check on the effectiveness of control measures or to protect the health of workers. |
| 11. When is health surveillance required? | Only where special circumstances require it (such as processes mentioned in the regulations or where certain diseases can be identified). |
| 12. What can happen if you do not make the assessments? | The enforcing authority (the HSE or Local Authority) can issue an improvement or prohibition notice or even prosecute in the criminal court in certain circumstances. |
| 13. If it is alleged that you have broken the regulations, what, if any, defence have you got? | You must prove that you took all reasonable precautions and exercised due diligence to avoid committing the offence. |
| 14. Who has to make the actual assessments? | It is the responsibility of employers to ensure that assessments are done, although they can employ a competent person to carry out the assessment. |
| 15. If a substance that can be inhaled does not have a control limit, what would be the adequate control standard? | Control would be considered adequate if the majority of the population could be regularly exposed to that substance at that level of exposure without any adverse effects on their health. |
| 16. Where will you find a list of substances that have a workplace exposure limit? | In HSE Guidance Note EH40 Workplace Exposure Limits (regularly updated). |
| 17. Which assessments have to be recorded? | All assessments must be recorded, unless they are very basic, simple and obvious. |
| 18. Can you use other people's assessments? | Yes, provided that they exactly fit your circumstances, or can be modified or adapted to suit your needs. |
| 19. When must you review an assessment? | When it is, or you suspect it may be, no longer valid because of changes in work methods, introduction of new types of control measures, or new information; or when monitoring shows that controls may not be working and, of course, when new substances are introduced. |

B
07

| Question | Emergency procedures |
|---|---|
| 20. Define the terms **hazard** and **risk**. | A **hazard** is the potential of a substance to cause harm.<br>A **risk** is the likelihood of that harm occurring in the circumstances that exist. |
| 21. To whom do you have a duty under the COSHH Regulations? | To employees and anyone else who may be affected, such as contractors and people working or passing nearby. |
| 22. What is the first step in the assessment process? | List all of the products and substances that you use, and determine which are substances hazardous to health. |
| 23. Who has the right to ask to see your assessments? | Enforcing authority inspectors (either the Health and Safety Executive inspector or Local Authority environmental health officer).<br>If you have safety representatives, they may also have a right to see your assessments. Principal contractors or your customers could also be included here, although they may not have a legal right. |
| 24. What is the best recommended control measure? | Elimination of the substance altogether or substituting a non-hazardous substance. |
| 25. When can the use of personal protective equipment (PPE) or respiratory protective equipment (RPE) be considered? | Only as a last resort, after every other type of control has been considered and PPE or RPE is found to be the only reasonably practicable method of achieving control. |
| 26. What is the general rule about the maintenance and inspection of control measures? | Anything provided as a control measure, except single-use RPE, must be properly maintained, regularly inspected and records kept. The regulations give details of inspections and records. |
| 27. What information, instruction and training do you have to give your employees? | Information, instruction and training on the risks to health of the substances that they work with the precautions they must take and any controls they must use. |
| 28. What is monitoring? | The use of a valid occupational hygiene technique to properly assess the exposure of employees to substances hazardous to health. |
| 29. When is monitoring necessary? | When it is necessary to ensure the adequacy of the control methods in use or it is otherwise needed to protect the health of employees. |

**How did you do?**

**Check which questions you could not answer, or got wrong. List the points covered then take a second look at the sections of this chapter that deal with them. Try the test again later.**

# 08

# Skin protection

**Contents**



## Supporting information

**G: Checklists and forms**



**GT 700 Toolbox talks**

## Overview

**Active concern for the welfare of employees will encourage their co-operation in reporting skin irritations at an early stage.**

**Workers are more likely to co-operate in preventative measures if they are provided with information on the causes of skin disease and given advice on how to identify the symptoms.**

## 8.1 Introduction

Under the Control of Substances Hazardous to Health (COSHH) Regulations employers have to make sure that employees' exposure to hazardous materials by skin contact and absorption through the skin is either prevented or, where it is not reasonably practicable, adequately controlled.

There are many different skin diseases that can occur and affect people at work. The most common work-related skin disease is contact **dermatitis**, caused by contact with an external agent, as well as other skin diseases such as acne, cancer and skin infections.

## 8.2 Important points

- Many of the substances used or created during construction work have the potential to cause severe skin problems.
- The fact that skin complaints (such as sensitising (allergic) dermatitis) are on the increase suggests that the threats to health are not being taken seriously.
- The COSHH assessment and the information on the accompanying data sheet and a substance's container should indicate the degree of risk and the preventative measures necessary.
- Ideally, the risk will be eliminated by avoiding the substance altogether, although this will often not be practical.
- Hazardous substances created by work processes will carry no health warning but must be identified in a COSHH assessment.
- Skin conditions can be prevented by simple actions (such as wearing the appropriate gloves or PPE).
- Barrier creams offer limited protection against some substances but should not be relied upon.
- Most substances can enter the body through openings (such as cuts and grazes). Other, more hazardous substances, can penetrate unbroken skin.
- Periodic self-checks or hand-checks, carried out by someone trained to recognise the symptoms, are an effective form of initial health surveillance.
- Prompt medical advice should be sought if there could be an emerging health problem.



## 8.3 Legislative requirements

### 8.3.1 Health and Safety at Work Act

The legal duties of employers, employees, manufacturers, importers and suppliers, as specified in the Health and Safety at Work Act 1974, and applicable regulations, are shown below.

#### 8.3.1.1 Employers' responsibilities

Employers have a duty to ensure that, as far as is reasonably practicable, safe systems of work are used, that adequate welfare facilities are available and that appropriate information, instruction, training and supervision are provided, as is necessary to ensure safety and the absence of risks to health in the use, handling, storage and transport of articles and substances.

There is a requirement on every employer to make a suitable and sufficient assessment of every work activity in order to identify any hazard to employees (or any other persons) that might be encountered as a result of the work having been carried out. The risk assessment must identify any substance to be used that can cause an adverse skin reaction and the control measures that are necessary to ensure that the substance can be used safely.

#### 8.3.1.2 Employees' duties

Employees are required to take reasonable care for their own health and safety, and that of other persons who may be affected by their work, and to co-operate with the employer so as to enable them to carry out their legal duties and requirements. In addition, employees must not intentionally or recklessly interfere with anything provided in the interests of health and safety.

#### 8.3.1.3 Manufacturers, importers and suppliers

Manufacturers, importers and suppliers of any articles or substances that are used in the workplace are responsible for ensuring that they have been tested for use, that information on their use is freely available and, so far as is reasonably practicable, that they are safe when properly used. This may include advice on appropriate PPE.

### 8.3.2 Control of Substances Hazardous to Health Regulations

These regulations are commonly known at the COSHH Regulations.

The principal points of the regulations place the following requirements on the employer to protect employees, or any other persons who may be affected by their operations.

- Assessing the health risks created by work involving substances hazardous to health. It should be noted that this is the same assessment as required under the Management of Health and Safety at Work Regulations. There is no need to carry out two assessments if the requirements of both sets of regulations are satisfied in a single assessment.
- Ensuring that the exposure of employees or others is prevented, or adequately controlled, by putting in place any measures necessary to control the exposure to risks.
- Ensuring that any control methods provided are properly used and maintained by monitoring the work environment, as necessary.
- Carrying out health surveillance in specified circumstances.
- Providing information, instruction and training for employees on the risks to health and precautions to be taken regarding any work with substances hazardous to health.
- Providing procedures for dealing with accidents, incidents and emergencies, including first aid and safety drills.

**For further information refer to Chapter B07 Control of substances hazardous to health.**

### 8.3.3 Personal Protective Equipment at Work Regulations

These regulations require that where a risk has been identified by a risk assessment, and it cannot be adequately controlled by other means, which are equally or more effective, then the employer must provide and ensure that suitable PPE is used by employees.

In essence, PPE may only be used as a last resort after all other means of eliminating or controlling the risk have been considered.

In deciding which type to issue, the employer must take into account the risk that the PPE is being used for, and that the PPE will fit the wearer and allow them to work comfortably.

Whilst the employer must take reasonable steps to ensure that any PPE supplied is worn, employees in turn must ensure that they wear the equipment provided and know the procedures for reporting any loss or defect to their employer.

**For further information refer to Chapter B06 Personal protective equipment.**

## 8.4 Harmful substances

Specifically in relation to skin protection, employers must ensure that the appropriate assessments have been made on any articles and substances used at work, and that they are:

- safe and free from any risk to health, when properly used
- used in accordance with the findings of risk assessments, procedures and conditions stipulated
- properly stored, transported and handled
- properly marked to indicate any special precautions that need to be taken.

They must ensure that persons using such articles and substances are:

- suitable and able to carry out the task that is expected of them
- properly and adequately trained in their use and aware of all necessary precautions that must be taken
- provided with appropriate personal protective clothing and equipment
- supplied with all necessary information
- educated in the dangers of skin conditions, and in methods to be used to prevent those conditions arising
- able to detect, and be aware of, the need to report any signs of skin infection or dermatitis.

Adequate washing and first-aid facilities must be provided, and barrier and cleansing creams should be available. In addition, the employer is responsible for providing supervision to ensure the above procedures, conditions and correct methods of work are maintained and that the proper facilities and equipment are available.

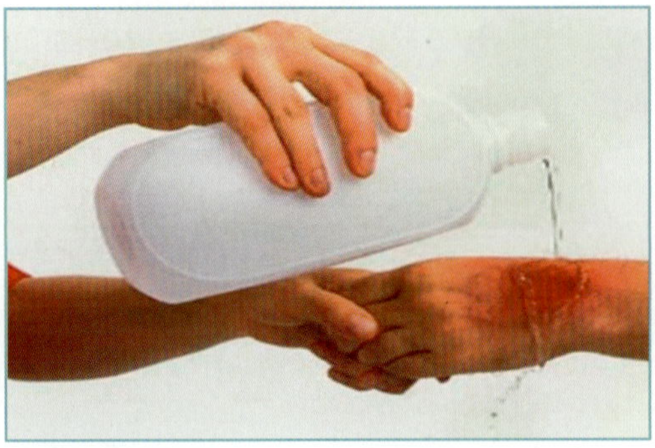

## 8.4.1 Potentially harmful substances and agents

The following substances and physical agents can be potentially harmful to the skin.

- ☑ Pitch, tar and bitumen.
- ☑ Cement or lime.
- ☑ Brick, stone, tile and plaster dust.
- ☑ Paints, varnishes, lacquers and stains.
- ☑ Certain types of timber.
- ☑ Fibreglass.
- ☑ Certain epoxy resins.
- ☑ Acrylic and formaldehyde resins.
- ☑ Chromates (in primers and cement).
- ☑ Organic solvents.
- ☑ Petrol, diesel and paraffin oils.
- ☑ White spirit and thinners.
- ☑ Acids or alkalis.
- ☑ Ionising radiation.
- ☑ Solar radiation.
- ☑ Other materials (depending on individual reactions).

## 8.4.2 Identifying hazardous symbols

| Globally harmonised pictograms | | | |
|---|---|---|---|
|  | **Toxic**<br>Toxic if swallowed. |  | **Corrosive**<br>Danger – causes severe skin burns and eye damage. |
|  | **New pictogram**<br>This replaces the previous CHIP irritant symbol. Refers to less serious health hazards (such as skin irritancy or sensitisation). May cause an allergic reaction. |  | **New pictogram**<br>May cause serious longer term health hazards (such as carcinogenicity and respiratory sensitisation). |

www. **For further information on labelling and packaging refer to the HSE website.**

## 8.5 Effects of contact with some materials

Skin contact with certain materials can cause a variety of reactions and some examples are given below. This list is not exhaustive.

**Mineral oils, including fuel oils and mould oils,** can lead to inflammatory skin conditions (such as dermatitis, oil acne or even skin cancer). These may be caused by constant contact with oil or oily clothes and rags (for example, when placed in overall pockets).

**Chemicals, including strong alkalis and certain acids, chromates, formaldehyde,** are substances that can penetrate the skin causing ulcers (for example, chrome ulceration) and dermatitis. Some chemicals can also cause skin cancer. The most significant chemicals for construction workers are polycyclic aromatic hydrocarbons (PAHs) from products containing coal tar or pitch. HSE research estimates that these caused over 450 cases of **non-melanoma skin cancer** in 2004 and fewer than five deaths in 2005. These risks are now significantly reduced as petroleum-based alternatives to coal tars are now used.

**Cement and lime** can also cause chronic dermatitis. Wetted cement and lime become more alkaline, corrosive and therefore potentially very damaging to the skin.

**Solvents and de-greasers, including paraffin, turpentine, petroleum products, thinners and similar solvents,** affect the skin by dissolving the natural oils (de-fatting), which renders it more vulnerable to attack by other substances and bacteria.

**Tar, pitch, bitumen products, including cresols and phenols like mineral oil,** cause inflammation, blisters and oil acne.

**Radiation, light and heat radiation, including X-rays, beta and gamma radiation, extremes of radiation, temperature and humidity,** make the skin more susceptible to dermatitis and other skin problems.

**Epoxy resin hardeners, glass fibres, certain woods, fungicides and insecticides** may irritate the skin and lead to dermatitis.

## 8.5.1 Dermatitis

Industrial dermatitis is a major cause of absenteeism, not only in the building and construction industry but across the whole spectrum of industry, and it accounts for over half of all working days lost through industrial sickness.

It is an inflammatory skin condition that is neither infectious nor contagious. It is caused by certain irritants contained in many industrial materials. Although dermatitis is not itself an infection, it can lead to infection when the skin's natural barriers break down.

There are two general types of dermatitis, shown below.

**Contact (irritant) dermatitis** is usually caused by the skin coming into contact with an irritant substance – usually a chemical, but it can be a mineral.

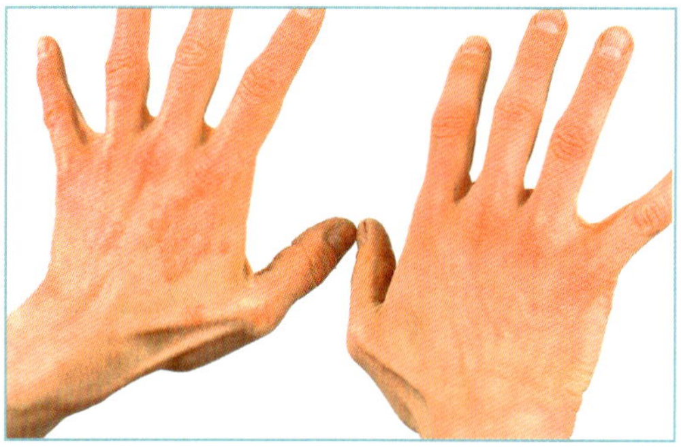

Repeated exposure to extreme heat or cold can lead to physical damage to the skin and make it more likely that irritant dermatitis will occur. Wet work, which involves the hands being wet for long periods (more than two hours a day) or repeatedly getting the hands wet, can also cause dermatitis. Anyone may be affected and the length of exposure, together with the strength of the irritant substance, will affect the seriousness of the complaint. Most cases of dermatitis are of this type.

**Sensitising dermatitis**, also known as allergic contact dermatitis, accounts for about 20% of all work-related dermatitis.

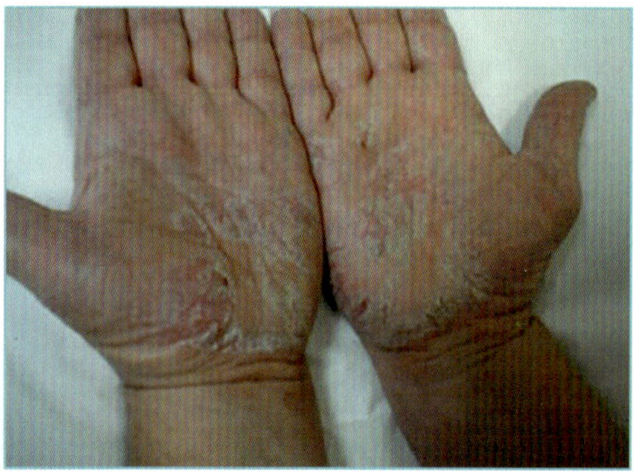

Some people develop a sudden allergic reaction following exposure to a specific substance. The reaction may be after weeks, months or even years of use or exposure to a substance without any ill effects.

However, once that sensitising dermatitis has occurred, any future exposure to the substance will again produce an adverse reaction. The exposure may be to an everyday chemical or mineral, and may be as simple as exposure to nickel in jewellery.

The outer layer of skin forms a natural defence against irritants, providing it is undamaged by cuts and abrasions, or by solvents (such as hydrocarbons, benzene, tetrachloride, spirits and thinners) that remove the skin's natural protective oils. Reaction of the skin to an irritant varies from one individual to another. The reaction may be only a mild redness or it can develop into swelling, blisters and septic ulcers that are both unsightly and painful.

Personal hygiene is particularly important when working with materials that may be irritants, as resistance to an irritant varies with the type of skin. Pores, ducts and hair follicles in the skin may admit irritants to the sensitive inner skin layer and, therefore, washing thoroughly to remove dirt and grime with soap and water is an essential preventative measure.

It is equally important that clothing is kept clean. Oil-stained overalls are a known cause of skin problems around the thighs.

The best course of action is to prevent skin contact with all potentially irritant substances, even if this is achieved by issuing personal protective equipment (PPE). When total avoidance of skin contact cannot be guaranteed, it will be necessary in some cases to implement occupational health screening (depending on the hazardous properties of the substance). Initially this should involve establishing whether the persons involved in the job have had any previous adverse reaction to the substance(s) in use.

**A poster on skin checks for dermatitis is available to download for free from the HSE website.**

Those people who are found to be allergic to one or more substance should be identified and not be allowed to handle or come into contact with them. Any part of the body that comes into contact with a skin irritant may be affected although it is usually the hands, wrists and forearms that are affected initially. Treatment for dermatitis should be sought as soon as possible because, if neglected, symptoms may spread to other parts of the body. Any treatment of dermatitis or its symptoms should be left to a doctor.

It should be noted that occupational dermatitis diagnosed by a doctor is notifiable to the Health and Safety Executive (HSE) under the provisions of the Reporting of Injuries, Diseases and Dangerous Occurrences Regulations (RIDDOR).

**Refer to Appendix A for examples of timber materials known to produce dermatitis or other irritant effects.**

**For further information refer to Chapter A13 Accident reporting and investigation.**

**Advice on screening can be obtained from the Employment Medical Advisory Service (EMAS).**

### 8.5.2 Skin burns

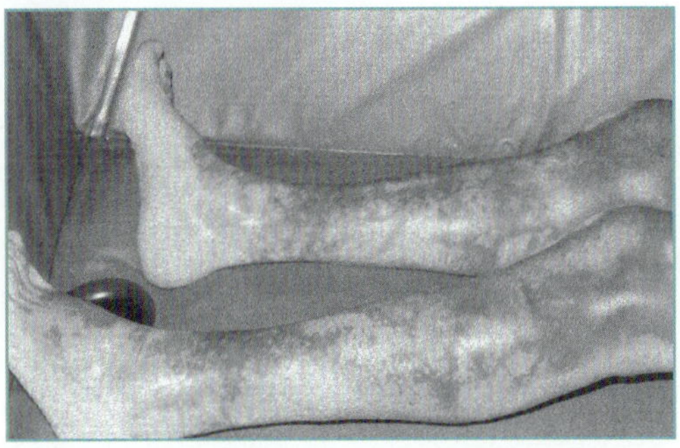

Many substances used in the construction industry have corrosive properties that can cause severe burns to the skin. These substances have either strong acid or alkali properties. Hot-work processes also have the potential to cause skin burns.

Wellington boots, for example, whether reinforced with protective toecaps, soles or not, are essential in preventing burns from wet cement or concrete. The cement content, when mixed with water, becomes highly corrosive and will cause severe burns to body tissue.

This picture shows the severely burnt legs of a man who was ignorant of the dangers of wet cement, the effect it can have on skin, and the need to wear wellington boots to protect the legs.

### 8.5.3 Abrasion and cuts

Manually handling objects with rough surfaces and sharp corners can cause damage to the skin of the hands if appropriate gloves (such as rigger gloves) are not worn. Repetitive manual handling may even make the situation worse. Such damage breaks the surface of the skin making it more vulnerable to absorbing other substances that could potentially have severe health effects.

Worn-out gloves must be thrown away and replacements obtained.

Where objects with sharp edges (such as sheet glass and sheet metal components) have to be manually handled, gloves with cut-proof material (such as Kevlar) woven into the fabric must be worn.

Ideally, work would be organised so that the manual handling of all such objects could be avoided. However, given the nature of construction, total avoidance is usually not possible. For example, a roof tiler may now use an inclined hoist to get the tiles up to roof level, but the hoist must still be loaded and the tiles distributed around the roof by hand.

With the increased emphasis on occupational health issues, tradespeople will often now wear gloves to carry out manual handling, tasks that at one time would have been carried out with bare hands.



## 8.6 Health risks from working in the sun

A sunny day usually makes most people feel good, but too much sunlight can actually damage the skin. It is not simply sudden exposure while on holiday that is harmful. Even a tan that has been built up gradually can be harmful to health. A tan is a sign that the skin has been potentially damaged.

Skin damage is caused by ultraviolet rays in sunlight. People whose jobs keep them outdoors for a long time (such as building, construction and civil engineering workers) may, if their skin is unprotected, get more sun on their skin than is healthy for them. They will then be at greater risk of developing skin cancer.

*Site sun cream dispenser with details of the day's UV level supplied by the principal contractor*

In the short-term, excess exposure of unprotected skin to the sun can cause blistering and peeling. Even mild reddening of the skin is a sign of skin damage.

In the long-term, too much sun will speed up ageing of the skin, making it leathery, mottled and wrinkled. However, the most serious issue is an increased chance of developing skin cancer.

There are two main types of skin cancer: **malignant melanoma**, which is less common but more serious, and **non-melanoma**, which is very common but not as serious.

In 2010 approximately 12,800 cases of malignant melanoma were diagnosed (about 35 per day), resulting in 2,203 deaths, and about 100,000 cases of non-melanoma were diagnosed, resulting in 546 deaths.

Men most commonly develop skin cancer on their chest or back, whereas for women it is on their legs.

Cases of skin cancer have more than quadrupled over the last 30 years and more than two young adults (aged 15-34) are now diagnosed with skin cancer every day in the UK.

Some medicines, and contact with some chemicals used at work (such as bitumen products), can also make the skin more sensitive to sunlight (photosensitivity).

www.

**For images of malignant melanoma and non-melanoma refer to the Cancer Research UK website.**

## 8.6.1 Skin types

Some people are more at risk than others. The effect that strong sunlight can have on the different types of skin is explained below. People with white skin are most at risk. Workers with the following characteristics should take particular care.

- ☑ Fair or freckled skin that does not tan, or goes red or burns before it tans.
- ☑ Red or fair hair and light coloured eyes.
- ☑ A large number of moles.

**Type 1.** White skin, never tans, always burns. Often person has red or fair hair, blue eyes, pale skin and freckles.

**Type 2.** White skin, burns easily, but may tan eventually. Person may have fair hair, blue eyes and freckles.

Workers with skin Types 1 or 2 must take extra care to avoid strong sunshine or cover up with tightly woven clothing and a hat.

**Type 3**. White skin tans easily and burns rarely. Person has dark hair and eyes and slightly darker skin.

**Type 4.** White skin, never burns, always tans. Person has dark hair, eyes and skin.

Workers with skin Types 3 or 4 should still take care in strong sunshine.

**Type 5.** Brown skin.

**Type 6.** Black skin.

Workers with skin Types 5 or 6 are still at risk from skin cancer. These skin types can still darken and even burn in stronger sunlight.

## 8.6.2 Protecting yourself

Even if their skin is not fair or freckled, workers should be particularly careful whilst working out of doors in summer in the three or four hours around midday when the sun is most intense.

Workers should:

- ☑ protect themselves with the type of clothing outlined below
- ☑ try to avoid the mild reddening, which is a sign of skin damage, as well as being a sign of early burning
- ☑ try to work and take breaks in the shade if they can (this will reduce the danger of harming the skin)
- ☑ not be complacent (the skin's most vulnerable areas are the back of the neck and the head – where possible, keep these areas covered)
- ☑ try not to get a tan; it might look good but it indicates that the skin has already been damaged.

www. **A leaflet for workers, who are working in hot weather, is available from the HSE.**

A suntan does not eliminate the long-term cancer risk, which is associated with prolonged exposure to the sun.

Using **protective clothing** to cover up is one of the main ways to avoid the dangers of developing skin cancer.

- ☑ **Work clothing** made from close-woven fabric, such as a long-sleeved shirt and jeans, will stop most of the UV rays.
- ☑ **Wear a hat.** A wide brimmed hat will shade the face and head. A safety helmet will afford protection and the addition of a hanging flap will protect the back of the neck.
- ☑ **Keep a shirt or other top on.**

Hats and other clothing are the best form of protection, but sun creams and lotions can add useful protection for parts of the body that are not easy to shade from the sun. A sun protection factor rating of 15 or more is recommended.

The first warning sign is often a small scabby spot that does not clear after a few weeks. Workers should be instructed to look for changed or newly formed moles or any skin discoloration. Workers should pay particular attention to any growths that appear on the face, especially around the eyes and nose, or on the backs of hands.

If these signs are noticed, medical assistance should be sought either from the company's medical staff or a local general practitioner, drawing attention to any moles that grow, change or bleed.

Many of these symptoms may prove to be non-cancerous – but they need to be checked to be absolutely sure.

Even if a spot is cancerous, simple modern treatments can usually cure them. This type of cancer very rarely spreads to other parts of the body. The smaller the spot, the easier it is to cure.

**! Don't delay If you think something might be wrong, get it checked out.**

Employers are strongly encouraged to develop a sun safety policy.

**For an example of a sun safety policy refer to Appendix B.**

B 08

## 8.7 Reducing risks

### 8.7.1 Substitute products

In line with the requirements of the COSHH Regulations, every effort must be made to ascertain which substances have the potential to cause dermatitis and, where possible, to substitute other materials that either eliminate or reduce the danger. An alternative, where possible, may be to use a more dilute form of the substance.

### 8.7.2 Reduce contact

If the outcome of an assessment is that there are no alternatives, and substances that cause dermatitis have to be used, methods of work should be implemented that eliminate contact between the skin and the substance.

The use of mechanical handling equipment may be possible but, if this is not available, simple devices and instruments, including splash guards, drip trays, tongs and scrapers will help to reduce the risk.

### 8.7.3 Healthy working conditions

It may be possible to use localised ventilation and exhaust systems to deal with dust, fumes and oil spray, which can be inhaled or absorbed.

Plentiful supplies of clean fresh air and comfortable working temperatures are vitally important, as is the general cleanliness of the working area, the machinery and any other equipment that is in use.

Wherever possible and appropriate, the display of warning and information signs should be prominently made, so that all employees are aware of the hazards existing in that area.

## 8.8 Protecting the worker



If an employer intends to use any items of PPE (including gloves and barrier creams) as part of their skin protection strategy in the workplace, then it is important that the correct PPE is selected.

All PPE for skin protection that is produced or imported by reputable companies is manufactured to British and European Standards.

As with all PPE for use at work, skin protection should be selected by a competent person who can ensure, in discussion with the supplier, that it meets the appropriate standards.

Most leading manufacturers and suppliers offer an advisory service on the selection of gloves and other items of skin protection.

### 8.8.1 Protective clothing

Protective clothing and other PPE provides one of the most practical ways of limiting contact between the skin and other substances. To be effective, all protective clothing must be the right size, fit for the purpose, maintained in good condition, cleaned regularly and stored carefully when not in use.

*Use appropriate PPE for the task*

Protective clothing may include gloves, overalls, eye protectors (such as goggles and face shields), aprons, boots and leggings, depending on the work being undertaken. Legislation requires the provision and wearing of protective clothing for specific processes and operations. The protective equipment provided must be suited to the requirements of the job.

Regular inspections must be made to ensure it remains sound and adequate.

### 8.8.2 Gloves

A glove suitable for handling abrasive materials may offer no protection against chemicals. The appropriate glove for sulphuric acid may not be approved for chromic acid.

Much care is needed in selecting the right type of glove to be used for a particular hazard. Manufacturers' charts and recommendations should be followed when selecting gloves to protect the wearer against specific hazards. A properly selected glove can be useful in the prevention of dermatitis if care is taken to avoid getting contaminants inside the gloves when putting them on and taking them off.

The modern materials from which gloves are now made enable them to be effective against hazardous substances whilst generally allowing the necessary amount of feel and dexterity where these factors are an issue.

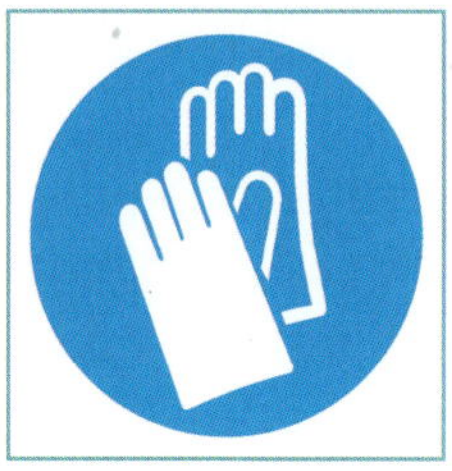

*Safety gloves must be worn*

| Industrial gloves – some types and uses | |
|---|---|
| **Hazard** | **Recommended type** |
| Acids, concrete, brickwork, stain removers, solvents and alkalis. | Neoprene, nitrile, PVC or rubber. |
| Esters, ethers, ketones (mastic, sealers), aldehydes and petroleum-based products. | Medium and heavyweight rubber, neoprene, nitrile or PVC. |
| High and low temperatures. | Nitrile, PVC or medium and heavyweight rubber. |
| Abrasion, unloading bricks and blocks and general materials handling. | Rubber, nitrile, PVC, neoprene or chrome-leather with reinforced palm. |
| Bitumen, hot work or similar. | Asbestos substitute or Nomex. |

**For further information on the selection of work gloves refer to Chapter B06 Personal protective equipment.**

## 8.8.3 Barrier substances

Where exposure of the skin is unavoidable, the use of barrier creams or other preparations may limit the degree of contact.

These substances are applied before starting work and removed by washing after each spell of work. Re-application is necessary before resuming work.

Water-soluble barrier creams are unsuitable where wet work is involved, and some substances are worn off with manual work.

There are many types of barrier substances available and it is essential that the right type is used for the work being done.

Most barrier substances afford only limited protection and should never be relied on as a sole means of protection.

## 8.8.4 Hygiene

Personal cleanliness is an important factor in the prevention of dermatitis. The necessary washing facilities and an ample supply of clean warm water, soap and clean towels should be made available near to the workplace, and workers should be encouraged to use these facilities.

Facilities for changing out of work-stained or contaminated clothing will also help to promote personal cleanliness.

All facilities should be kept clean and be inspected regularly.



## 8.8.5 Skin cleansers

Soap and water will help restore the skin to its natural state after the use of barrier creams. Skin cleansers may be required where soap and water are not adequate (such as insoluble barrier substances). With some skin cleansers (sanitisers), an additional moisturiser may be needed.

Solvents (such as paraffin, turpentine, thinners and petrol) remove the natural oils from the skin and must not be used for skin cleaning. Conditioning creams, designed to replace the natural oils of the skin, removed through frequent cleansing, should be used when necessary.

## 8.8.6 First aid

A healthy, intact skin is an effective barrier against some substances and infection, but the slightest cut or other injury may admit infection.

All abrasions to the skin, however minor, should be treated at once. However, be aware that some substances can penetrate unbroken skin.

## 8.8.7 Educating staff in prevention

Regular inspections of the workplace, work methods and precautionary procedures adopted will help ensure that the risk of dermatitis, or other skin complaints, is kept to a minimum. At-risk employees should be encouraged to carry out self-checks for the first signs of dermatitis and, ideally, supervisors should be trained to identify dermatitis. In appropriate circumstances, arrangements should be made for workers to have regular examinations by an occupational health professional to detect early signs of skin complaints, such as dermatitis and skin cancer.

Active concern for the welfare of employees will encourage their co-operation in reporting skin irritations at an early stage. Workers are more likely to co-operate in preventative measures if they are told positively what dermatitis is and what can be done to prevent it from occurring.

**The HSE *Skin at work* website contains basic practical advice for employers and employees on the prevention of skin diseases. The site also contains in-depth technical advice for occupational health nurses and health and safety practitioners, plus other resources.**

**CITB publishes a DVD-based occupational health training package entitled *If only I'd known* (DVD 064). This covers many of the points dealt with in this chapter.**

## Appendix A – Some timbers known to produce dermatitis and other irritant effects

| Commercial name | Harmful effects | Severity | Frequency |
|---|---|---|---|
| Afrormosia | Dermatitis and asthma. | Can be severe. | Quite frequent. |
| African mahogany | Dermatitis. | Severe. | Infrequent. |
| Boxwood | Dermatitis, rhinitis and asthma. | Mild. | Frequent. |
| Chestnut | Dermatitis, conjunctivitis and asthma. | Usually mild. | Infrequent. |
| Dahoma | Irritation of the chest and dermatitis. | Severe. | Frequent. |
| East African camphor wood | Asthma and dermatitis. | Fairly severe. | Infrequent. |
| Ebony | Irritation of nose and throat, and dermatitis. | Fairly severe. | Frequent. |
| Guarea (also West African cedar) | Nasal irritation, severe vomiting, chest irritation, blisters and dermatitis. | Effects vary from mild to severe depending on sensitivity. | Quite frequent. |
| Iroko | Skin and eye irritation, asthma and symptoms of the common cold. | Usually mild, occasionally serious. | Very infrequent. |
| Machaerium | Dermatitis. | Severe. | Infrequent. |
| Mansonia | Irritation of mucous membrane, nasal haemorrhage, sore eyes, dizziness and dermatitis. | Severity varies with individuals. | Frequent. |
| Satinwood | Dermatitis, headache and coughing. | Quite severe. | Infrequent. |
| Teak | Dermatitis and eye inflammation. | Can be severe. | Frequent. |
| Western red cedar | Asthma, bronchial trouble, dermatitis and septic wounds from splinters. | Severe. | Fairly frequent. |
| Yew | Bronchial asthma and dermatitis. | Quite severe. | Infrequent. |

## Appendix B – Sun safety policy example

1. This company is committed to protecting and educating its workers about the risks to health arising from excessive exposure to strong sunlight. The policy will be implemented as appropriate for all workers who are at risk.
2. Sun protection advice will be provided as part of routine health and safety training for all employees, including supervisors and managers. All new employees will be made aware of the sun safety policy.
3. Wherever possible, working hours and tasks will be scheduled to avoid the midday sunshine. Wherever possible, work that can be carried out indoors or in the shade will be scheduled during periods of strong sunshine.
4. All workers who are liable to be at risk will receive appropriate training on how to protect themselves from prolonged exposure to strong sunlight, regardless of their skin type or hair colour.
5. Workers who are at risk will be encouraged to wear full-length trousers and long-sleeved shirts throughout the year. They will be made aware that, ideally, clothing will be loose fitting and made from a close-weave fabric.
6. In most circumstances, the mandatory wearing of a safety helmet will provide the necessary protection for the head. In the rare circumstances where a safety helmet need not be worn, workers at risk will be advised to wear a hat.
7. Workers at risk will be given information on the appropriate use of sunscreen creams, including advice on the minimum recommended level of protection.
8. Drinking water will be provided in the shade and all workers will be encouraged to drink plenty of water to avoid dehydration.
9. Rest areas in the shade will be provided and workers at risk will be encouraged to use them for their rest breaks.
10. All contractors working on the site will be made aware of the contents of the sun safety policy and will be required to adhere to its guidelines.
11. The effectiveness of this policy will be monitored and it will be reviewed and updated as necessary.

# 09 Asbestos

Contents



## Supporting information

**GT 700 Toolbox talks**

## Overview

**Asbestos is a risk to health when airborne fibres are breathed in. Asbestos fibres are biopersistent and the greater the number of fibres inhaled, and the longer the period over which they are breathed in, the greater the risk of incurable asbestos-related diseases developing. These include cancers in the lungs and chest lining.**

**Almost 5,000 people die each year as a result of past asbestos exposure.**

## 9.1 Introduction

An understanding of this chapter alone will not be deemed sufficient for any person to be considered as a competent person under the Control of Asbestos Regulations (CAR). The purpose of this chapter is to give users information on the subject of asbestos.

- ☑ What to look for.
- ☑ The dangers to health that can occur due to exposure to asbestos.
- ☑ The requirements of the current regulations.
- ☑ The duty to manage asbestos.

**At the time of authoring the Health and Safety Executive (HSE) is working on a range of updated guidance documents to support the recently published Approved Codes of Practice (ACoPs).**

Asbestos removal work will normally be considered to be construction work as defined in the Construction (Design and Management) Regulations (CDM). Asbestos removal work may be required on larger or smaller jobs where CDM will also apply. Asbestos removal work must always be undertaken in accordance with all relevant legislation, regardless of the size and complexity of the asbestos removal task.

The HSE has previously expressed a number of concerns regarding aspects of health and safety, often associated when working with asbestos but that can be overlooked, such as working at height, the risk of fire, working in confined spaces, the use of machinery, burning, cutting and lifting. It is important not to view asbestos as a hazard in isolation. All associated hazards must be effectively managed, with due consideration given as to how the use of respiratory protection may exacerbate some of these risks. For example, a respirator used for confined space work may not be suitable for working with asbestos.

Not surprisingly, the emphasis of the regulations is on exposure risk management, not only for those who may be working directly with asbestos, but also for those who undertake work in premises where asbestos might be present. Work with the most high risk (dangerous) products must be carried out by a licensed contractor and appropriately trained operatives. Work with less hazardous products can, in most cases, still be carried out by people providing they are trained and competent and they are maintaining records of these non-licensed works.

The key to safe working is a risk assessment, which must be carried out by someone who is competent in terms of the following.

- ☑ Assessing the likelihood and extent of exposure to asbestos.
- ☑ Implementing the requirements of the legislation and supporting guidance.
- ☑ Understanding the controls needed.

*Damaged asbestos lagging*

All work with asbestos must comply with the Control of Asbestos Regulations (CAR). The classification of work and risk are determined by a material friability. Those **materials capable of releasing high levels of fibre will generally require a licensed contractor**. Generally, work with undamaged asbestos cement products, older textured coatings (such as Artex) and some other **materials where the asbestos fibres are tightly bound into a base material is non-licensed**, but in some circumstances may require *notification*.

Some work with asbestos cement products (for example, clearing up fire damaged debris where the cement has been badly damaged and the asbestos fibres are no longer well bound into the base material matrix) is likely to need the services of a licensed contractor.

**Asbestos is a risk to health when airborne fibres are breathed in. The greater the number of fibres, the age of first exposure and the longer the period over which they are breathed in, the greater the risk of incurable asbestos-related diseases developing. These include cancers in the lungs and chest lining. Smokers exposed to asbestos have a greatly increased risk of lung cancer.**

B 09

The use of asbestos materials in construction products was very common from the mid-1940s, reaching its peak in the mid-1970s. However, asbestos that is in a good condition, which is not damaged and is not likely to be worked on or disturbed, does not pose any immediate problem and may not need to be removed. The HSE advises that it is usually better to leave it in place, and then to manage its presence on an ongoing basis. However, on construction projects the HSE state: *'in the case of demolition of major refurbishment, the plan of work must specify that all asbestos is removed before any other major work begins, where this is reasonably practicable and does not cause a greater risk to the employees than if the asbestos had been left in place'.*

In the past, asbestos was widely used in the manufacture of building materials and products. Current legislation now prohibits the use of asbestos for all of these purposes. As a result, there should be no asbestos issues with any newbuild premises or refurbishment after 1999, where the full removal of asbestos has been undertaken. It is important to note that asbestos has not been banned worldwide and from time to time may be found in imported products. Appropriate due diligence should be applied to imported plant and machinery, arriving from areas around the world where asbestos is not a banned material.

Although asbestos building materials and products have been largely replaced by safer alternatives, there remains the issue of the ongoing and long-term management of existing asbestos where its removal is not practicable.

Consequently, the regulations place a duty to manage asbestos on the owners or occupiers of non-domestic premises.

www.

**There are many resources available on the HSE website, including video support, which can indicate the likely locations where you may find asbestos.**

## 9.2 Important points

- CAR applies to employers, as well as those who manage premises or who remove asbestos.
- The regulations are designed to protect everyone who might be at risk from asbestos exposure, not just those tasked with the removal of asbestos-containing material (ACM).
- ACM is hazardous when airborne and dangerous when fibres are inhaled.
- Asbestos was widely used in the UK until it was banned in late 1999; disturbance of the fabric of any building built before this time has the potential to expose asbestos.
- As part of the requirements of the duty to manage, all non-domestic premises should have an asbestos management plan in place. This document should be available to anyone who might work within or will undertake any maintenance of the building.
- The requirements for the control of asbestos removal are cascading, and relate to the friability of the material. The most friable materials require higher levels of control and competency than the least friable materials.
- Anyone who may encounter asbestos as part of their daily work operations should have asbestos awareness training. This includes most people within the construction and maintenance sector. It is currently estimated that 20 people from the construction sector die each week as a result of past asbestos exposure.
- All work with asbestos must comply with CAR. The requirements for licensed work remain the same: in the majority of cases, work with asbestos needs to be done by a licensed contractor. This work includes most asbestos removal, all work with sprayed asbestos coatings and asbestos lagging and most work with asbestos insulation and asbestos insulating board (AIB). Other types of asbestos may require the use of a license subject to an assessment of risk and potential fibre release.
- If you are carrying out non-licensed asbestos work, this still requires effective controls.
- Some non-licensed work needs to be notified to the relevant enforcing authority. This is referred to as notifiable non-licensed work (NNLW).
- Written records should be kept of non-licensed work, which has to be notified (such as copy of the notification with a list of workers on the job), plus the level of likely exposure of those workers to asbestos. This does not require air monitoring on every job, if an estimate of degree of exposure can be made based on experience of similar past tasks or published guidance.
- Before any work that has the potential to expose anyone to asbestos is carried out, a survey must be carried out and a written risk assessment made.
- The priority for any employer is to prevent exposure to, and the spread of, asbestos. This is not only important during asbestos removal operations, where effective containment is required, but it should also be considered during maintenance and refurbishment work.
- A written, site-specific plan (or register) of work must be kept on site and followed.
- Anyone who does any work with asbestos must be specifically trained to do it, and this training must be repeated at least annually.
- Contractors producing hazardous asbestos waste must check that the site receiving your asbestos waste is authorised to receive asbestos. They should have an environmental permit.
- Be aware of other hazards that may arise from working with or managing asbestos (such as working at height, in a confined space or where the presence of live services must be managed) and how the use of respiratory protective equipment (RPE) can change these risks by, for example, restricting all round visibility.
- The HSE, or the appropriate authority, must be notified of the following.
  - All work involving the disturbance of asbestos. This applies to licensed asbestos work and notifiable non-licensed asbestos work. Only non-licensed work does not require notification to the HSE.
  - Separately, if the project is notifiable under the Construction (Design and Management) Regulations.

- ☑ CAR requires anyone who issues a site-clearance certificate to be accredited to ISO 17025 by an appropriate accreditation body as competent to carry out such work. In the UK the sole source of this accreditation is through the United Kingdom Accredited Service (UKAS).
- ☑ CAR requires all those who may be exposed to asbestos to have had appropriate asbestos awareness training. The HSE has identified specific groups deemed at risk, which includes all construction personnel.

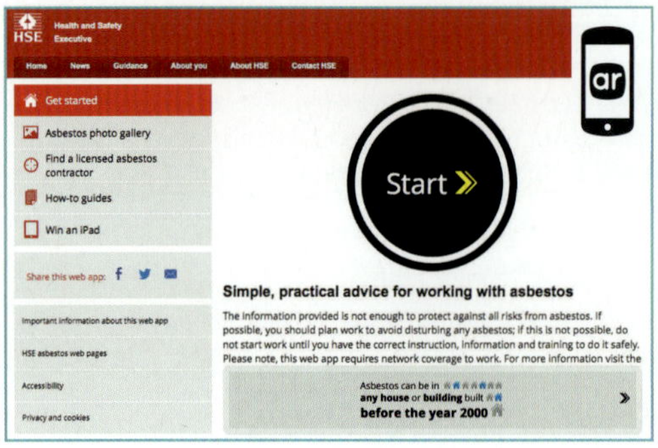


The HSE has developed a web tool, which is freely available to help contractors work safely with asbestos. It includes a number of images and how to guides.

In 2014 HSE research identified that 1.3 million tradespeople are at risk from the dangers of asbestos. This includes construction workers, carpenters, painters and decorators. The research also found that one in seven people believed that drinking a glass of water would help protect them from the deadly dust and one in four thought that opening a window would help to keep them safe.

**www.** **For further information on the research into the dangers of asbestos refer to the HSE website.**

## 9.3 Control of Asbestos Regulations

CAR defines the following terms.

**Licensed work.** All high risk work, other than very minor work, with the following products.

- ☑ Asbestos insulation.
- ☑ Coating (excluding textured coatings and paint).
- ☑ Asbestos insulation board.
- ☑ Work on any material that exceeds the control limit of 0.1 fibres per $cm^3$ over four hours, or the short-term exposure limit of 0.6 fibres per $cm^3$ over ten minutes.

**Notifiable non-licensed work.** Work that will normally fall into this category may involve minor work involving the repair of asbestos insulation, minor work with AIB that meets the short duration criteria, maintenance of and removal of damaged asbestos cement and removal work of decorative coatings that contain ACM.

For work not to require a licensed contractor, an assessment by a competent person must conclude that the planned exposure is sporadic and low intensity, and will not exceed the control limit.

The work itself must meet the following requirements.

- ☑ Be short, non-continuous maintenance; or removal of materials where the asbestos fibres are firmly linked to the base material matrix.
- ☑ Encapsulate or seal the materials that are in good condition.
- ☑ Be subjected to air monitoring, gathering samples or other analytical work.

Work with the following materials will be notifiable and non-licensed providing the risk assessment accurately confirms that the exposure over a four-hour period will not exceed the control limit of 0.1 fibres/$cm^3$, and the maximum exposure will be below a peak of 0.6 fibres/$cm^3$ averaged over ten minutes. It is worth noting that 0.1 fibres $cm^3$ equates to 100 fibres per $m^3$.

- ☑ Asbestos cement.
- ☑ Textured decorative coatings containing asbestos.
- ☑ Paints that contain asbestos.
- ☑ Items of bitumen, plastic, resin or rubber, which do contain asbestos, but the asbestos was not used for its thermal or insulation properties (such as dampproof course, roofing felt, vinyl floor tiles and toilet seats).
- ☑ Gaskets, packers and washers.
- ☑ Items (such as asbestos rope) **where the material is not being used for insulation** (for example, asbestos rope used as a gasket/packer in the joint between two sections of an asbestos cement drainpipe). (It should be noted that asbestos rope wrapped around a pipe, to keep the heat in or stop it from freezing, is acting as insulation.)

**!** **Written records should be kept of notifiable non-licensed work.**

B 09

**Non-licensed work.** Work that will normally fall into this category is shown below.

- Short, non-continuous work with asbestos insulating board (attaching cables, cleaning light fittings and lifting ceiling tiles for inspection).
- Short, non-continuous maintenance and removal work with asbestos cement that is in good condition.
- Short, non-continuous work with decorative coatings (drilling and fixing screws).

It includes minor work on the repair or removal of asbestos-containing items, where the asbestos is well bonded and the removal of these items will not result in the degradation of the materials. Some examples are shown below. *(For further information refer to 9.12.5 Non-licensed work.)*

- Work with asbestos cement sheets, where the material is in a good condition and can be removed intact.
- Work on textured decorative coatings, applied to plasterboard, where the material can be removed, attached to the plasterboard.
- Thermoplastic floor tiles.

**Sporadic and low intensity.** The concentration of air cannot exceed, or be liable to exceed, 0.6 fibres/cm$^3$ in air measured over a ten-minute period by a UKAS laboratory.

**Control limit.** Average exposure measured by a UKAS laboratory for a four-hour period, which is currently set at 0.1 fibres/cm$^3$ for all types of asbestos fibre. This should not take into account any RPE worn.

**Risk assessment.** An assessment of the risk of anyone being harmed through exposure to asbestos, as carried out by someone with both the theoretical and practical experience of the intended work with asbestos-containing materials. This degree of specialism necessary to carry out such a risk assessment may be beyond the competence of many people who would otherwise be considered to be a source of competent health and safety advice under the Management of Health and Safety at Work Regulations.

www.

**Competence is detailed in the ACoP, which is available on the companion website.**

## 9.3.1 Prohibitions

These parts of the regulations prohibit the importation, supply, use and reuse of all types of asbestos, as articles or substances for use at work, and also prohibit the supply of products containing them. Further restrictions prevent their use for the manufacture and repair of any product. Any existing products that contain asbestos should be properly disposed of.

If, for example during a refurbishment, asbestos cement sheeting is removed from the roof of a building, it cannot be sold or given away. It must be disposed of properly.

It is important to note that the requirements of the REACH Regulations may apply in circumstances where items of plant and machinery, which have an asbestos content, are being sold or moved.

# 9.4 Locating asbestos

This is often a job for an asbestos surveyor and it can be difficult, as the appearance of the asbestos may be changed by surface coatings, heat or ageing. It may also be encapsulated by, or be concealed beneath, other materials, particularly where asbestos removal was carried out to a poor standard in the past. However, original plans or specifications may help to confirm its presence.

*Asbestos insulation board*

It is important to note that asbestos might have been introduced to properties through historic maintenance and refurbishment and it will not always be possible or practicable to locate all asbestos materials within a building.

If a building was constructed or refurbished prior to 2000 there is a probability that it may contain asbestos.

The asbestos industry estimates that over 3,500 products have been produced with an asbestos content, many of which have been used for a variety of reasons within the construction industry.

Asbestos material is fire resistant and thermal efficient, and so it was commonly used for heat insulation and fire compartmentalisation. Its high tensile strength made it ideal for incorporation into fabrics and yarns. This quality also made it a perfect binding material with cement and other matrices.

## 9.4.1 Products that asbestos can be found in

The following items are an example of the types of products that asbestos can be found in. It has been estimated that over 3,500 building products have been produced with an asbestos content.

#### 9.4.1.1 Insulation and sprayed coatings using moulded or pre-formed lagging

- ☑ Boilers, plant and pipework.
- ☑ Fire protection to steel work.
- ☑ Thermal and acoustic insulation of buildings, including loose packing.

#### 9.4.1.2 Insulation board

- ☑ Fire protection to doors.
- ☑ Claddings on walls and ceilings.
- ☑ Partitioning.
- ☑ Ceiling tiles.
- ☑ Fire breaks in ceiling voids.
- ☑ Electrical equipment and service risers.
- ☑ General building board.

#### 9.4.1.3 Asbestos cement

- ☑ Corrugated roof sheets.
- ☑ Flat sheets for cladding and partitions.
- ☑ Roof and rainwater drainage goods.
- ☑ Underground pipes.
- ☑ Bath panels.
- ☑ Artificial roof slates.
- ☑ Flue pipe.
- ☑ General building board.

#### 9.4.1.4 Other materials

- ☑ Vinyl or thermoplastic floor tiles.
- ☑ Insulation of electrical equipment.
- ☑ Some textured coatings.
- ☑ Bakelite sanitary ware, and other products.
- ☑ Bitumen.

Asbestos-based friction materials were widely used in brake and clutch linings in vehicles and plant, including lift equipment, together with gaskets and packing in engines and heating or ventilation systems. Substitute materials have been developed in most cases.

**For further information on places and materials that can contain asbestos refer to Appendix C.**

B 09

## 9.5 Types of asbestos

Asbestos is a naturally occurring fibrous silicate mineral material, which does not burn and is resistant to most acids and alkalis. The fire protection and insulating properties of asbestos were the main reason for its use over the years.

*Asbestos mining*

CAR applies to all asbestos types but the three main types that have been used in the construction industry are shown below.

- ☑ Chrysotile (white).
- ☑ Amosite/grunerite (brown).
- ☑ Crocidolite (blue).

Although the colours are often quoted to differentiate between the types of asbestos, the actual colour of a material suspected of being asbestos is not necessarily an accurate indication as to whether or not it is asbestos or an asbestos-containing material, or if it is, of what type. Only laboratory testing can definitively prove that a material is asbestos and confirm what type.

**It is impossible to rely on colour or appearance to identify different forms of asbestos. This must be undertaken by laboratory analysis.**

Changes in colour may occur due to the following.

- ☑ It ageing or simply becoming dirty.
- ☑ The effects of heat.
- ☑ Surface coatings or dyes being applied.
- ☑ Encapsulation.
- ☑ Oil or chemical splashes.

It is important to ensure a full depth sample is taken whenever materials are suspected of containing asbestos. In the case of asbestos used in the lagging of boilers and pipework this can be particularly difficult as differing layers of the material may have different contents. Repairs and modifications can mean that boilers or pipework may be lagged by a mixture of different types of asbestos.

*Asbestos fire blanket*

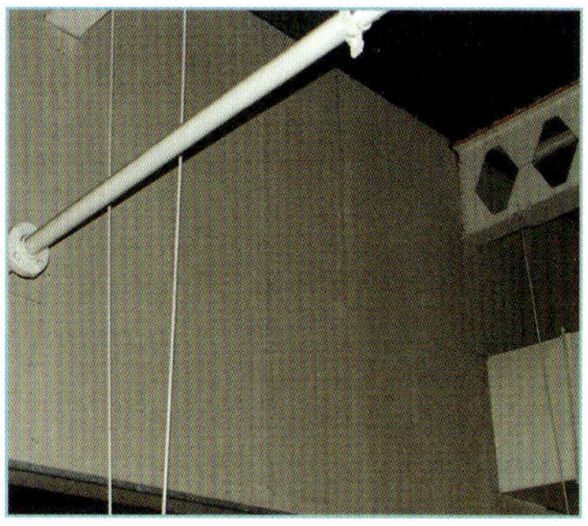

*Asbestos (AIB) panels at high level*

*Damaged asbestos spray applied acoustical ceiling material*

*Asbestos floor tiles*

*Asbestos soffit*

Asbestos was widely used as fire protection in building materials, for thermal insulation and also as a sprayed coating to steel structural members. All of these uses now present significant management issues associated with the maintenance of the asbestos over the remaining life span of the building or the removal of the asbestos during renovation, refurbishment or demolition.

Safe working in situations where asbestos might be exposed or damaged demands stringent control, and compliance with recommended precautionary measures and methods of work. These are detailed in the Approved Code of Practice (ACoP) *Work with materials containing asbestos* and CAR.

**In addition the HSE publication *Asbestos: the licensed contractor's guide* (HSG247) provides specific guidance for high risk (licensed) asbestos work.**

## 9.6 Duty to manage

This is perhaps the most important part of CAR for the long-term protection of the health of employees and others. It states that any person who owns, occupies, manages or has responsibility for part or all of non-domestic premises that may contain asbestos has a legal duty to manage the risk from asbestos or asbestos-containing materials within those premises, or co-operate with whoever has the duty to manage the risk.

It should be noted that domestic housing that is owned and/or managed by Local Authorities, housing associations, or similar is not deemed to be non-domestic property and therefore the duty to manage under the regulations will apply to the owner or manager. However, the common parts of blocks are deemed to be within scope of the requirements.

**It should also be noted that although Regulation 4 of CAR does not apply wherever maintenance or refurbishment work is planned in any property, including domestic dwellings, Regulation 5 places an obligation on the employer to identify asbestos before work starts, regardless of whether the requirements of Regulation 4 apply.**

The requirements of the duty to manage can be a shared responsibility depending upon contractual requirements. In the construction industry when taking possession of a site you are likely to be taking on an element of duty holder responsibilities. Responsibility may also change during the contract, as work progresses. A contractor in charge of a site during development is likely to be the duty holder.

Asbestos insulating board (AIB)

Damaged asbestos panels

**HSE publications *Asbestos hidden killer* and *A short guide to managing asbestos in premises* provide simple precautions to be undertaken and explains the duty to manage in general terms. Both are available to download free from the HSE website.**

If you have any maintenance and/or repair responsibilities for non-domestic premises, either through a contract or a temporary agreement, or because you own or occupy the premises, then you have a duty to manage. It is important to note that the responsibility can be shared and several people could have duty holder responsibilities at any time.

Your duty to manage will require you to manage the risk from asbestos by the following.

- Find out if there is any asbestos or suspected ACMs in the premises, how much of it there is, where it is, and what condition it is in.

  ***Note:*** *if work will be carried out that will disturb the fabric of pre-2000 premises, an appropriate asbestos survey must be carried out by a competent person, as outlined in the HSE publication Asbestos: the survey guide (HSG264). There are now two types of survey:*

  – *management survey*

  – *refurbishment or demolition survey.*

  *(Refer to Appendix A for further details of commissioning a competent asbestos surveyor to carry out a suitable survey.)*

  *Prior to any refurbishment or demolition work it is a client's duty to ensure an invasive refurbishment/demolition asbestos survey is undertaken in accordance with HSG264. It is important to ensure that this survey has considered the work planned and is reviewed should the work change, to ensure it provides an appropriate record of asbestos materials.*

- Always presume that it is asbestos or an ACM unless you know or you have strong evidence proving otherwise.

  ***Note:*** *it is better to overprotect than to expose employees and others to asbestos.*

- Make and keep up to date, a record (an asbestos register) of the location and condition of all the asbestos, ACMs or presumed ACMs in your premises.

  ***Note:*** *a plan of the premises showing where the materials are will always be extremely useful, and will be essential in larger premises. Such a plan would form an integral part of the ongoing management of the asbestos or ACM. Where applicable, details of asbestos should also be added to the health and safety file.*

- Assess the risk that the materials pose to employees and others.

  ***Note:*** *a risk assessment should be undertaken by a competent person who has sufficient knowledge of the subject.*

  *If the materials are in good condition, not liable to be damaged, and will not be disturbed or worked on, then the risk is probably low. If the materials are flaky, crumbling, in a place where they can be damaged by, for example, forklift trucks, then the risk is high. Given the known ill health caused by asbestos, then a high risk of damage calls for urgent action. When assessing this risk the surveyor may need additional information about how the space containing the ACM will be used. This is known as the* ***priority assessment****. Completion of this is the responsibility of the duty holder.*

- Prevent any work on the premises that may disturb asbestos or ACMs until control measures to manage the risk have been put in place.

  ***Note:*** *this could be work by your employees or any contractors or sub-contractors brought in for carpentry, flooring, partitioning, ceiling fixing, plumbing, electrical or other work.*

- Prepare a plan that sets out in detail how you are going to manage the risk from the material.

  ***Note:*** *if material is not going to be removed by a licensed asbestos removal contractor, consider how you are going to manage the long-term presence of the asbestos. If it is in good condition and not liable to be damaged, then routine inspection and monitoring may be enough if records are kept. A sealing coat may be needed, or other protective work necessary, to lower and to further control the risk.*

- Take all of the steps needed to put your plan into action.

  ***Note:*** *make it happen. What is the organisation, what are the arrangements for the implementation of the plan and who has the responsibility?*

- Review and monitor your plan and the arrangements that you made to put it in place.

  ***Note:*** *a regular review of the action plan will ensure that it is working, that the control measures are still effective and that inspection, monitoring and recording are in fact taking place. It may be the case that procedures, notices and policies that have been in place for a length of time tend to be overlooked. A fresh approach may therefore be needed.*

- Provide information on the location and condition of the material to anyone who is liable to work on or to disturb it.

  ***Note:*** *part of this information involves the use of the signs that will have been placed to identify the location of asbestos or ACM. In a large workplace or premises, this will also mean keeping a detailed plan of the building or register that describes every individual room or workplace and the asbestos or ACM that is in there. This will inform staff, visiting contractors, maintenance workers and visiting specialists (such as IT data installers) of the areas and features of the building that they must not disturb. Wherever possible, it should be ensured that actions are traceable and contractors should sign to confirm they have inspected the register or management plan before starting work.*

  Asbestos will pose a significant risk to health if it is in a condition that allows easy release of fibres that can then be inhaled.

B 09

- ☑ Ensure that anyone who has information on the whereabouts of asbestos in your premises makes this available to you as a duty holder.

  ***Note:*** *those who are not duty holders, but control access to the premises (for example, contractors who remove panelling and find what could be asbestos or ACM) have a duty to tell you what they have found. However, you may need to remind them about this duty before they start work. Regarding the control of premises, the duty may be with the landlord or management agency.*

  *The regulations also impose duties on employers for the protection of employees who may be exposed to asbestos at work, and other persons affected or who may be at risk of being affected by such work.*

  *Similar duties are placed on self-employed persons.*

- ☑ Provide information to the emergency services.

  ***Note:*** *in practice this is more important where buildings have large amounts of asbestos products in them. The presence of, for example, one or two rainwater goods products is unlikely to be a major issue.*

- ☑ If you are a contractor working on someone else's premises where asbestos is likely to be present, you must be given access to the asbestos register, which must outline the location and condition of known asbestos within the building.

**If you are not given access to the asbestos register, you should not start any work that will disturb the fabric of the building.**

**For a checklist on managing asbestos refer to the HSE website.**

## Failure to provide asbestos information 1

In early 2014 a building contractor failed to plan, manage and properly monitor the construction work at a school. He was fined £50,000 and ordered to pay £26,217 after admitting a breach of Section 3(1) of the Health and Safety at Work etc. Act 1974.

After the hearing the HSE inspector said: 'This was a serious failing on the part of the company. Having correctly commissioned an asbestos survey, it looks as though no-one at the company bothered to read it. Or, if they did, they disregarded its contents and failed to act to protect site workers from exposure to what is one of the deadly killers in the construction industry. As a result, several people, including the young apprentice, were unnecessarily exposed to the risk of inhaling asbestos fibres. One can only wish and hope that there are no serious consequences for these workers in the future. It is vital that companies are fully aware of not just the duty to get an asbestos survey done, but then to act on its findings. There is considerable guidance freely available from the HSE to assist duty holders to deal with asbestos materials properly'. *(Source HSE.)*

## Failure to provide asbestos information 2

The court heard how an employing company failed to ensure that information about the location and condition of asbestos materials was provided to those liable to disturb it. The contractor had conducted the work without carrying out the necessary assessment to determine whether asbestos was present, and had failed to take any measures to prevent the spread of asbestos fibres. The personal involvement of both directors meant that they had also been prosecuted as individuals.

The work carried out by the contractor meant that asbestos debris was scattered over the working area, which exposed workers there, and on neighbouring sites, to a potential health risk. The employing company had to have the site environmentally cleaned.

The contractor was fined a total of £12,000 and ordered to pay £3,804.20 in costs after pleading guilty to breaching Regulations 5(a) and 16 of CAR. The employing company was fined £10,000 with £2,243.40 costs after pleading guilty to breaching Regulation 4 of the same legislation. A director was fined £1,000 and ordered to pay £204.80 in costs after pleading guilty to breaching Regulation 5(a) of the same legislation. A second director was fined £650 (with no order for costs) after pleading guilty to breaching Regulation 16 of the same legislation.

Speaking after the case the HSE inspector said: 'Asbestos is the single greatest cause of work-related deaths in the UK and there is a lot of industry in the area that still uses or occupies premises that have old chemical processing plant dating back to the 60s. Almost all of it was lagged with asbestos in those days. Site operators and contractors working at these sites should always assume that old pipework is lagged with asbestos, unless there is reliable evidence that says otherwise. Those involved in the construction and refurbishment industry also have a clear duty to ensure that work is managed so as to prevent the spread of asbestos. This incident occurred because the employing company's asbestos management systems did not include anything relating to informing others of the presence of asbestos on the site. The contractor failed to carry out an asbestos assessment before starting work and did not take any measures to prevent the spread of asbestos fibres. This put the directors themselves, their own employees and others working nearby at risk of exposure to asbestos fibres and the court agreed that both companies were equally culpable for the offences'. *(Source HSE.)*

## 9.7 Representative sampling

If representative samples are needed for laboratory analysis, they must be taken in a prescribed manner to retain their integrity and the safety of anyone who may handle them. It is a legal requirement that any laboratory carrying out analysis has the necessary facilities, expertise and quality control procedures. Laboratories that meet these standards are accredited under ISO 17025 by the United Kingdom Accreditation Scheme (UKAS).

To confirm or identify the type of asbestos or ACM on the premises, a series of bulk samples may have to be taken for laboratory analysis by a UKAS-accredited laboratory. Methods employed in taking samples of asbestos will vary according to its type and location. HSE guidance on taking samples should be followed.

Anyone removing samples for analysis must be competent to do so and use appropriate protective clothing and respiratory equipment, particularly if the work involves cutting, boring, drilling or otherwise creating airborne dust or fibres.

**Guidance covering licensed asbestos removal, sampling, analysis and clearance procedures is available from the HSE.**

## 9.8 Certificate of reoccupation

The importance of ensuring that a previously contaminated area is totally clear of asbestos before reoccupation cannot be stressed too strongly. The wellbeing of everyone who will occupy the premises is dependent upon it.

The regulations require that anyone who certifies premises as being safe to reoccupy following licensed asbestos work must be accredited by an appropriate body as competent to carry out such work. Organisations accredited under UKAS to ISO/IEC 17025 will have appropriate quality management schemes in place.

Clearance monitoring is carried out as part of the four-stage clearance.

- ☑ Verification of work through document review.
- ☑ Visual inspection of the enclosure, waste and transit routes (to ensure no visible asbestos remains).
- ☑ Disturbed air tests in the enclosure to ensure the levels are <0.01 fibres/$cm^3$.
- ☑ Subject to satisfactory previous stages, a post enclosure removal inspection.

The above procedures involve the analyst following a set procedure of looking at the site set-up and the cleanliness of the asbestos enclosure and asbestos decontamination unit.

Having completed a detailed visual inspection (which is likely to include a search on hands and knees), the analyst carries out an air monitoring clearance test. This will include vigorously brushing the floor, and surfaces around each air monitoring pump, to disturb any trapped asbestos. The analyst then allows the removal contractor to take down the enclosure before a final visual check of the area is undertaken. **A certificate of reoccupation is then issued.**

Finally, prior to the decontamination/hygiene unit leaving site, it is inspected and air tested to ensure the asbestos levels are less than 0.01 fibres/$cm^3$, followed by a UKAS analyst leaving an air test certificate in the clean end of the unit.

It is important to review these documents and add any additional information to the management plan. It is also important to note areas where asbestos has not been removed, for whatever reason (for example, where insulation material has to be left in situ where pipes pass through walls).

The HSE is currently undertaking a project within the asbestos industry, looking at the quality of work and links to contractual relationships. Evidence has indicated that, where appointed directly, the quality of the work is completed to a higher standard.

**The HSE strongly recommends that the organisation undertaking this monitoring is appointed independently of the asbestos removal contractor.**

## 9.9 Monitoring

Monitoring of asbestos work should be undertaken during the asbestos work to ensure asbestos fibres are not being released from the enclosure. This is of greater importance the more friable the asbestos and the longer the duration of the work.

Air monitoring, to reduce the risks from the spread of asbestos, is required for the following reasons.

- ☑ Measure the background concentration of asbestos fibres in the work area during work.
- ☑ Check that control measures are effective.
- ☑ Measure background fibre levels outside the enclosure, particularly when the enclosure is in occupied premises.
- ☑ Check for fibre leaks around the perimeter of the enclosure and at the air lock and bag lock positions.
- ☑ Conduct testing at the discharge location of the air extraction equipment, where it is sited internally.
- ☑ Measure the background fibre levels inside the enclosure when the asbestos work is complete, to ensure that it has been thoroughly cleaned and decontaminated before dismantling.
- ☑ Carry out measurements for reassurance (for example, after accidental release of asbestos fibres).

B 09

For non-licensed and notifiable non-licensed work asbestos monitoring can be used to confirm that effective controls are in place. Examples of appropriate monitoring would include perimeter monitoring during asbestos cement sheeting removal or monitoring within dwellings that are to be occupied immediately after floor tile removal. This data can be used to reassure occupiers or those in the immediate vicinity of the work.

Where licensed asbestos work is being undertaken consideration should be given to the need for monitoring to determine the effectiveness of controls. Prior to the commencement of any work the asbestos enclosure should be subject to a smoke test to ensure the adequacy of the containment measures. Where possible this should be witnessed by a third party (such as the analyst), who will undertake subsequent monitoring of the work.

Where work is going to result in the removal of friable asbestos or is in areas where building occupants or other trades may be present, consideration should be given to leak monitoring outside of the enclosure. This monitoring is designed to identify when asbestos fibres are escaping from enclosures as a result of containment failures, or failures in decontamination procedures.

Monitoring should also be undertaken within the asbestos work area to ensure that controls on fibre release are effective and in accordance with the contractor's plan of the work.

*(For further information on health surveillance and monitoring refer to 9.14.1.)*

## 9.10 Asbestos surveys

Two types of survey are defined within the HSE publication HSG264.

- ☑ **Management survey.**
- ☑ **Refurbishment and demolition survey.**

To understand the difference between a management and a refurbishment/demolition survey, the simplest explanation is to consider a studwork wall that forms a firebreak. It was originally clad in asbestos insulation board, which was later covered over with plasterboard. In a management survey, the surveyor would correctly identify the outer surface as being plasterboard. However, as there would be no invasive testing, the asbestos would remain undiscovered. An invasive refurbishment and demolition survey would break through the cladding and discover the inner asbestos cladding.

Just because the surveyor did not find any asbestos does not mean that no asbestos is present. In all cases it is important to remember that surveying is as much an art as a science and there will be mistakes. Within some types of building asbestos will only be found by dismantling the building in a controlled manner.

There are also some asbestos-containing materials that would only be found by luck rather than judgement (for example, asbestos cement shuttering in a slab, or asbestos insulation board used as packers inside a studwork wall). It is important to be wary of unidentified building products and for everyone to have sufficient asbestos awareness training. Management should be in a position to stop work if necessary and question the presence of any 'funny looking plasterboard' found.

It is important to consider the type of building, especially system build properties, where information about concealed ACMs can be found on similar types of property. In such an instance, it could be reasonable to assume that ACMs will be in similar locations to that of a surveyed property.

The HSE strongly recommends the use of UKAS-accredited organisations to carry out asbestos surveys. It is the employer's responsibility to ensure surveying organisations are competent. This can be achieved by the use of UKAS-accredited organisations. If the employer chooses a non-accredited organisation they should keep records of the checks undertaken to assess competence.



**Refer to Appendix A for further details on asbestos surveys.**

## 9.11 Working with asbestos

The following is a brief overview of the main requirements of the regulations, as they are likely to affect the readers of this chapter, as opposed to the detail of the much more stringent requirements that affect asbestos-removal contractors and others whose business involves working with asbestos.

www.

**The HSE website provides comprehensive and understandable guidance on the types of work methods to be used.**

An employer or self-employed person who is required to carry out any work in a building or structure must ensure the following.

- Have appropriate awareness training, as detailed in CAR Regulation 10.
- Make a suitable and sufficient assessment as to whether asbestos is, or is liable to be, present in the premises where work is being carried out. Under CDM, the client has a duty regardless of the size of the project to provide information to the contractor on the known hazards associated with the structure (such as the presence of asbestos).
- Note that:
  - this information should normally be in the form of refurbishment and demolition surveys, as defined in HSG264 for most invasive construction work
  - any existing information on the presence of asbestos, supplied by the client based on a management survey, must be closely scrutinised to ensure that the construction work will not disturb more of the structure than the surveyor checked (do not regard a management survey as appropriate for any construction work; a management survey is for occupation and day to day operations needs, not construction needs). Asbestos surveys typically focus on buildings so it is important that other areas (such as external ducts) are considered within any survey.
- Identify that the material does not contain asbestos or assume it contains brown or blue asbestos if not known (fail-safe system).
- A competent person carries out an assessment to decide the likely exposure for the proposed work methods and if the work will, therefore, be licensable or non-licensed.
- Prepare a suitable written plan of work.
- Provide adequate information, instruction and training for employees and others.
- Training is repeated on an annual basis for any work with asbestos.
- When working with asbestos, prevent or reduce asbestos exposure to the lowest level reasonably practicable by means other than the use of RPE (for example, use an asbestos H class vacuum cleaner (BS 8520-3:2009) or other fibre suppression techniques (BS 8520-1:2009)).
- When working with asbestos, the proper use of RPE and that face-fit testing is carried out (minimum P3 filter).
- When working with asbestos, maintain respiratory equipment in a clean and efficient state, good order and repair. Regularly examine and test exhaust ventilation equipment (BS 8520-2:2009).
- Provide adequate and suitable protective clothing (minimum Type 5/6 overall) and ensure that it is cleaned or disposed of appropriately.
- Prevent the spread of asbestos from the workplace.
- Premises and plant involved in work with asbestos are kept clean.
- Monitor the air where employees are exposed to asbestos and keep suitable records for a specific period.
- Provide medical surveillance of staff, where necessary, and retain records for a period of 40 years.
- Air monitoring is only carried out by an accredited laboratory.
- Provide washing and changing facilities that are adequate and suitable for employees exposed to asbestos, and storage for protective clothing and personal clothing (not worn during working hours).
- Regulate raw asbestos, asbestos waste storage and disposal, ensuring adequate packaging, sealing and marking in accordance with the regulations.

*(For further information refer to 9.5 Asbestos waste.)*

### Working with an expired asbestos licence

In August 2014 an asbestos removal contractor was fined £15,000 and ordered to pay £4,000 in costs after admitting breaching Regulation 8(1) of the Control of Asbestos Regulations.

After the hearing the HSE inspector said: 'The contractor obviously decided to ignore the fact that its asbestos licence had expired and also that the application to renew had been refused. Instead it carried on regardless and went ahead with work at the premises, removing a ceiling that contained asbestos insulation board. When the contractor's licence expired, the firm should have ceased to carry out any work with asbestos-containing materials that is required by licence. The company were fully aware of what types of activities are covered and knew perfectly well that it was illegal to undertake the work they did'.

### Property developer guilty of exposing employees to asbestos

A property developer pleaded guilty to a total of 12 breaches, including exposing employees to asbestos. He was sentenced to eight months in prison, suspended for two years, for the breach of the prohibition notice. He was also fined £55,000 and ordered to pay a further £45,000 in costs.

The court was told that the defendant disregarded the presence of asbestos insulation board at the site of a former school. He knew the potentially dangerous material formed part of the pre-fabricated buildings on the site, but ignored advice on its safe removal.

The HSE visited the school, which was being converted into a retirement complex, during a construction safety initiative. An inspector identified the type of building known to contain asbestos, and gave the defendant advice on what he needed to do to comply with the relevant legislation surrounding its removal.

Eight days later, the HSE received a complaint from a member of the public advising that the asbestos was not being removed properly. The contractor was told to have surveys carried out and to arrange for the licensed removal of the material. However, when inspectors later re-visited the site they found building rubble containing asbestos that had not been properly disposed of. A prohibition notice was immediately served to stop all work with, or liable to disturb, the material asbestos and a direction to 'Leave undisturbed' was imposed on the piles of contaminated rubble.

HSE inspectors made a third unannounced visit later that year and found workers in breach of the prohibition notice. They found two workers putting asbestos insulation board into a lockable skip and dry sweeping the dust, which resulted in large clouds of contaminated dust billowing across the site. Work was again stopped until arrangements were made for safe and proper removal of the asbestos materials.

The court heard that although employees had been wearing disposable overalls and face masks, no other controls were in place, so not enough was done to protect them from the risk of exposure. Dust would have contaminated their clothes and there was no water on site to enable decontamination. The asbestos-containing material should have been dampened down and double-bagged in special bags, before being removed by a licensed contractor. High efficiency vacuum cleaners should then have been used to remove smaller pieces of asbestos and dust, rather than a broom.

Speaking after the hearing, the HSE inspector said: 'The defendant showed a wilful disregard for the health and safety of his employees and others. Our investigation uncovered a catalogue of serious errors, safety failings and a general ignorance of the laws around the safe and correct removal of asbestos. This was an appalling case of failing to properly plan, manage and resource this project, which led to workers being exposed to risks to their health from asbestos. Workers who have been exposed to asbestos could have posed a health risk to others in the long-term, even their families and loved ones, by taking home their contaminated clothing. Asbestos is the single greatest cause of work-related deaths in the UK. Building owners and contractors have a duty to ensure they protect their workers from risk of exposure. The defendant failed in that duty by choosing to ignore the dangers of this hidden killer'.

**For a summary of ways to prevent exposure to asbestos, which can be given as a toolbox talk, refer to Appendix B.**



## 9.12 Licensed and non-licensed work

All work with asbestos must comply with CAR. Some materials are licensed due to the high risk they present and require the use of licensed contractors. Other work is deemed lower risk and therefore lower levels of control and requirement apply. CAR has a hierarchal approach to asbestos controls and, based upon this approach, identifies three categories of asbestos removal work.

1. Licensed asbestos work. Applies to the highest risk materials.
2. Notifiable non-licensed asbestos work (NNLW).
3. Non-licensed asbestos work. Applies to the lowest risk materials.

**The HSE has published a flowchart in their leaflet *Advice on non-licensed work with asbestos* to assist with deciding the status of asbestos work.**

### 9.12.1 Licensed work

The regulations prohibit the removal or work on all types of sprayed asbestos, asbestos insulation, asbestos coating and asbestos insulation board, unless it is carried out by a company holding a licence granted by the HSE.

An exception is made in the case of repair or maintenance work of short duration.

**For further guidance on this term refer to the section on notifiable, non-licensed work and non-licensed work.**

An assessment made by a competent person will determine whether work should be licensed.

Work with most other forms of asbestos-containing materials will not generally require a licensed contractor.

A licence is not required for undertaking sample collection, analysis or air monitoring.

The decision on whether work is licensed or not licensed is the responsibility of the contractor undertaking the work (not the client). In some instances a licensed asbestos removal contractor may choose to notify work in order to avoid any ambiguity in the notification requirements, or where certainty cannot be guaranteed on the duration of the work.

## 9.12.2 Licences

There are three types of asbestos licence.

- **Full removal licence** – normally held by a licensed contractor.
- **Supervisory licence** – required where a third party actively supervises the work. A client, principal or main contractor does not need one. This type of licence is gradually being phased out as unnecessary. This is not to be confused with laboratories or consultants undertaking monitoring of contractor performance, who do not need a licence for these activities.
- **Ancillary licence** – needed to carry out work associated with the main asbestos removal work, typically by scaffold companies who erect scaffolds to form enclosures for licensed asbestos removal work. A separate notification must be sent to the HSE by the company carrying out the ancillary work.

  Companies that service and maintain asbestos removal equipment may also require this type of licence, particularly where there is a high probability of disturbing high-risk asbestos materials.

**All licences for work with asbestos insulation, AIB or asbestos coatings are granted by the licensing unit of the HSE.**

A new asbestos licence will last one year and, upon renewal, it may, depending on performance, be renewed for a period of three years. However, this is not guaranteed and the HSE can grant licences of any duration, up to three years. The HSE can revoke the licence completely, shorten the term of the licence or impose extra conditions on the licence. It is good practice to look at the licence held by a licensed contractor and question the period of its validity, along with any conditions.

Licensing conditions are not obvious on a licence so you may need to ask the contractor to clarify the conditions that are applicable. Many conditions are standard but some contractors can have special conditions applied to the licence that may restrict the type of work they can undertake.



## 9.12.3 Notification of work with asbestos

Licensed asbestos removal contractors are required to notify the HSE or Local Authority (whichever is the enforcing authority) of all proposed licensed work at least 14 days in advance, using the ASB5 form. Where a scaffold is to be built, that will be used to give access to a workplace where asbestos will be removed or will provide a working platform, then the scaffold contractor may need to be an ancillary licensed contractor.

**Notification is not an approval of the work by the HSE.**

The HSE uses notifications, along with contractor information, to undertake focused site visits based on contractor performance and risk.

In an emergency, it is sometimes possible to obtain a dispensation (waiver) from the 14-day period of notification. This should be discussed with the proposed licensed contractor. However, these dispensations are only available for emergencies and should not be applied for as a result of bad planning.

All questions on the removal of asbestos should be referred either to the HSE or a competent person.

**Details of where to find competent advice can be found in Appendix A.**

The unlicensed removal of asbestos, as well as being an offence under the regulations and potentially subject to a prison sentence, may also expose employees and others to high levels of airborne asbestos fibres and the subsequent risk of later ill health.

## 9.12.4 Notifiable non-licensed work

Work that will normally fall into this category may involve minor work on low risk materials that are already in a poor condition (for example, textured coating ceiling affected by fire or flood), or those where the materials are likely to deteriorate during work (such as falling fragile asbestos cement sheeting).

Other examples include involving the repair of asbestos insulation, minor work with AIB that meets the short duration criteria, maintenance of and removal of damaged asbestos cement and removal work of decorative coatings that contain ACM.

A contractor who does not hold an asbestos licence may normally carry out work with certain low risk asbestos products in situations where the planned exposure is sporadic and low intensity, and will not exceed the control limits (0.1 fibres/cm$^3$ in four hours or 0.6 fibres/cm$^3$ in ten minutes).

Any measurements required to check the exposure limit must be carried out by a UKAS-accredited laboratory and should not take into account the effect on any RPE used.

After April 2015, if a job is notifiable non-licensed work (NNLW) it must be done by persons who have had a medical examination in line with the requirements in the law.

**Notification of this type of work will be necessary. Once you have confirmed the work is NNLW, you need to notify it to the relevant enforcing authority. Do this using the online notification form.**

This is the only method of notification. You cannot notify by phone or post.

Notice should be given before the work starts – there is no minimum notice period. You do not need to wait for permission from the enforcing authority – the database will provide a PDF copy of your notification. A licensed asbestos contractor carrying out NNLW work will still need to notify.

**Any other work with asbestos-containing materials is subject to the requirements of CAR and may require an asbestos licence.**

## 9.12.5 Non-licensed work

Work that will normally fall into this category is work that is not licensed or is not NNLW. Some materials can be both NNLW and non-licensed. For example, where a textured decorative finish has been applied to a concrete surface the work will be NNLW, as to remove the material requires its deterioration. Whereas the same material applied to a plasterboard finish will be non-licensed as it can be removed intact with the plasterboard.

The key distinction is whether the material is already in a less than good condition and whether, during the removal work, the material is likely to suffer further deterioration or degradation.

**Where employers are considering undertaking small works themselves, they should read the relevant HSE publications and ensure they have appropriate insurance cover in place.**

There is an absolute requirement for anyone who undertakes any work with asbestos to have received practical training for the tasks they will be performing within the preceding 12 months, and more often if the method or equipment used changes.

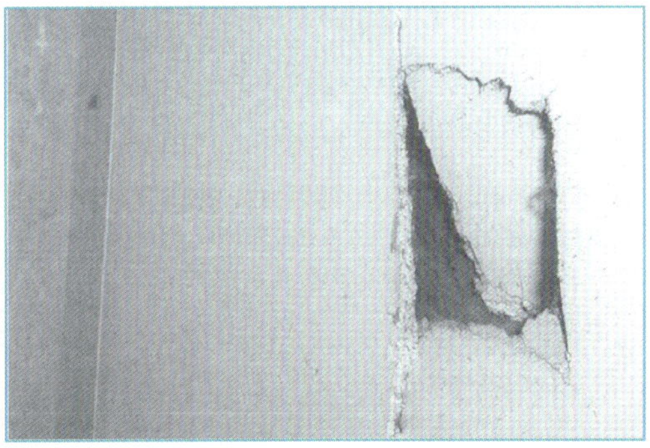

*Broken asbestos insulation board (typically contains 40% asbestos)*

The following products are likely to fall into non-licensed work.

- Short, non-continuous work with asbestos insulating board (attaching cables, cleaning light fittings and lifting ceiling tiles for inspection).
- Short, non-continuous maintenance and removal work with asbestos cement that is in good condition.
- Short, non-continuous work with decorative coatings (drilling and fixing screws).

The work itself must be:

- short, non-continuous maintenance, **or**
- encapsulation/sealing of materials in good condition, **or**
- air monitoring, gathering samples or other analytical work.

**For advice and examples of non-licensed work on asbestos, refer to the HSE website.**

Non-licensed work does not require the following.

- Notification to the relevant enforcing authority.
- A licensed contractor to carry it out.
- Asbestos medicals or health records for the workers doing it.
- Specific emergency procedures.
- The area around the work to be identified as an asbestos area.

**The HSE publication HSG247 provides comprehensive practical guidance on how a licensed asbestos removal contractor should work.**

## 9.13 Assessment prior to the removal of asbestos

In the planning phase, and before carrying out any work involving asbestos or ACMs, including minor repairs, the employer must make an assessment to determine the following.

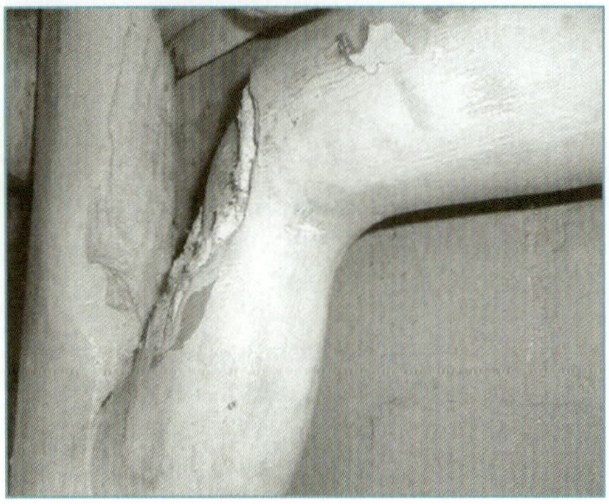

*Damage to pipework insulation*

- Type of work and its possible duration.
- Type and quantity of asbestos involved (using analysis results if available) and if more than one type of asbestos is present.
- Likely nature and degree of exposure to the asbestos.
- Steps that need to be taken to prevent or reduce such exposure to asbestos (the control measures).
- Procedures for the removal of any waste from the site.
- Procedures in place for dealing with any emergencies.
- Reasons for the choice of the proposed work method.

Some of the information should come from the asbestos management plan for the building. This may be augmented, if necessary, with additional survey work. Under CDM, the client has a duty to provide information on the presence of asbestos. These requirements will be the responsibility of the contractor when working upon domestic premises. However, in the case of the Local Authority or housing associations some of this information may already be available.

The assessment should be prepared in writing, including where it is for maintenance, repair or small-scale work involving:

- the handling of existing pre-formed and package bonded asbestos materials in situ
- small-scale repair or maintenance work not involving the cutting or breaking of asbestos or ACMs.

A competent person with adequate knowledge of the job should carry out the assessment. Where work is of a repetitive nature, covering various locations within a building or site, then a single assessment may be sufficient.

When planning any asbestos removal it is important to consider what might be present behind the ACM. For example, if removing plasterboard that has been covered with an asbestos-containing textured finish, what would happen if asbestos lagged pipes were present in the ceiling void? The assessment should also consider what additional risks could be present (for example, electrical risks if working on ceiling tiles).

Large quantities of asbestos board were previously used within premises to form fire compartments. Where clients are planning the removal of these materials, consideration should be given to the potential impact that this could have upon the building and its fire protection.

### 9.13.1 Designated areas

Where licensed asbestos contractors are working, certain designated areas may be created (such as one or more asbestos area and respirator zone).

In most situations the asbestos area and respirator zone will be the same. However, in certain circumstances there may only be an asbestos area, where the control limits are not exceeded (for example, a transit route/waste route for asbestos). It is advisable to exclude non-essential persons from this asbestos area. Where this is not possible then appropriate monitoring should be undertaken.

### 9.13.2 Asbestos areas

Where a licensed asbestos removal contractor is undertaking the removal of asbestos, in order to ensure that people other than those involved in asbestos work are not exposed to asbestos by entering asbestos areas, such areas should be designated and clearly identified, using notices that meet the requirements of the Health and Safety (Safety Signs and Signals) Regulations.

### 9.13.3 Respirator zones

Areas where the removal contractors are working, and where control limits for exposure to airborne fibres are liable to be exceeded, will be designated as respirator zones to ensure that only removal contractors wearing RPE are allowed to enter.

### Workers exposed to asbestos during refurbishment work

A cladding installation business owner was fined after he exposed workers to a potentially fatal risk from airborne asbestos fibres at a house.

The employer instructed an employee and a casual labourer to remove and replace soffit boards during refurbishment work at a property. The Magistrates' Court, however, heard that the employer had not carried out a suitable survey in advance to determine whether asbestos was present and did not hold a licence to undertake work with the dangerous material.

A neighbour informed the employer that the soffits were made of asbestos insulating board, but he allowed work to carry on. A complaint was made to the HSE and an inspector visited the site and immediately halted further work. The HSE investigation found the employer was aware from some of his previous jobs that soffit boards may contain asbestos but had not taken this into account when assessing this job. He had also failed to provide information and training to workers who could be exposed to asbestos fibres.

The employer was fined £7,015 and ordered to pay £3,200 in costs after pleading guilty to four breaches of CAR.

After the hearing an HSE inspector said: '(The employer) as a person running a cladding installation business, should have been in no doubt about the dangers posed by asbestos and of the regulations governing work with this material. Despite this, he progressed this work without testing the material to be removed for the presence of asbestos. This resulted in those working there being exposed to risk of inhaling airborne asbestos fibres without taking any suitable precautions.

This incident was entirely preventable and highlights the importance of having a robust asbestos management system in place. Duty holders should identify the type, location and condition of all asbestos-containing materials, and establish appropriate precautions, before starting removal operations. This is all the more important for this type of higher risk notifiable work, which should only have been performed by a licensed contractor.'

## 9.14 Health issues

### 9.14.1 Monitoring

The HSE strongly recommends that the client of the licensed contractor, rather than the licensed contractor, appoints the UKAS analysts who will carry out any **air monitoring**. It is felt that this is likely to give a greater degree of independence.

The HSE is currently undertaking a research project into these types of contractual relationships and the impact they have upon quality. Evidence suggests that the quality of final work is improved where the analyst has been employed by the client, and this is increased further where the analyst acts in a management or supervisory capacity for the client. The analyst is one of the few people, apart from the contractor, with the necessary skills and equipment to enable them to enter a live asbestos enclosure, if required.

There are various types of monitoring that can be performed. The analysts carrying out the air monitoring must either hold the Royal Society for Public Health (RSPH) Certificate for Asbestos Analysts (Air) or the British Occupational Hygiene Society P403 and P404 certificates.

**Background monitoring** is usually carried out before any asbestos removal work starts to enable the fibre concentration to be measured and any possible problems identified.

**A certificate of re-occupation is testing undertaken following the removal of treatment ACMs within an enclosure. This is a four stage process and is sometimes referred to as a four stage.**

**Static monitoring** can be carried out during work with asbestos. Typically, this will be outside the asbestos enclosure to demonstrate that there are no leaks (leak monitoring), or it may be performed on the site boundary during work with asbestos cement to show that there is no off-site fibre emission.

**Personal monitoring** may be carried out for two reasons.

- Specifically to demonstrate that the RPE being used is effective.
- To measure the fibre levels that whoever is carrying out the work with asbestos is being exposed to.

It would be important to discuss what type of personal monitoring is required with the UKAS analyst, as the monitoring strategy would be different.

Any employer or self-employed person must monitor the exposure during work with asbestos unless they know that the exposure will not exceed the control limit, or they have access to other ways of showing what the level of exposure is. This may be by referring to previous monitoring.

### 9.14.2 Medical surveillance

Asbestos removal contractors must ensure that their employees, who are liable to be exposed to asbestos above the control limit, are under regular medical surveillance by an HSE-appointed doctor; the local HSE office can supply the names of the appointed doctors who are able to carry out this specialist health surveillance.

Medical examinations should be provided before work with asbestos starts and at prescribed periods thereafter, currently every two years.

Health records containing information on medical examinations have to be maintained and kept for 40 years after the date of the last entry.

**After April 2015, if a job is NNLW, it must be done by persons who have had a medical examination in line with the requirements in the law.**

### 9.14.3 Washing and changing facilities

Asbestos removal contractors must provide adequate and suitable washing and changing facilities for their employees. Where protective clothing and respiratory equipment are in use, storage must be provided for contaminated items. Separate storage must be provided for personal clothing not worn during working hours.

The hygiene facilities (decontamination unit) are usually mobile, single (or more) showers, with three compartments. They should always be accompanied with the appropriate test certificates (electric, gas, dioctyl phthalate, and so on) and have a clean air-test certificate from the previous job (unless it's a new unit).

## 9.15 Asbestos waste

Asbestos waste is considered to be of two types: combined or fibrous. Combined was previously called bonded and effectively the asbestos is well bound into the material.

Roofing felt, vinyl floor tiles and most asbestos cement is categorised as combined. Asbestos insulation board, pipe lagging and sprayed coating are fibrous. Professional advice may be needed to ensure that the waste is correctly categorised.

Where asbestos waste has been identified for disposal, details of the type, estimated quantities and disposal options should be included in the project site waste management plan in accordance with the Site Waste Management Plan Regulations. These regulations currently apply in England for projects with an estimated value of £300,000 and above with greater detail required when the value exceeds £500,000.

It is good practice to bag or wrap asbestos cement sheets, or other asbestos cement products. If not wrapped they must at least be placed in a suitable skip that has been lined with polythene. The skip should be secured if it is left overnight. It is good practice to bag or wrap waste from internal work to guarantee that when the waste is carried outside there will be no asbestos debris dropped. If a van is being used to carry small volumes of asbestos waste, the waste must be double bagged and the bags secured (for example, by putting them in a lidded bin). The waste must also be physically separated from the driver, any passengers or any other equipment or materials that are being transported in the vehicle.

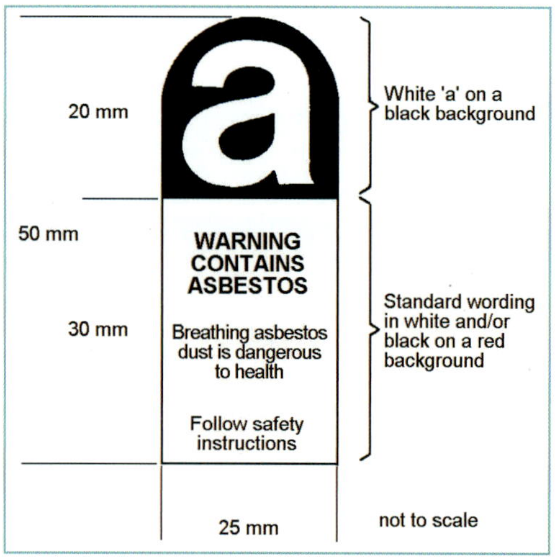


*Labelling requirement of asbestos waste*

Any fibrous asbestos removed from an enclosure should be double-wrapped or bagged. Bagged waste should consist of an inner red bag and an outer clear bag. These should be correctly marked.

The packaging (bagging) and labelling must satisfy the requirements of current legislation and, where asbestos waste is to be transported by road, there is further legislation controlling its safe movement.

Containers should be designed and constructed so as to retain the asbestos without any spillage or loss during normal handling.

Where the asbestos removal contractor uses labels on waste or removed asbestos, the label must be clearly and indelibly printed so that the words in the lower half can be easily read. These words must be printed as specified in the diagram.

The label has to be firmly affixed to the packaging using an adhesive type label, or directly printed onto the packaging (plastic bag).

### 9.15.1 Disposal of removed asbestos

Any material containing more than 0.1% asbestos on a gravimetric (weight for weight) basis should be disposed of in accordance with the Hazardous Waste Regulations in England and Wales, or the Special Waste (amendment) Regulations in Scotland (as amended).

In practice, this will be most asbestos-containing materials. Sites producing hazardous asbestos waste need to be registered with the Environment Agency or Natural Resources Wales (unless exempt). A unique site code will be issued and used on new consignment notes for all future arisings. At present there is no requirement to register sites producing hazardous waste with SEPA in Scotland.

The waste must be carried by a registered carrier and taken to a licensed or permitted site for disposal. There are very few waste disposal sites in the UK that have asbestos cells, and it is becoming common to take the waste to an intermediate waste transfer site. These are licensed facilities, which are allowed to store waste on a temporary basis prior to subsequent disposal to a licensed tip. They normally bulk up the waste to reduce transport costs.

A contractor can have a skip on site for temporary storage during work. Where a skip is used on a client's site it should not be used for consolidating waste from other sites. Unless the yard was designated as an intermediate waste transfer facility, it is illegal to have an asbestos skip there.

There are slight differences in the respective legislation for England and Wales, Northern Ireland and Scotland. Contractors who work in any of these areas must comply with the relevant national legislation.

In essence, there is a duty of care put on everyone in the waste disposal chain. Clients, whether they are at work or domestic, have a responsibility to ensure that the waste is disposed of correctly. They can be prosecuted if the waste is fly-tipped. Where asbestos has been removed as part of a project, a prudent contractor would ensure that proof of disposal formed part of the information that was given to the client. In England, where a site waste management plan is required under the Site Waste Management Plan Regulations, the plan should be updated to include details of the disposal of the asbestos waste and the waste carrier.

The principal contractor or contractor may suggest to the principal designer that this information is placed in the health and safety file to confirm that the asbestos has been transported and disposed of legally.

### 9.15.2 Crushed secondary aggregate

Crushed secondary aggregate from construction and demolition work (C&D waste) may occasionally have small fragments of asbestos, typically as pieces of asbestos cement. The general rule when supplying or receiving this material is that you should not see (by the naked eye) any visible asbestos debris in the product. If you see a fragment of suspected asbestos cement, further investigation should be undertaken to ascertain the extent of contamination, the source material and reasons for this occurring.

**A number of different working groups are looking at the issues surrounding crushed secondary aggregate, including groups focused on the testing of these materials and acceptability of future uses.**

It is generally accepted that very small fractions of asbestos will occasionally get missed and end up in these products. However, quantitative analysis should confirm that this level is at least 10 times lower than the threshold of 0.1% w/w for hazardous waste (that is less than 0.01%). As to whether you send or receive this material is a decision that should be carefully considered by a competent person who may require further advice from authoritative organisations (such as the National Federation of Demolition Contractors, the Institute of Demolition Engineers, the Environment Agency or Natural Resources Wales, or the HSE).

The issue arises where asbestos has been removed so far as is reasonably practicable from a concrete surface. It is foreseeable that there will be some asbestos fibre present. This is most likely to occur where a spray coating or textured coatings have been removed, as it is physically impossible to remove all traces of fibre without removing the top surface of the concrete by grit blasting.

The issues are whether the:

- crushed concrete would be considered to be a product to which asbestos had been added
- product would be considered to be hazardous waste.

The health risks are minimal but the potential financial risks associated with incorrect disposal and/or land being deemed contaminated is high. It is suggested that advice is sought regarding this issue if relevant on any projects.



## 9.16 Training

The regulations have cascading training requirements, based upon risk of exposure. The training needs to be appropriate for the work and the roles undertaken by individuals. There are three types of asbestos training.

- Awareness training.
- Training for work with asbestos that does not require a licence from the HSE. To include practical training based on the tasks to be performed.
- Training for asbestos work that does require a licence from the HSE. To include practical training based on the tasks to be performed.

### 9.16.1 Awareness training

This training is for persons who are liable to disturb asbestos while carrying out their normal everyday work, or those who may influence how work is carried out. This could include, for example, general maintenance staff, electricians, plumbers, gas fitters, painters and decorators, joiners, plasterers, demolition workers, construction workers, roofers, heating and ventilation engineers, telecommunications engineers, fire and burglar alarm installers, computer installers, architects, building surveyors and other such professionals. However, this list is not exhaustive and there are other occupations that are liable to disturb asbestos in addition to those listed.

Training should, in the first instance, be delivered in a classroom environment. It should then be supplemented with e-learning or toolbox talks, and updated as regulations and requirements change. It may also be prudent, on sites where asbestos is present and construction work is planned, to have site-specific asbestos awareness training incorporated into site induction processes.

### 9.16.2 Asbestos work that does not require a licence (non-licensed asbestos work)

This training is for those workers who plan to carry out any work with asbestos that does not require a licence and who may knowingly disturb lower risk asbestos-containing materials. It should be provided in addition to asbestos awareness training and should be job specific. Typically, workers who may need this training include those listed under asbestos awareness training and who carry out tasks, such as the following.

- Drilling holes in asbestos materials (including for sampling and analysis purposes).
- Laying cables in areas containing undamaged asbestos materials.
- Removing asbestos-containing floor tiles.
- Cleaning or repairing asbestos cement sheet roofing or cladding.

Topics covered by this type of training are shown below.

- How to make suitable and sufficient assessments about the risk of exposure to asbestos.
- Safe working practices and control measures, including an explanation on the correct use of control measures, protective equipment and work methods.
- Selection and appropriate use of protective equipment.
- Waste handling procedures.
- Emergency procedures.
- Relevant legal requirements.

This training should incorporate elements of both classroom based training and practical training for the tasks that will be performed. Any training programme for employees undertaking this work will also need to consider refresher training.

### 9.16.3 Asbestos work that does require a licence (licensed asbestos work)

Most work with higher risk asbestos-containing materials must be carried out by licensed contractors. Only suitably trained workers, using appropriate RPE and who are under suitable medical surveillance can undertake licensed asbestos work. This type of training is therefore required for operatives, supervisors and managers working for a licensed contractor, but note that the training requirements for operatives and supervisors are different.

This training should incorporate elements of both classroom based training and practical training for the tasks that will be performed. Any training programme for employees undertaking this work will also need to consider refresher training.



### 9.16.4 Refresher training

Refresher training should not be a repeat of the initial training. It should be given at least once a year and be appropriate to the workers' familiarity with the work. Therefore, depending on the individual training need, it could be a structured update training session or a short toolbox talk refreshing experienced workers on the main principles/expectations. The training should be tailored to meet the training needs, for example, if work methods change, the type of equipment used to control exposure changes or the type of work being carried out changes significantly.

### 9.16.5 Management training

The HSE is currently working with a number of trade associations and other representative bodies on the development of wider ranging training requirements, including training for those who manage asbestos removal work. In addition, it is expected that competency schemes will be developed for both managers and operatives within the asbestos removal industry.

## 9.17 Insurance

It is imperative to ensure that anyone who proposes to carry out work with asbestos is insured to do so. In addition to employers' liability insurance, asbestos contractors also usually have public liability insurance for carrying out asbestos work.

**Employers' liability insurance** provides insurance cover in the event of an injury or death caused to a employee. As such it does not exclude risks but insurers will refuse cover if they discover asbestos work is being carried out that has not been declared on proposal forms.

**Public liability insurance** is in place to protect members of the public from the acts and omissions of contractors. Unless working with asbestos is specified, this cover will be specifically excluded for almost all construction related public liability insurance policies. It is important to check that this is in place for any contractor who is employed.

If people are insured to work with asbestos it normally says openly on the insurance documents.

If in doubt you should check with the broker or underwriter of the insurance policy to confirm the mandatory employers' liability insurance covers them for work with asbestos, noting any specific exclusions (for example, non-licensed work only).

There have been instances of roofing contractors working with asbestos cement who created contamination of occupied premises and simply were not insured for the clean up costs.

When employing contractors to undertake asbestos survey and testing work they must be competent and hold employers' liability and public liability insurances. They must also hold appropriate levels of professional indemnity insurance, which protects clients where the standard of service is below the acceptable threshold.

## 9.18 Development and the future

At the time of writing the HSE is developing guidance documentation to support the ACoP, which are expected to be released in early 2015. They will include guidance for those undertaking asbestos removal (both licensed and unlicensed), along with guidance for laboratories undertaking sampling and analysis, and organisations undertaking asbestos surveys.

Work has commenced in Europe on revisions to the European Asbestos Worker Protection Directive. This work is at a very early stage and is yet to be consulted upon.

Two significant suggestions at the very early proposal stages are shown below.

- ☑ The potential introduction of a requirement to remove all asbestos from public buildings.
- ☑ The introduction of a background exposure level, considerably lower than that currently deemed acceptable within the UK. The possible introduction of this requirement is likely to have an impact on some buildings and how properties are managed.

Should these two changes become reality they will significantly affect the way asbestos is managed in UK premises.

Compensation for asbestos-related health consequences continues to increase and considerable publicity has been given to those claimants who would not traditionally be viewed as being exposed to asbestos. Recent cases have been brought by employees of high street retailers, who have not been involved in construction.

### Lady dies following exposure to asbestos at school

A significant case was when a claim was made on the basis of asbestos exposure occurring whilst a pupil was attending school. The lady later passed away (aged 46) as a result of the mesothelioma she had developed following the exposure.

The claim was subject to a number of appeals by the Local Authority. The final successful claim has established is that even very low levels of exposure can result in compensation and that a risk is present above natural background levels.

### Employee paid undisclosed sum by Marks & Spencer

An employee, who worked for Marks & Spencer between 1978 and 1987, claimed she was exposed to asbestos at the store. At the age of 53 she developed mesothelioma as a result of this exposure. In 2011 Marks & Spencer was fined £1 million as a result of failings during asbestos work.

The HSE stated: 'The court heard that the client, Marks & Spencer plc, did not allocate sufficient time and space for the removal of asbestos-containing materials at the store. The contractors had to work overnight in enclosures on the shop floor, with the aim of completing small areas of asbestos removal before the shop opened to the public each day. The HSE alleged that Marks & Spencer plc failed to ensure that work at the store complied with the appropriate minimum standards set out in legislation and Approved Codes of Practice. The company had produced its own guidance on how asbestos should be removed inside its stores, and the court heard that this guidance was followed by contractors inappropriately during major refurbishment'.

## 9.19 Supporting information

The trade associations listed below can provide information on their members (who can demonstrate having met certain standards of performance) and general advice on work with asbestos.

www.

- ☑ **Asbestos Control and Abatement Division (ACAD).**
- ☑ **Asbestos Removal Contractors Association (ARCA).**
- ☑ ***Trade associations for analysts* – provide advice on air monitoring, asbestos surveys and asbestos project management and regarding any of the member laboratories.**
- ☑ **Asbestos Testing and Consulting (ATAC).**

The British Occupational Hygiene Society (BOHS) and the Royal Society for Public Health (RSPH) offer a range of competency training courses for those undertaking asbestos assessments and asbestos monitoring.

The United Kingdom Asbestos Training Association (UKATA) and the Independent Asbestos Training Providers (IATP) are organisations offering membership to other organisations who offer asbestos training to people undertaking asbestos removal activities.

## Taking risks with asbestos

Over 5,000 people per annum die as a result of asbestos exposure. It is estimated that over 75% of these deaths have a construction industry link.

HSE Research Report RR558 outlines the reasons why people still take chances when working with asbestos even though they know the risks. The report highlights the fact that many people deny the importance or relevance of the risk because they think:

- as most asbestos has been removed, there isn't enough around to worry about
- exposure only occurs in extreme cases (such as when handling asbestos lagging)
- some levels of asbestos are actually safe
- new materials (such as MDF) pose a greater risk
- more visible risks (such as working at height) are more important
- contact with asbestos is a lottery – there is always some present.

There are also economic factors and pressure from employers (creating a fuss versus keeping your job) and the lack of safety culture (a failure of the employer to promote safe working practices). However, the Working Well Together (WWT) initiative, in conjunction with commercial organisations and local safety groups run Safety and Health Awareness Days (SHADs) around the country for SMEs. These raise awareness of asbestos and other hazards encountered when undertaking maintenance work.

**Information on the risks from asbestos can be found on the HSE website.**

# Appendix A – Asbestos surveys in accordance with HSG264

## Survey planning

Good planning is essential to ensure the effectiveness of any survey. The level of planning required will largely depend upon the complexity of the structure to be surveyed and the extent of the survey.

As part of the planning process, the client should be clear as to why the survey is needed and what they want to get out of the survey report. Adequate planning, particularly with regard to establishing the areas where the surveyor would need access (to carry out the survey) and overcoming potential access problems, and agreeing the amount of intrusive inspection to be carried out could significantly reduce the number of caveats in the survey report.

### Prior to the survey

**1. What the surveyor will need from the client.**

- ☑ The details of the structure or part of it to be surveyed.
- ☑ The structure's use, work processes, known hazards and any priority areas.
- ☑ Plans and prior survey reports on design, structure and construction.
- ☑ Safety and security information (such as fire alarm testing).
- ☑ Access arrangements and any permit systems in operation.
- ☑ Contact details of relevant staff for operational or health and safety issues.
- ☑ The opportunity to carry out a walk-through inspection of the structure in the interests of familiarisation to enable potential problem areas to be identified.

**2. What the client should expect from the surveyor.**

- ☑ Details of qualifications and experience.
- ☑ The significant findings of their risk assessment.
- ☑ References from previous work.
- ☑ Details of professional indemnity insurance.
- ☑ Costs.
- ☑ Proposed scope of work.
- ☑ Plan of work.
- ☑ Timetable of work.
- ☑ Details of any caveats (for example, restrictions or limitations in the survey).

After the survey has been completed, the surveyor must supply the client with a comprehensive survey report that includes details of any areas not accessed or surveyed.



## Competence of surveyors

The duty holder who commissions the asbestos survey must be satisfied that the prospective surveyor, whether an organisation or an individual, is technically competent to carry out the range of work required and will allocate adequate resources to it.

In line with the principles of CDM, it is essential that searching questions are put to each prospective surveyor to ensure their technical competence will be translated into a satisfactory survey that fully meets the duty holder's requirements. The client can satisfy themselves that these requirements have been met by appointing a UKAS-accredited asbestos surveying organisation.

www.

**For further information refer to the HSE publication *Asbestos: the survey guide* (HSG264).**

Alternatively they can check by making reasonable enquires via a two-stage process.

**Stage 1.** Assess the company's or individual's survey expertise, along with their knowledge of health and safety.

**Stage 2.** Assess the company's or individual's experience and track record to establish if they are capable of doing the work and that they recognise their limitations.

As a minimum this should entail the following.

- ☑ Seeking evidence of their training and experience in such work.
- ☑ Confirming that they are qualified and experienced in carrying out the type of work to be done.
- ☑ Checking that they are going to carry out the survey in accordance with the HSE guidance contained in *Asbestos: the survey guide* (HSG264).
- ☑ Ensuring that at least two surveyors will carry out the survey and that in doing so **they will** be working together.
- ☑ Seeking evidence that they have suitable liability insurance.

If choosing to follow this path it is important that evidence of these investigations is retained, in the event that a decision may need to be justified at a later date.

## Personal competence

Individuals may be able to demonstrate sufficient competency through a combination of qualifications and experience.

As a minimum, an individual should hold a British Occupational Hygiene Society (BOHS) P402 certificate, or a PSPH asbestos survey qualification, plus a minimum of six months' full-time, relevant, field-based experience, working under the supervision of an experienced and suitably qualified surveyor.

## Corporate competence

Organisations can demonstrate their technical competence to carry out asbestos surveys through accreditation to ISO/IEC 17020, which is the quality standard against which the performance of inspection bodies (such as asbestos surveying companies and analytical laboratories) can be independently assessed. The standard is awarded by UKAS.

## Survey risk assessment

Before a survey is commenced the risks to the surveyor, sampling staff and others, including the building occupants, must be assessed. The risk assessment would normally be conducted by the asbestos surveyor and should cover asbestos risks and non-asbestos risks. Depending upon the type of survey to be carried out and the nature of the premises, the non-asbestos risks could include the following.

- ☑ Working at height.
- ☑ Working in confined spaces.
- ☑ Noise, vibration and machinery hazards.
- ☑ Lone working.
- ☑ Electrical and chemical hazards.

The above list is far from exhaustive.



## Types of survey

Since the introduction of HSG264 there have been two categories of asbestos survey.

**1. Management survey.** The purpose of this type of survey is to locate, so far as is reasonably practicable, the presence and extent of any suspected ACMs, which could be damaged or disturbed by daily work (such as normal occupancy and building maintenance). Management surveys will often involve minor intrusive work and some disturbance, and can involve sampling of materials and/or presumptions that asbestos is present.

Management surveys have replaced the older surveys commonly referred to as Type 1 or Type 2 surveys. These surveys may still be appropriate but they often excluded areas where routine maintenance is required (such as false ceiling voids), so it is therefore important to ensure that any report caveats do not exclude these areas. When using or relying on a report it is important to ensure it is robust and up to date. This will include ensuring any recommended actions have been completed and that the client has undertaken the necessary re-inspections.

**2. Refurbishment and demolition survey.** As its name suggests, this type of survey must be carried out before any refurbishment or demolition is commenced. (It replaces what used to be called the Type 3 survey.) However, this type of survey might also be necessary for other work (such as engineering construction projects).

The survey will locate and describe, as far as is reasonably practicable, all ACMs in the area to be refurbished or the whole structure if it is to be demolished. This type of survey is fully intrusive and involves destructive inspection, as may be necessary, to gain access to all areas, including those that are difficult to reach.

It is important that both the surveyor and client understand the scope of the survey, as the degree of investigation within a survey may differ from a refurbishment project to a demolition project. Refurbishment surveys may be very specific in the areas in which they apply (for example, a survey focused on the installation of a new door opening). It is therefore important that the remit of the survey is clearly understood, especially if the survey is being provided by a third party.

Construction work is rarely fixed so the survey should be reviewed following any revisions to the scope of work.

Additional consideration should be applied to demolition sites where work may involve ground work. In these instances it is important to ensure the survey has considered the presence of underground services away from buildings (for example, central boiler systems with buried services).

It is also important to consider whether additional investigation work should be undertaken behind identified ACMs. Typically, the asbestos survey will stop when a suspected ACM is identified, but this may not represent the true extent of the work. For example, an asbestos survey might identify an asbestos insulation board ceiling, at which point the survey would cease. However, it is possible that additional ACMs may be present in the ceiling void, which could delay the work, or the materials could mean a significant change to the contractor's notifications (such as the discovery of pipe insulation), which would warrant a re-notification of the work and a delay of at least 14 days.

Within the life cycle of a building the expectation should be that the building will have at least one management survey, numerous refurbishment surveys and, finally, a demolition survey.

## Caveats

Anyone applying the results of a survey should initially check if the surveyor has written any caveats on the survey. In the past it was common for surveyors to exclude access to areas that are over three metres above ground level, as it is not possible for a single surveyor to safely use a ladder higher than this because they cannot foot it. Hence, in such circumstances there should always be a minimum of two surveyors. There may be other areas that have not been accessed.

Caveats are restrictions put on the scope of the survey, or the investigative methods to be used. Caveats can be imposed by either party.

- ☑ They can be imposed by the building owner to reduce the intrusive damage that would otherwise occur to the building as a part of the survey process or on a listed building.
- ☑ Conversely, the asbestos surveyor may find it necessary to include caveats in the survey report to cover areas of the building where asbestos could be present but, for whatever reason, access could not be achieved (this may apply to live plant or, in the case of refurbishment surveys, areas that are permanently occupied).

Hence, caveats can seriously reduce the usefulness and value of a survey and should only be imposed when absolutely necessary and where they can be fully justified.

Asbestos surveyors are taught to identify the spaces where asbestos is likely to be found and to survey accordingly. The meaning of spaces can be anything from a boiler room to a roof void, an office, an underground duct, a cavity between the two leafs of a wall or anywhere else that asbestos or an asbestos-containing material might have been used. By preventing access to an area or restricting the investigative method necessary, the client could seriously reduce the usefulness of the survey report.

A 'no access' comment on an asbestos report could be simply because of any of the following reasons.

- ☑ The door of a room was locked and the surveyor could not gain entry.
- ☑ The space was an underground duct and a mini digger was required to lift the covers.
- ☑ A suspended floor had no access other than by destroying the floor.
- ☑ The electrical system was live during the survey.

Effective planning should help to overcome such obstacles.



## Survey report

The outcome of the survey should be a survey report that fulfils the requirements of the client.

A comprehensive report will include a plan of the building with the areas where ACMs have been identified clearly marked. Similarly, areas where access could not be gained, but where asbestos could be present, should also be marked.

HSE guidance recommends that the information is also presented in a tabulated format, room-by-room, for ease of interpretation. This table could then be incorporated into the asbestos register for the building.

The survey report must identify the following.

- ☑ Locations where ACMs have been found.
- ☑ The extent of the ACM in each location.
- ☑ What type of ACM it is.
- ☑ The level of confidence that it is an ACM (for example, identified through analysis, strongly presumed or presumed).
- ☑ The asbestos type within the ACM.

For management surveys (and refurbishment and demolition surveys where work will not start for some time), the following information should also be provided.

- ☑ How easy to access the ACMs are.
- ☑ The extent of damage or deterioration.
- ☑ If it has received any surface treatment.
- ☑ An indication of the priority for dealing with each ACM identified.
- ☑ How each ACM should be dealt with.

Some asbestos surveys will be prepared with both a material assessment and a priority assessment. The priority assessment is the responsibility of the duty holder, as it forms part of the management plan and, where provided, this information should be carefully reviewed.

The client must ensure that the asbestos report fulfils the requirements for which it was commissioned. This will entail checking that the report:

- ☑ complies with the tender requirements
- ☑ contains no unagreed caveats or disclaimers
- ☑ confirms the survey was of the type required
- ☑ covers all the rooms and areas required
- ☑ contains clear and accurate diagrams and plans
- ☑ confirms that an adequate number of samples were taken
- ☑ indicates that sample numbers reflect variations in the same ACM (for example, where two types of suspended ceiling tile have been used in the same room)
- ☑ does not contain any other obvious omissions, discrepancies or inconsistencies.

# Appendix B – Preventing exposure to asbestos

## Manager

- ☑ Avoid disturbing asbestos-containing materials, if possible.
- ☑ If you are not a licensed contractor, make sure you know what work can be carried out on asbestos-containing materials.
- ☑ Ensure that anyone going to work on asbestos material has received adequate training.
- ☑ Use the HSE's *Asbestos essentials* to ensure the job is carried out properly.
- ☑ Prepare a plan of work, explaining what the job involves, the work procedures and what controls to use.
- ☑ Ensure that those doing the work understand the plan of work.
- ☑ Provide the right protective clothing and equipment, including properly fitted respirators and overalls.
- ☑ Make sure the work area is inspected visually at the end of the job and there is no debris or dust.
- ☑ Make arrangements for the safe disposal of any asbestos waste.
- ☑ Consult with others who may be affected by the work.

## Worker

- ☑ Make sure you have been properly trained for work with asbestos and understand what is required of you in the plan of work.
- ☑ Use the HSE's guidance to help you carry out the job properly and ensure that exposure to asbestos is kept as low as possible.
- ☑ If you have any concerns, stop work and talk to your supervisor.
- ☑ Don't eat, smoke or drink in the work area.
- ☑ Use any equipment provided, including that for personal protection; ensure it is clean and in good working order.
- ☑ Make sure the work area is clean at the end of the job. Don't sweep up dust and debris – use a Type H vacuum cleaner and wet rags.
- ☑ Ensure asbestos waste is disposed of safely.

## Links to HSE guidance

www. **An HSE *Asbestos essentials* task sheet can be found on its website.**

## Planning – prioritising decisions and managing risk

- ☑ Identify where there might be asbestos-containing materials.
- ☑ Consider eliminating the need to work with asbestos. Can you avoid disturbing asbestos by doing the job some other way?
- ☑ Does the work need to be done by a licensed contractor?
- ☑ Where it is not possible to eliminate the risk, develop a plan of work that highlights the risks and identifies the controls that must be used. Communicate this so that it is understood by all involved.
- ☑ Workers must be provided with the appropriate RPE and any other protective equipment identified in the plan of work. This must be properly fitted, clean and in full working order.
- ☑ Ensure all workers are trained in non-licensed asbestos work and follow the appropriate task guidance sheets.
- ☑ Use an asbestos waste container and dispose of asbestos waste safely.

# Appendix C – Places and materials that can contain asbestos

## Building fabric

- ☑ Corrugated roofing, tiles, slates, soffits, gutters, downpipes, walls and panels.
- ☑ Insulation under the roof, on beams and stanchions.
- ☑ Boards and panels, and any insulation between these.
- ☑ Insulation around pipes, on a heater, boiler, calorifier, in storage heaters.
- ☑ Decorative coatings on walls or ceilings.
- ☑ Insulation around windows.
- ☑ Water cistern.
- ☑ Flues, waste water pipes.
- ☑ Plastic floor tiles.

Also check **outbuildings**.

## Equipment

- ☑ Oven, brakes, soundproofing, ironing surfaces and insulating mat.
- ☑ Fire blanket, fire insulation in or on doors and insulating gloves.

Note down the **condition** and **amount** of materials that might contain asbestos.

**Where you can't get access (for example, roof void, undercroft, wall cavities) presume that these contain asbestos.**

## Materials that do not contain asbestos

The following materials **do not** contain asbestos, but they **may conceal** asbestos:

- ☑ stone
- ☑ brick or breeze-block and mortar
- ☑ concrete
- ☑ metal
- ☑ glass
- ☑ wood
- ☑ most furnishings and fabrics (but see 'Equipment' above).



**Steel frames that were clad in asbestos for fire protection may have underlying lead paint coatings and thus a lead paint survey will also be required.**

### The HSE website contains further guidance on asbestos

It covers:

- ☑ identifying asbestos risk
- ☑ licensed work with asbestos
- ☑ other work with asbestos
- ☑ waste
- ☑ instruction and training.

# 10

# Dust and fumes

**Contents**



## Supporting information

**GT 700 Toolbox talks**

## Overview

**Each year thousands of construction workers contract or die from respiratory diseases due to breathing in dust and fumes. The amount breathed in each day as they work from site to site can seem small or insignificant. In some cases the effects of exposure may be immediate but generally it can take years before the symptoms of ill health become apparent. Because of this, respiratory risks are often overlooked or underplayed.**

**This chapter explains what dust is, what it can do to the human body, and what must be done to minimise exposure to protect the workforce.**

## 10.1 Introduction

Managing and controlling long-term exposure to dust and fumes is a challenge facing the industry. Many workers are exposed daily, but may only work for short durations on various sites and frequently change employers.

The exposure to airborne dust or fumes can result in skin diseases and severe respiratory illnesses. These illnesses include cancer, silicosis, asthma and chronic obstructive pulmonary disorder (COPD). Asbestos fibres, silica and lead dust are particularly hazardous if inhaled. Such diseases can be totally disabling, causing those affected to give up work or change their employment.

Work-related ill health has devastating consequences for individuals and their families but it is very much misunderstood or underestimated.

- There are approximately 12,000 deaths each year as a result of occupational respiratory diseases. About two-thirds of these are due to asbestos-related diseases or COPD. These are long latency diseases (they take a long time to develop following exposure to the agent that caused them). Therefore current deaths reflect the effect of past working conditions.
- Approximately 28,000 people who worked between 2013-14 and 127,000 who had ever worked currently have breathing or lung problems that they believe were caused or made worse by their work.
- There are an estimated 10,000 new cases of breathing or lung problems caused or made worse by work each year.
- In 2012 there were an estimated 179 new cases of occupational asthma (asthma caused directly by work). Other data sources suggest the total number of new cases in the wider category of work-related asthma (asthma caused or made worse by work) each year could be more than 10 times higher.
- In 2005 over 500 construction workers are believed to have died from lung cancer caused by silica dust (from cutting blocks, kerbs, and other items). This is about 10 people per week.

Raising the awareness of managers, supervisors and workers, to ensure effective control measures are always put in place and followed, is fundamental in helping reduce these numbers.

**At any one time there are far more people off work through occupational ill health than there are because of a work-related accident.**

The construction dust partnership has been formed to raise awareness within the construction industry about lung diseases related to hazardous workplace dust. It is also in place to promote good practice, to prevent these diseases, particularly for those undertaking high risk tasks. It offers advice for both employers and workers.

www.

**For further details on the construction dust partnership refer to the CITB website.**

## 10.2 Important points

- The creation of airborne dust or fumes should be prevented or eliminated where reasonably practicable, by:
  - substituting and using a less harmful substance or material
  - using a different process (such as a block splitter instead of mechanical cutting)
  - manufacturing or cutting materials off site.
- Where the prevention of dust or fumes is not possible, the extent of exposure must be controlled to a level that is safe.
- Control of dust can be achieved by:
  - extracting dust and fumes through stand-alone extractor units
  - collecting dust in collector bags attached to powered hand tools
  - wet cutting solid materials (such as thermal blocks, bricks or ceramic tiles)
  - where practical, carrying out of work in the open air rather than in enclosed spaces.

- Hazardous fumes usually result from the following situations.
  - Processes in which materials are heated (such as welding, lead burning or grinding).
  - Uncontrolled use of substances (such as solvents and adhesives).
  - The use of equipment and plant powered by internal combustion engines.
  - Activities on site (such as cutting and welding).

**The creation of dust and fumes, regardless of amount, must be controlled. All risk assessments and methods statements should state how exposure to dust or fumes will be minimised. It is no longer acceptable to expect workers to work unprotected in dusty conditions.**

**For further information on asbestos, lead or carbon monoxide refer to the individual chapters covering those topics.**

## 10.3 Respiratory diseases

With an accident on site, the injury or other effects are usually immediate and obvious. The effects of exposure to most work-related ill health hazards are not immediate or not even felt (unlike an accident that causes injury).

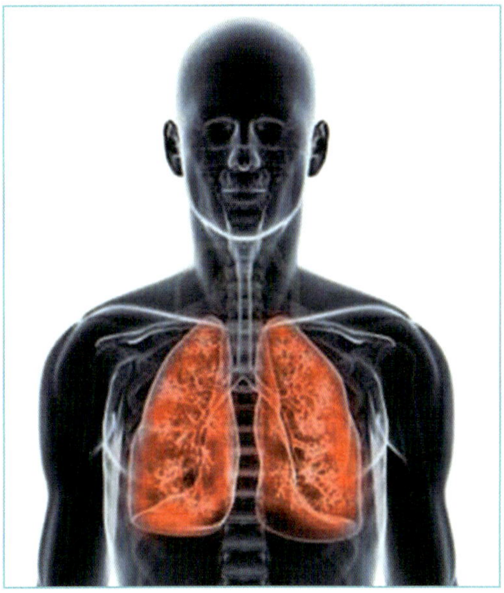

*Damaged lungs*

As workers are repeatedly exposed to small doses of dust and fumes, these start to damage their body.

Workers may go home from work feeling more or less the same each day and are none the wiser. It can take many weeks, months or even years before symptoms of exposure become a problem to them and irreversible damage may well have occurred.

Work-related ill health can often result in employees being unable to work as hard or as efficiently as before, and sometimes they may never work again.

During 2010, 1,105 people were assessed for the industrial injuries disablement benefit for asbestosis.

Typical symptoms and illnesses are respiratory diseases, such as those listed below.

- Silicosis.
- Asbestosis.
- Mesothelioma.
- Pleural thickening.
- Occupational asthma.

### 10.3.1 Silicosis

Silicosis is a huge problem within the construction industry. Respirable crystalline silica (RCS) is found in stone, rocks, sands and clays, and so is contained in many construction products (such as concrete, blocks, bricks, ceramics, and so on). Common day-to-day work produces RCS and many workers are exposed to it knowingly and unknowingly by breathing in silica particles.

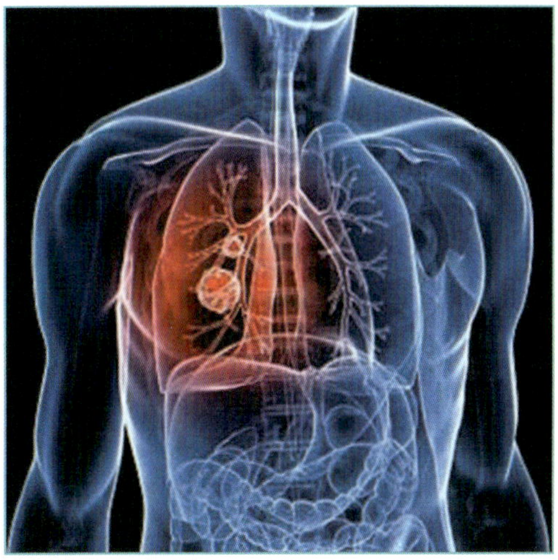

*Early stages of lung scarring*

Exposure to RCS over a long period can cause fibrosis (hardening or scarring) of the lung tissue with a consequent loss of lung function. Sufferers are likely to have severe shortness of breath and may find it difficult or impossible to walk even short distances or upstairs. The effect continues to develop after exposure has stopped and is irreversible. Sufferers usually become house- or bed-bound and often die prematurely due to heart failure.

Acute silicosis is a rare complication of short-term exposure to very large amounts of silica. This condition is life-threatening and associated with significant clinical consequences.

Silica may also be linked to lung cancer. Precautions taken to control the risk of fibrosis will serve to control the risk of lung cancer. Workers with silicosis are at an increased risk of tuberculosis, kidney disease and arthritis. Exposure to RCS may also cause chronic obstructive pulmonary disease (COPD).

*(For further information on silica dust, exposure levels and good practice refer to 10.11 Silica dust.)*

### 10.3.2 Asbestosis

This is a chronic lung disease, characterised by scarring of the lung tissue due to previous asbestos exposure, which leads to long-term breathing complications.

It is only caused by exposure to long, thin asbestos fibres. Extended exposure can lead to an accumulation of fibres in the lung tissues, which can then create scarring (long-term fibrosis). Over time the lung tissue thickens, causing pain and restricting breathing. Individuals may not be diagnosed until years after the exposure occurred.

Asbestosis is not a form of lung cancer or mesothelioma, so people can live with the disease. However, the condition will get worse over time and therefore treatment is required.

### 10.3.3 Mesothelioma

Mesothelioma, otherwise known as mesothelioma cancer, is commonly caused by exposure to asbestos. It affects the thin, protective membrane surrounding the lungs, heart and abdominal cavity.

When microscopic fibres are breathed in or swallowed the human body is sometimes unable to release them. These fibres can then become trapped and cause inflammation, scarring and damage.

The disease can lay dormant for years. It can take from 20 to 50 years after exposure before signs and symptoms develop.

### 10.3.4 Pleural thickening

This is also known as diffuse pleural thickening. It causes chest pain and a decline in breathing, and is one of the most commonly diagnosed symptoms of asbestos exposure.

Pleural thickening is a lung disease caused by inhaling asbestos fibres. These fibres become embedded in the pleura (the thin membrane that covers the lungs), which then triggers scarring. The scarring thickens the pleura and, as the scar tissue grows, it can encase the lung and close off the space between the lungs and the pleura.

Pleural plaques or pleural thickening caused by asbestos are not the same as asbestosis; in these conditions the pleura is damaged by asbestos, but the lungs themselves are unharmed.

### 10.3.5 Occupational asthma

This is caused by exposure to respiratory sensitisers at work. These are inhaled into the lungs, over a period of time, and cause asthma symptoms. It can be a serious condition, leading to severe chronic asthma, if there is a prolonged exposure to respiratory sensitisers.

Respiratory sensitisers can be chemicals such as isocynates (from spraying), wood dusts, colophony (from soldering) or some glues.

## 10.4 Types of dust and fumes

The following paragraphs describe the main respiratory hazards that may be encountered on site.



### 10.4.1 Dust

Dust is produced when solid materials are broken down into finer particles. The longer that the dust stays in the air then the easier it is to breathe in. Airborne dust is usually respirable dust.

Not all harmful dusts are visible. Dusts that are too fine to be seen by the naked eye are the cause of many serious health problems. Like most occupational health problems, it can take several years for symptoms of ill health to manifest themselves.

Skin irritation, dermatitis and ulceration can be caused by contact with some types of dust. Other types of dust, being soluble, may be absorbed through the skin via cuts and abrasions.

The inhalation of dust can cause wheezing, coughing, breathlessness, bronchitis, nasal and other types of cancer. Dust also contains bacteria and viruses and therefore has the potential to cause stomach disorders. These can result from ingesting airborne dust or from eating food with contaminated hands.

### 10.4.2 Mists

Tiny liquid droplets are formed by atomisation of the liquid (for example, when spraying or using an aerosol). Mists may be a combination of several hazardous substances.

### 10.4.3 Vapours

These are the gaseous state of substances that are liquids or solids at room temperature. They usually form when substances evaporate. One example is the vapour from a tin of glue or solvent that has been left open.

### 10.4.4 Fumes

Fumes can be produced when some building materials are heated or otherwise worked. A common form of respiratory illness, which has flu-like symptoms, is caused by the inhalation of welding fumes. Other sources of hazardous fumes are uncontrolled exposure to the use of equipment and plant that is powered by internal combustion engines.

**Metal fumes** occur when metal is vaporised at high temperatures (for example, when welding and gas cutting). The physical properties of fumes can be confusing, particularly when identifying suitable respiratory protective equipment (RPE). Usually, metal fumes are actually a solid particle by the time they are inhaled.

When welding is taking place the temperature of the metal at the weld is sufficiently high for the elements in the metal to become gaseous. However, 2–3 mm away from the weld the gases have cooled down sufficiently for the fumes to solidify out as small particles.

Consequently, when purchasing RPE to protect against fumes, a device that protects against solid particles rather than gases is required.

### 10.4.5 Gases

Gases are airborne at room temperature and normally mix with the air that we breathe. Examples include propane, butane, acetylene, carbon monoxide and hydrogen sulphide. Gases can spread very quickly.

## 10.5 Exposure limits

It is widely known that almost any excess levels of construction dust can cause health problems. Harmful effects range from simple skin irritation to severe respiratory illness.

*Operative working with dust suppression to prevent exposure*

Such problems are not likely to arise if occupational exposure limits and the appropriate regulations are observed and safe systems of work are maintained.

Exposure to any unlisted substance or general nuisance dust should be limited by reducing dust levels to the minimum reasonably practicable. These levels should not exceed 10 milligrams of dust per cubic metre of air, when measured over an eight hour period (10 mg/m$^3$ 8H TWA). Within that figure, only 4 mg/m$^3$ should be respirable dust. When these levels are exceeded the dust will become a substance hazardous to health under COSHH.

Generally speaking, if dust can be seen in the air, it is highly possible that the 10 mg limit is being approached (or exceeded).

When dust is inhaled, the body's defence mechanisms can usually deal with the larger particles. However, they struggle to cope with the very small particles, which can pass through the lungs and, as they may stay in the air for more time, they can remain a hazard for longer.

In occupational hygiene terms, dust is divided into the following two categories.

- ☑ Inhalable dust, sometimes called total dust.
- ☑ Respirable dust, which is much smaller particles.

Because dust is a mix of very small particles, all dusts have been assigned a concentration in air above which they are considered hazardous. It is important to remember that this applies to all dusts, for example those caused by the following methods.

- ☑ Sweeping a dusty floor.
- ☑ Mechanically cutting concrete products.
- ☑ Mixing sand and cement to make mortar.
- ☑ Sanding down MDF or timber.
- ☑ Driving plant on dusty sites.

Technical descriptions of the two types of dust are shown below.

- ☑ Total inhalable dust approximates to the fraction of airborne material that is inhaled and is available for deposition in the respiratory tract.
- ☑ Respirable dust approximates to the fraction of airborne material that is inhaled and penetrates to the gas exchange region of the lung (the alveoli).

Any concentration of **inhalable** dust in the air, equal or greater to **10 mg/m$^3$** (10 milligrams of dust per cubic metre of air) averaged out over **eight hours**, or any **respirable** dust in excess of **4 mg/m$^3$** averaged over **eight hours**, is deemed to be a substantial concentration of dust and therefore within the definition of a substance hazardous to health.

The official list of exposure limits is updated periodically and published in the HSE Guidance Note EH40. This has been supplemented by a table on the HSE website under COSHH, which has an up to date list of workplace exposure levels.

The lists specify workplace exposure limits (WEL) for a number of dusts, in addition to other substances.

**Dusts are classified as substances that are hazardous to health.**

B
10

## 10.6 Managing the risk

The Control of Substances Hazardous to Health (COSHH) Regulations require that every employer shall **not** expose any employees to any hazardous substance, unless a suitable and sufficient assessment of the risks has been carried out, and that adequate precautions are put in place.

Any such assessment should apply the principles of hierarchy of control (see explanation below).

### e.g. Hierarchy of control – Follow 'ERIC-PD'

E **Eliminate.** (Is there a safer substance that can be used? Can the activity involving the hazardous substance be substituted or discontinued? Can the concentration of the substance be reduced?)

R **Reduce.** (Reduce the frequency and length of exposure to the substance.)

I **Isolate.** (Isolate the substance away from the user.)

C **Control.** (Control the use of the substance by enclosing the material, or provide a different method of application, such as extraction or wet cutting.)

P **Personal protective equipment.** (Should always be seen as the last resort. Wear appropriate gloves, goggles, respiratory masks, and so on.)

D **Discipline.** (Follow a safe system of work, providing training and information.)

Similarly there are legal duties on every employer to make a suitable and sufficient assessment of every work activity to identify any hazard that employees or any other person might encounter as a result of the work being carried out.

Employers are required to assess the health risks to their employees arising out of exposure to hazardous dusts and fumes, and, if reasonably practicable, put control measures in place to eliminate the work processes and the use of substances that cause exposure. If this is not reasonably practicable, employers must ensure the following.

- ☑ Exposure is controlled to an acceptable level.
- ☑ Employees are informed of the hazards involved and the control measures in place.
- ☑ The effects of any exposure are mitigated by providing health surveillance where necessary.

Designers have the potential to eliminate or reduce the exposure of operatives, and possibly others, to dust or fumes through their designs, as outlined in the examples below.

- ☑ Specifying construction methods that avoid hot works and therefore the creation of fumes, particularly in enclosed areas and confined spaces.
- ☑ Stoning up site and haul roads, using vehicle wheel washes and dampening down surfaces will help control dust, both for workers and those near to site (such as neighbouring communities).
- ☑ Specifying that construction materials are cut to size at the point of manufacture, eliminating the need for cutting, planing, sanding and so on.
- ☑ On-site designing of enclosures to contain hazardous dust where its creation is unavoidable.

Principal contractors, contractors or sub-contractors and the self-employed have the potential to reduce exposure to dust and/or fumes by co-ordinating work, co-operating with each other and adopting work methods explained elsewhere in this chapter.

### Dust suppression techniques

Rubbing down tape and jointing. Traditionally rubbing down creates a lot of dust, which is hazardous to health, has to be cleaned up and is manually intensive. This drywall sander with collection system minimises all these issues to the extent that the operative does not need RPE.

Cement boarding used as part of a vertical cladding system had to be cut to size on site. A circular saw complete with vacuum collection was used in a designated cutting area and the operator also wore FFP3-rated RPE.

**www. Follow recognised, industry or HSE guidance, which can be downloaded from the construction section of the HSE website.**

HSE
Health and Safety Executive
Time to clear the air!
Protect your lungs when using cut-off saws

HSE
Health and Safety Executive
Dust control on cut-off saws used for stone or concrete cutting
HSE information sheet
Construction Information Sheet No 54 (Revision 1)
Introduction
Health effects

## 10.7 Respiratory protective equipment

Given the nature of some work, it is not always practical to completely contain the airborne dust or fumes created. In these circumstances, if no other control measure is reasonably practicable, respiratory protective equipment (RPE) and other personal protective equipment (PPE) as necessary, must be provided for each person working with, or otherwise exposed to, airborne dust or fumes.

Selecting the wrong type of RPE could have serious, even fatal, consequences. Selection must be carried out by a competent person and must be adequate in reducing exposure to an acceptable level, which is suitable for the wearer, task and environment, to ensure the wearer can work freely and without additional risk caused by the RPE.

The Health and Safety Commission instigated the reduction in the workplace exposure level (WEL) of **crystalline silica to 0.1 mg/m$^3$**, due to concerns about the severe lung disease, silicosis and a form of cancer that can occur as a result of inhaling this substance.

**It is recognised good practice to use RPE with an FFP3/P3-rating to protect against all construction dust (such as silica), which is created when mechanically cutting concrete, bricks, slabs, and so on – even when wet cutting (which only removes about 75% of airborne particles). FFP3/P3-rated offers maximum protection compared to FFP1/P1 or FFP2/P2.**

There are various types of RPE approved for use. Details of types and permissible uses are available from the manufacturers.

- Disposable face mask respirators.
- Nuisance dust masks.
- Half face respirator.
- Half masks.
- Powered respirators.
- Ventilated visor and ventilated helmet respirators.
- Self-contained breathing apparatus.

*Disposable valved dust respirator*

*Reusable respirator*

**For further information on respiratory protective equipment refer to Appendix A and Chapter B06 Personal protective equipment.**

## 10.8 Monitoring

Sampling is usually carried out by using metered pumps with membrane filters or workers wearing personal dose meters. The dust collected is weighed in relation to the amount of air sampled. Dust samples can also be examined for type, and monitoring can also be static or personal.

There are some direct-reading dust sampling monitors available. However, there is some doubt as to the accuracy of these instruments. They are very useful for a long-term project where they can be calibrated regularly by comparing their readings against samples taken from membrane filters. However, they are not recommended as the sole means of measuring a personal exposure to dust. It is also important to be aware that there are a number of different laboratory techniques required for analysis (for example, measuring exposure to silica normally requires x-ray diffraction). This is not a piece of equipment that is commonly available and the best source of advice is the British Occupational Hygiene Society (BOHS).

## 10.9 Training and supervision

It should be noted that all these sets of regulations place a legal duty on the employer to provide employees with adequate information, instruction, training and supervision to be able to carry out any work task safely and without risks to their health.

Information, instruction, training and supervision, as required by the regulations, must be provided for supervisors and personnel who work in dusty conditions. New employees should receive full instruction before starting work and should be familiarised with the following.

- ☑ The health risks associated with dust and the preventative measures in operation, as identified by the risk assessment.
- ☑ The correct use and cleaning of protective clothing and equipment.
- ☑ The reasons for air sampling.
- ☑ Their duties in respect of the correct use of equipment and of safe systems of work in operation.
- ☑ The procedures for reporting defective or inadequate equipment.

## 10.10 Summary of managing dust hierarchy

### 10.10.1 Raise dust awareness

Construction dust is the most significant risk to workers' health after asbestos. Silica dust alone is thought to accelerate the deaths of around 500 construction workers annually – far greater than those killed by accidents. Many more suffer from a reduced quality of life.

www. **For an information sheet on construction dust refer to the HSE website.**

### 10.10.2 Control methods

#### 10.10.2.1 Design and different work methods

The first focus should be on reducing the risk at the design stage. Paving can be planned so that the smallest number of cuts is needed. Different sized materials can be chosen so that cutting is minimised. Routes for services can be designed in.

Where a risk remains, this can be reduced by working another way. Cables can be protected and covered with plaster or board instead of chasing. Brackets and cable trays can be directly fixed instead of using drill holes. Block splitters can be used instead of a cut-off saw.

#### 10.10.2.2 Water suppression

Water can be used with some tasks to effectively damp down the dust. Most modern cut-off saws can be attached to a water supply. The water can come directly from the mains or a portable source (such as a hand-pressurised freestanding container). Other devices (such as masonry saw benches) can be selected that come with an in-built water reservoir.

#### 10.10.2.3 Local exhaust ventilation and on tool extraction

Water suppression is not suitable for controlling all dust risks. It cannot be used with most electric tools, on wood or where the waste slurry would create a problem (such as in an inhabited building). Extraction is an effective alternative. This sucks the dust away as it is being created and stores it until emptied. An extraction vacuum can also be used for general cleaning instead of dry sweeping.

Correctly working on-tool extraction is made up of a number of different parts. A specially designed hood is needed to collect the dust at the point it is being created. This should be shaped and designed around the cutting/contact point. The hood is attached to an industrial vacuum extraction unit via a hose. For most tasks the industrial vacuum should be either an M or H class. If using local exhaust ventilation this should be checked every 14 months to ensure it is working as expected.

#### 10.10.2.4 Respiratory protective equipment

RPE is often used to protect against dust risks. It takes two main forms: a disposable mask or half mask with filters. It should be used as a back-up measure to water suppression or extraction. It should not be used as a replacement for those controls where they can be used.

RPE needs to be to the correct specification if it is to provide the protection needed. For most tasks involving power tools this will be a disposable FFP3-rated mask or a half mask with a P3 filter.

### 10.10.3 Other considerations

The right controls still have to be used correctly. A worker may not know what to do or there may be a problem with the control due to poor maintenance. Poor planning might mean no more water is available to refill containers or electricity for extraction. Spare masks may have run out. Supervision may be lacking. Management arrangements are important for tackling this.

The control of dust also needs the user to play their part. The best controls and systems will not work if they are not followed.

**One of the reasons for people not following work methods is that they do not fully appreciate the risks, or have not been involved in any discussions about them.**

## 10.11 Silica dust

Silica occurs as a natural component of many materials used in construction work. Crystalline silica is present in substantial quantities in sand, sandstone and granite, and often forms a significant proportion of clay, shale and slate. Products (such as concrete and mortar) also contain crystalline silica.

The health hazards of silica come from breathing in the dust. Work that can expose workers or members of the public to the dust include working with stone, grit blasting, scabbling, cutting or drilling, demolition and tunnelling.

The use of power tools leads to high exposures if exhaust systems/wet cutting processes are not used and maintained.

For some work, exposure will depend upon how confined the working space is, and the presence or absence of ventilation. For example, tunnelling through dry, silica-bearing rock will always lead to high exposures for workers at or near the cutting face unless precautions are taken.

Breathing fine dust of crystalline silica can lead to the development of silicosis. This involves scarring of the lung tissue and can lead to breathing difficulties.

Exposure to very high concentrations over a relatively short period of time can cause acute silicosis, resulting in rapidly progressive breathlessness and death within a few months of onset.

| | |
|---|---|
| **Materials** | Sand, sandstone, granite, clay, shale and slate. |
| **Common products** | Concrete, mortar, bricks, blocks, ceramics, kerbs and paving slabs. |
| **Common operations** | Sweeping up, demolition and strip out. Drilling or breaking. Cutting (disc cutter/chasing machine/floor saw). Grinding, polishing, rubbing down, sanding and blasting. |
| **Control measures** | Manufacture off site/isolate process. Substitute process (for example, use hand block splitter not disc cutter). Extraction/vacuum collection/forced extraction. Local exhaust ventilation. Water suppression (typically only 75% of particles are controlled). Dampen down. |
| **Respiratory protective equipment** | Half face respirator or disposable face mask, P3 or FFP3-rated. |

## Company fined for silica failings

A natural stone supply company has been fined for failing to protect workers from exposure to hazardous substances – despite a previous warning.

The Magistrates' Court heard that exposure to respirable crystalline silica (RCS), a substance that can cause fatal lung disease, was not being adequately controlled. Inspectors also found that the required health surveillance for the silica was not being carried out by the company.

The court was told that a previous inspection had identified similar concerns, and that the company was given advice on suitable control measures. However, the HSE investigation established that, despite tests revealing a high level of exposure to silica, little action had been taken to improve the control measures in order to reduce the exposure.

The current inspection identified that equipment was not maintained in efficient working order, in good repair and was not in a clean condition. The court also heard that although health surveillance on employees was previously carried out once, no further health surveillance had been provided for employees exposed to RCS.

The company pleaded guilty to breaching Regulation 7(1) of the Control of Substances Hazardous to Health Regulations. They were fined £4,000 and ordered to pay £2,525.40 in costs.

After the hearing the HSE inspector said: 'Cutting stone can cause a lot of dust which, if it is not controlled, can cause serious health effects – the most serious being silicosis, which in its most acute form can be fatal. There is plenty of guidance available for stonemasons to help them improve existing control measures, and the health risks from silica dusts are insignificant when exposure to dust is properly controlled. There is no need to become ill through work activities and there is no excuse for companies not following the guidance'.

### 10.11.1 Health surveillance for silicosis

Health surveillance should be considered when there is a reasonable chance that an employee could contract silicosis through exposure to respirable silica dust. However, if there is only a low exposure risk then health surveillance, involving x-rays and a survey, could be unnecessary.

A health professional would be able to advise the employee on the type of surveillance (such as the examples shown below) that would be required.

- ☑ Chest X-rays.
- ☑ A baseline assessment or pre-employment checks.
- ☑ Training in how to identify symptoms and who these should be reported too (the responsible person).
- ☑ Fit for work assessments.
- ☑ The requirement to keep health records.
- ☑ Identifying patterns of employee sickness absence.

B 10

### 10.11.2 Good practice methods – Silica

| Drilling masonry | Control measures |
|---|---|
|  | ■ Can material be pre-drilled?<br>■ Ensure drill bits are sharp.<br>■ Drilling, especially horizontal at chest or eye level or above head means additional exposure to dust.<br>■ Where possible use dust collection systems that use a vacuum (not clip on dust bags).<br>■ Avoid sweeping; instead, vacuum up drill dust, otherwise the dust will disperse around the area and continue to be a hazard.<br>■ Use RPE (P3 or FFP3-rated). |

| Cutting slabs, kerbs or concrete | Control measures |
|---|---|
|  | ■ Can pre-sized material be purchased?<br>■ Can a block splitter be used?<br>■ Use a petrol or compressed air cut saw with a constant water feed.<br>■ Use RPE (P3 or FFP3-rated).<br>***Note:*** *water feed on its own will only remove approximately 75% of the airborne particles. RPE still needs to be worn.* |

| Chasing walls | Control measures |
|---|---|
|  | ■ Check for live services.<br>■ Ensure eye protection is impact-rated.<br>■ Use a proprietary system that incorporates a dust extraction system.<br>■ Regularly empty the vacuum collector.<br>■ Regularly clean the filter.<br>■ Consider using additional dust extraction (such as room filter cubes).<br>■ Use RPE (P3 or FFP3-rated).<br>■ Check that any escaping dust is not contaminating other areas or affecting others. |

| Sweeping up – General | Control measures |
|---|---|
|  | ■ Set up designated cutting areas.<br>■ Use dust extraction/collection units on equipment.<br>■ Vacuum the area rather than sweeping.<br>■ Provide good ventilation.<br>■ Dampen down area before sweeping.<br>■ Place dust in bags.<br>■ Use RPE (P3 or FFP3-rated).<br>■ Provide a vacuum to clean down equipment and clothing. |

## 10.11.3 Examples of controls for common high risk tasks

| Task | Ways to eliminate or limit the dust | Control measures |
|---|---|---|
| Cutting concrete kerbs, blocks and paving with a cut-off saw | ■ Limiting the number of cuts during design/layout<br>■ Using lower energy equipment (such as block splitters)<br>■ Getting material cut off site and delivered | ■ Water suppression<br>■ RPE* with an APF of 20 |
| Chasing concrete and raking mortar | ■ Limiting the need for chasing at the design/layout stage<br>■ Using a work method that limits/does not need chasing (such as over-covering cables) | ■ On-tool extraction using an H or M Class extraction unit<br>■ RPE* with an APF of 20 – consider powered RPE for longer duration work |
| Cutting roofing tiles with a cut-off saw | ■ Hand cutting natural/fibre cement slates and other tiles where possible<br>■ Using ½ and 1½ tiles<br>■ Correct setting out/design<br>■ Minimising valleys/using dry valleys | ■ Water suppression<br>■ A dedicated cutting area with scaffold board protection<br>■ RPE* with an APF of 20 |

| Task | Ways to eliminate or limit the dust | Control measures |
|---|---|---|
| Scabbling or grinding with hand-held tools | ■ Specifying architectural finishes that do not need scabbling<br>■ Using (ultra) high-pressure water jetting<br>■ Using chemical retarders and pressure washing<br>■ Casting in proprietary joint formers (such as mesh formwork) | ■ Where possible use on-tool extraction using an H or M Class extraction unit<br>■ RPE* with an APF of 20 |
| Short-duration drilling totalling 15-30 minutes with hand-held rotary power tools | ■ Limiting the number of holes during design/planning<br>■ Using direct fastening or screws | ■ Where possible use equipment that stops dust getting into the air. The larger the holes the better this needs to be. Options range from:<br>– drilling through a dust 'collector' or using cordless extraction attached to the drill (for smaller drill bits)<br>– on-tool extraction using an H or M Class extraction unit<br>■ Otherwise use RPE* with an APF of 20 |
| Drilling holes with hand-held rotary power tools as a 'main activity' | ■ Limiting the number of holes during design/planning<br>■ Using direct fastening or screws | ■ Where possible on-tool extraction using an H or M Class extraction unit<br>■ RPE* with an APF of 20 |
| Dry coring | ■ Limiting the number of holes during design/planning | ■ On-tool extraction using an H or M Class extraction unit<br>■ Longer duration work (for example, over 15-30 minutes accumulated time over the day) will also need RPE.* Use an APF of 20 |
| Wet coring | ■ Limiting the number of holes during design/planning | ■ Water suppression<br>■ Long periods of wet coring in enclosed spaces will also need RPE.* Use an APF of 20 |
| Using a hand-held breaker in enclosed spaces with limited ventilation | ■ Limiting the amount of breaking during design/planning stage<br>■ Bursting, crushing, cutting, sawing or other techniques<br>■ Remote controlled demolition<br>■ Hydrodemolition | ■ On-tool extraction using an H or M Class extraction unit<br>■ RPE* with an APF of 20 |
| Abrasive pressure blasting | ■ Using a different method of work like (ultra) high-pressure water jetting<br>■ Using 'silica free' abrasive material | ■ Wet or vacuum blasting<br>■ RPE* will depend on silica content of building materials, blasting equipment and length of work:<br>– in most instances use RPE with an APF of 40<br>– use RPE with an APF of 20 for lower risk work (including the 'potman' nearby)<br>■ Shrouds or screens to contain the flying abrasive<br>■ Certain restricted/enclosed working places may also need general mechanical ventilation |
| Soft strip demolition | ■ Carefully planning the work<br>■ Limiting the number of people that need to be in the work area<br>■ Screening off areas to prevent dust spreading | ■ Use water suppression or on-tool extraction for those tasks where it is possible<br>■ RPE* with an APF of 20 – consider powered RPE for longer duration work<br>■ Enclosed spaces may also need general mechanical ventilation to remove dusty air |
| Removing small rubble, dust and debris | ■ Limiting waste materials during design/planning<br>■ Considering where waste material is created and how frequently it needs removing<br>■ Using the correct dust controls when making rubble/debris | ■ Damping down and using a brush, shovel and bucket for minor/small 'one-off' amounts<br>Or for regular removal/site cleaning:<br>■ Water spray for damping down<br>■ Rake, shovel and bucket/wheelbarrow to remove larger pieces<br>■ Covered chutes and skips where needed<br>■ Vacuum attachments fitted to an H or M Class extraction unit<br>■ RPE* with an APF of 20 depending upon location, duration and type of work |

| Task | Ways to eliminate or limit the dust | Control measures |
|---|---|---|
| Cutting wood with power tools | ■ Using a less toxic wood[1]<br>■ Ordering pre-cut materials<br>■ Using dedicated cutting areas to minimise spread | ■ On-tool extraction using an H or M Class extraction unit<br>■ Longer duration work (for example, over 15-30 minutes accumulated time over the day) will also need RPE[†] suitable for the wood dust – particularly in enclosed spaces |
| Sanding wood with power tools | ■ Using a less toxic wood[1]<br>■ Using 'pre-finished' materials | ■ On-tool extraction using an H or M Class extraction unit<br>■ RPE[†] suitable for the wood dust in most situations |
| Sanding plasterboard jointing | ■ Using other finishes/systems | ■ On-tool extraction using an H, M, or L Class extraction unit |

****Table 2** Common RPE types for construction dust.*

| APF | Common RPE types for construction dust |
|---|---|
| 10 | ■ FFP2 disposable mask or half mask with P2 filter |
| 20 | ■ FFP3 disposable mask or half mask with P3 filter<br>Or for longer duration work:<br>■ Powered RPE such as a TH2 powered hood/helmet |
| 40 | ■ Abrasive blasting helmet with constant flow airline |

*[†]RPE for wood dust*
*The risk from wood dust is specific to different types (species) of wood.*

*[1]Knowing the species is important in establishing the right RPE to use. In general RPE with an APF of 20 is appropriate; particularly for higher residual dust levels, such as when sanding, and for all work with more toxic woods such as hardwoods, western red cedar and MDF. RPE with an APF of 10 is suitable for work with less residual dust and when the wood is lower risk (e.g. pine).*

*(Reproduced from the HSE Construction Information Sheet no. 36 Revision 2)*

B 10

## Appendix A – Respiratory protective equipment selection

Each type and class of respiratory protective equipment (RPE) is categorised by an assigned protection factor (APF) that gives the user some idea of the level of protection that the device will provide. For example, a filtering half-mask respirator marked:

- ☑ **FFP1 or P1** is a low efficiency device offering a **protection factor of four**
- ☑ **FFP2 or P2** is a medium efficiency device offering a **protection factor of 10**
- ☑ **FFP3 or P3** is a high efficiency device offering a **protection factor of 20**.

A protection factor of 10 means that, in controlled conditions, for every 10 units of contaminant outside the mask, only one unit or less will get inside the mask, or for every 20 units outside the mask there will be two units inside, and so on. It is important, therefore, that the correct filter is selected for the type and level of contaminant in the air.

**Always choose an APF above the calculated value.**

**Use RPE with an FFP3 or P3 rating to protect against dust (such as silica) that is created when mechanically cutting concrete, bricks, slabs and so on – even when wet cutting, which only removes about 75% of airborne particles.**

There are many types of RPE, including:

- ☑ disposable face mask respirators
- ☑ half-mask dust respirators
- ☑ high-efficiency dust respirators
- ☑ positive, pressure-powered respirators
- ☑ ventilator visor or helmet respirators
- ☑ compressed, air-line breathing apparatus
- ☑ self-contained breathing apparatus.

**BS EN 529 provides details on the APF and RPE.**

**Cheap nuisance masks (cup-shaped filters often held in place by a single strap with no BS EN 529 markings) are not classed as PPE or RPE. They do not meet any current standards or legislative requirements and offer very little or no protection to the wearer.**

B 10

### Common failings

- ☒ There is an assumption that workers know how to put on and use RPE.
- ☒ RPE misuse is common – but it is generally blamed on the workers.
- ☒ There is limited management input or involvement when it comes to RPE.
- ☒ There is little information provided to the worker wearing the RPE.
- ☒ There are poor standards of training, hazard awareness and RPE use.
- ☒ There is little supervision and enforcement of correct RPE use.

**Respirators must not be used in oxygen-deficient atmospheres.**

**For further information on respiratory protective equipment (RPE) and selection refer to Chapter B06 Personal protective equipment.**

# 11
# Carbon monoxide

**Contents**

## Overview

**Every year construction workers and occupants of properties where work is being undertaken suffer from the effects of carbon monoxide (CO) poisoning.**

**Although some of the effects can be immediate, they can also manifest over a period of time. The impact can be gradual and difficult to attribute to particular sites, equipment or instances given that many operatives generally work across a number of sites over a period of time.**

**Carbon monoxide effects are often overlooked as they can easily be attributable to a number of other illnesses making diagnosis difficult. This chapter gives a general overview of carbon monoxide, its identification, symptoms, impact and management and outlines the legal framework that regulates it.**

## 11.1 Introduction

Managing and controlling exposure to carbon monoxide is a vital challenge facing the industry as it can impact, sometimes lethally, both on operatives working on site and also on any occupants of property where work is being undertaken.

Every year 200 people are taken to hospital with suspected CO poisoning, with around 40 subsequent deaths. This poisoning can have devastating effects on workers and their families that could lead to long periods of sickness from work and, in the case of fatalities, the emotional and financial impact this brings.

One of the main problems is that carbon monoxide is odourless, colourless, tasteless, non-irritating and therefore difficult to detect or diagnose. As operatives tend to work on multiple sites, exposure may occur over a period of time and symptoms can easily be associated with many other illnesses.

- ☑ Every year around 12 people die from CO poisoning caused by gas appliances and flues that have not been properly installed, maintained or that are poorly ventilated.
- ☑ About 200 people are diagnosed annually by the NHS as having been poisoned by CO. This may be just the tip of the iceberg, as under-reporting, lack of awareness and difficult diagnosis means that a greater number may be living with low levels of CO poisoning without their knowledge. This potentially means their condition may deteriorate to the extent where, if not treated, fatalities could occur.
- ☑ Whilst an injury caused by an accident is in most cases instantly obvious, the symptoms of CO poisoning may not necessarily be immediately obvious.
- ☑ CO poisoning can lead to workers having long periods of sickness from work and, in extreme cases, paralysis and brain damage can be caused by prolonged periods of exposure.
- ☑ Even short-term sickness absence can have an adverse effect on business. People exposed may show similar signs to having the flu or food poisoning.
- ☑ The prevention of CO poisoning can be achieved through:
  - a suitable assessment of the risks to health being carried out and reviewed as necessary
  - adequate control measures being identified, put in place and adjusted as necessary
  - the persons at risk fully using the control measures provided
  - effective personal protective equipment (PPE).
- ☑ In some circumstances employers have a legal duty to provide health surveillance to employees.

Raising managers', supervisors' and operatives' awareness to ensure effective identification, management and control measures are always put in place and monitored is important in helping to reduce the impact of CO on operatives and, where appropriate, occupants.

**You can't see it or taste it, but CO can kill quickly, without warning.**

## 11.2 Important points

- ☑ The creation of CO fumes should be prevented or eliminated where reasonably practicable by:
  - identifying the potential health risks arising from the work to be carried out
  - investigating what can be done about them and deciding how they are going to be addressed
  - giving staff information, instructions and training on the health risks and the control measures to be followed
  - monitoring the work to make sure that the procedures are being implemented and are effective
  - introducing health surveillance where necessary.

- ☑ Control of CO can be achieved by:
  - – raising general awareness of the risks associated with CO by communicating the relevant information to friends, family and work colleagues
  - – being aware of the sources of CO, especially in domestic properties where a number of appliances could be responsible
  - – getting appliances professionally installed and regularly serviced to ensure they work efficiently and safely
  - – ensuring adequate ventilation for all fuel-burning appliances
  - – installing monitoring devices for the early detection of excess CO
  - – recognising the early signs and symptoms of carbon monoxide poisoning, particularly when more than one family or work member is affected, and seeking medical advice promptly.
- ☑ Hazardous CO fumes usually result from:
  - – domestic heating systems
  - – blocked flues/chimneys
  - – inadequate ventilation in living areas
  - – inadequate ventilation in adjoining car garages
  - – leakage from faulty appliances and chimneys/flues
  - – fumes from generators
  - – the use of equipment and plant powered by internal combustion engines.

## 11.3 Formation of and exposure to carbon monoxide

Carbon monoxide (CO) is produced by the incomplete burning of carbon based fuels (such as domestic or bottled gas, coal, oil, coke and wood). Gas stoves, fires, heating boilers, gas-powered water heaters, paraffin heaters and solid fuel-powered water heaters are all potential sources of CO. Diesel plant exhaust emissions also contain CO. The problem arises when such appliances are poorly installed, maintained, not serviced, and housed or used in poorly ventilated areas.

When the waste products of combustion are not effectively removed (for example, because of blocked flues and chimneys) then poisonous gas mixtures may re-enter the room. This problem is not just associated with older or poorer homes – it can also affect the occupants of newer homes with gas central heating. Exhaust fumes from cars, vans or generators are other sources of CO.

CO is formed when any fire burns and, if in an enclosed room, the amount of oxygen available gradually decreases whilst the amount of carbon dioxide increases. As the amounts of these two gases change, this causes the combustion process to alter from one of complete combustion to one of incomplete combustion. This results in the release of CO.

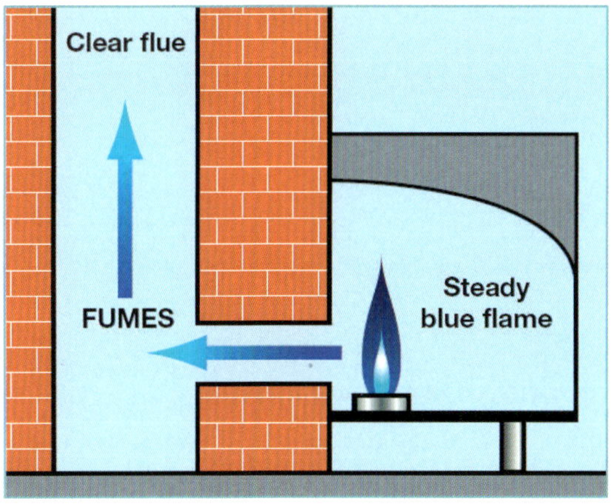


*A safe gas appliance*

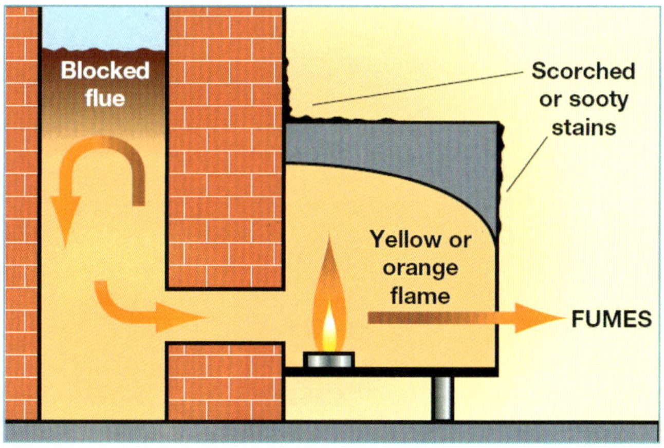


*A dangerous gas appliance*



Even perfectly designed and maintained heating appliances, or any kind of combustion device, will eventually begin producing dangerous amounts of CO if used in confined and poorly ventilated areas. Having poorly operating appliances only makes the problem worse more quickly. Maintaining appliances and ensuring sufficient fresh air is available are two easy ways of avoiding potentially lethal scenarios.

CO poisoning occurs when small amounts of CO fumes are breathed in. It gets into the bloodstream and prevents red blood cells from carrying oxygen, which causes body tissue and cells to die. CO also has direct effects on the blood vessels of the body, causing them to become leaky. This is seen especially in the brain, which swells, leading to unconsciousness and neurological damage.

Levels that do not kill can still cause serious harm to health when breathed in over a long period of time. Long-term effects of carbon monoxide poisoning include paralysis and brain damage.

Individuals can either be exposed to high levels of CO over a relatively short period of time (acute exposure), or to lower levels of exposure over a longer period of time (chronic exposure).

Acute exposure is easier to diagnose as the symptoms are more pronounced, but it is the common chronic exposure symptoms that are more subtle and difficult to tell apart from other conditions. Where whole families are affected by suspected food poisoning, in some cases this is actually due to CO poisoning. Where such symptoms are reported repeatedly, CO poisoning should be suspected.

The following clues point towards a problem within a specific location.

- ☑ If more than one person is affected.
- ☑ When symptoms appear or get worse when appliances are in use.
- ☑ When symptoms are worse in the winter when gas boilers/heaters are in use.
- ☑ When symptoms improve when operatives or occupants leave a location, but come back on their return.

Important information can also be obtained by inspecting appliances or machinery that run on combustion of carbon-containing fuels. The main problems could include black soot marks on gas fire burners or on walls near cookers, boilers or gas fires, or a yellow gas flame colour, rather than the blue colour it should be.

## 11.3.1 Symptoms of CO poisoning

Carbon monoxide symptoms are similar to flu, food poisoning, viral infections and simply tiredness, so it is quite common for people to mistake this dangerous poisoning for something else.

| Symptoms to look out for |
| --- |
| **1.** Headaches or dizziness |
| **2.** Tiredness |
| **3.** Pains in chest or stomach |
| **4.** Erratic behaviour |
| **5.** Visual problems |
| **6.** Nausea |
| **7.** Breathlessness |
| **8.** Collapse |
| **9.** Loss of consciousness |

Other signs that could also point to CO poisoning are that symptoms only occur when a person is in one place for a period of time, symptoms disappear or get better when the person leaves a location and come back when they return, and if others in the location experience symptoms appearing at a similar time.

Often the onset of symptoms is gradual, occurring without the individual or doctor being fully aware of what is happening. Coupled with this is the fact that the severity of the poisoning depends on the following factors.

- ☑ How much CO is actually present in the environment.
- ☑ The duration that the person is exposed to CO.
- ☑ The age of the individual concerned. (Babies, young children, pregnant women and people with heart or breathing problems are all at greater risk.)
- ☑ The person's general state of health.
- ☑ The extent of physical activity the person is undertaking (effects are increased with higher activity levels).



**Pets could be the first to show signs of carbon monoxide poisoning, as they are vulnerable to the effects of gas.**

## 11.3.2 Action for suspected CO poisoning

Effectively treating individuals suspected of CO poisoning could make the difference between survival, and short and long-term damage. Move the affected individual(s) away from exposure to the CO source. Their signs and symptoms will indicate whether there has been exposure to CO, but a blood sample will confirm the amount of carboxyhaemoglobin in the blood. A level of 30% indicates severe exposure.

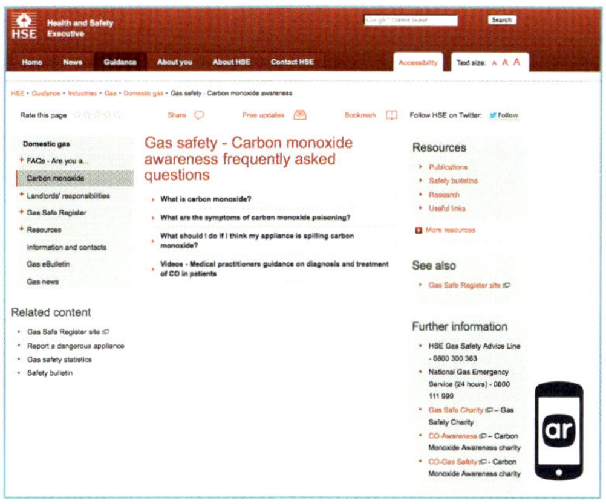


Mild CO poisoning does not usually need hospital treatment but it is still important to seek medical advice.

Exposure to a high amount of CO is treated with 100% oxygen (normal air contains about 21%). This enables the body to replace carboxyhaemoglobin more quickly.

The HSE has provided guidance for medical practitioners on the diagnosis and treatment of CO in patients. *(For further information refer to the AR link provided.)*

### What should I do if I think an appliance is spilling carbon monoxide?

- **Call the National Gas emergency service on 0800 111 999.**
- Switch off the appliance and shut off the gas supply at the meter control valve.
- Open all doors and windows to ventilate the room.
- Visit your GP and explain that you believe you may have been exposed to carbon monoxide.

## 11.4 Employers' responsibilities

Employers are required to complete the following.

- Identify the potential health risks arising from the work to be carried out.
- Investigate and decide how they are going to be addressed.
- Give staff information, instructions and training on the health risks and the control measures to be followed.
- Monitor the work to make sure that the procedures are being implemented and are effective.
- Introduce health surveillance where necessary.
- Look for the benefits and the improvements.
- Report any injury, disease or dangerous occurrence, as specified under the Reporting of Injuries, Diseases and Dangerous Occurrences Regulations (RIDDOR).

The management of health on site includes areas of confined or enclosed spaces (lack of ventilation, fire trap/risk) and competence, knowledge, skills/training and experience.

Health risks that need to be considered include respiratory problems and the potential for contracting serious respiratory diseases (such as occupational asthma resulting from the inhalation of existing harmful substances).

## 11.5 Managing the risk

The law says you must identify any work that may expose workers or the public to CO gas, and manage any risk accordingly.

All gas work carried out in the home and in certain commercial premises should be done by a Gas Safe registered engineer.

There are three main ways in which construction work can interface with CO gas issues.

- Site worker and security staff facilities.
- Refurbishment work on existing buildings (including use of diesel plant).
- Gas Safe register for gas engineers.

Site gas-fired appliances, refurbishment work on existing buildings and work on gas systems have all lead to deaths from CO poisoning.

### 11.5.1 Site worker and security staff facilities

Inadequately ventilated liquefied petroleum gas (LPG) cookers and heaters can produce CO gas. Flammable gas may also escape from leaking cylinders.

Site workers and night security staff have died from CO poisoning on construction projects where such gas-fired appliances have been used in site welfare or rest facilities.

### Security guard dies from carbon monoxide poisoning

A construction company and a security company manager have been fined after a security guard died from carbon monoxide poisoning while at a work.

The Central Criminal Court heard how the deceased had been working as a security guard. The semi-derelict building was due to be turned into a self-storage facility. The construction company were managing the refurbishment and had employed a security company to provide 24-hour security to the site. The company engaged a self-employed security guard.

A petrol-powered electricity generator had been provided by the construction company to power a portable heater and lights, as there was no electricity supply to the building.

The security company manager attended the site at about 1.45 pm. He had not heard from the security guard, who was on the night patrol shift and had been due to call in at 6 am. The security guard was found lying on a second storey office floor, with the generator in another room off the same corridor. An ambulance was called and the security guard was declared dead at the scene. The postmortem revealed he had died of carbon monoxide poisoning.

The HSE investigation showed that the construction company failed to take reasonable measures to ensure, so far as was reasonably practicable, that the generator provided for their use was safe and without risks to the health of the security guards. The manager of the security company failed to take effective steps to ensure that the petrol generator, provided for the use of the security guards, was not operated within the building and he did not carry out or implement the findings of a risk assessment for the provision of a 24-hour security presence. He had also not provided the security guard with appropriate information, instruction and supervision in respect of the use of the generator.

The construction company pleaded guilty to breaching Section 4(2) of the Health and Safety at Work etc. Act 1974. The company was fined £60,000 and ordered to pay costs of £24,515.

The manager of the security company pleaded guilty to breaching Section 3(2) of the Health and Safety at Work etc. Act 1974. He was fined £30,000 and ordered to pay costs of £15,000.

Using properly maintained electrical equipment can eliminate the risks associated with LPG heaters. If LPG is used you can reduce the risks in the following ways.

- ☑ Using and storing the cylinders in safe, well-ventilated places, outside of the accommodation (including overnight) or in purpose-built ventilated storage areas.
- ☑ Ensuring that appliances have been properly installed, checked and maintained by a competent person.
- ☑ Providing adequate combustion ventilation with fixed grilles at high and low level.
- ☑ Checking that the ventilation provided is not blocked (for example, by newspaper or rags in cold weather to stop draughts).
- ☑ Checking that cylinders are properly turned off when not in use.
- ☑ Using wall or ceiling-mounted CO detectors.

## 11.5.2 Refurbishment work on existing buildings

*Gas membrane fitting*

Members of the public have died from CO poisoning after refurbishment work (such as roof work) has disrupted gas flues or ventilation systems, causing CO to build up in occupied premises.

The impact of refurbishment work on existing gas-fired systems must be identified during the planning stage and managed throughout the project.

A competent gas engineer should be involved where there is any likelihood that refurbishment work will affect gas-fired systems.

### Loft conversion work causes risk of carbon monoxide poisoning

Two partners in a home improvement company have been fined after building work at a house exposed a woman and her foster children to the risk of carbon monoxide poisoning.

The company was contracted to carry out loft conversion work at a property in November 2010. As part of the improvement work the company had to replace a flue from the gas fire. However, this was then left in an immediately dangerous condition, with potentially lethal fumes escaping into the loft space.

The householder had concerns about the quality of the work carried out by the company, and found that there were faults with the plumbing system. The Gas Safe register sent an officer to investigate. They found that the flue from the gas fire had been removed just below the level of the loft, allowing poisonous carbon monoxide gas into the loft space. This was classified as immediately dangerous.

The HSE's investigation identified that the company did not obtain advice from a Gas Safe registered engineer before the chimney and flue were removed. The gas fire was still connected and used during the winter, resulting in potentially deadly carbon monoxide gas building up within the loft space.

The householder said: 'My son started complaining of headaches and feeling sick and I put it down to him playing computer games, not carbon monoxide. When the Gas Safe register inspector found that the flue had been removed, I realised just how lucky we were'.

The partners in the company each pleaded guilty to a breach of the Gas Safety (Installation and Use) Regulations and both were fined £1,500.

An HSE inspector said: 'The partners failed in their duty to ensure the gas fire was made safe before they removed the chimney and flue. The shoddy and careless work by the contractors could have cost a family with young children their lives. Anyone carrying out work on or near a flue should get advice from a Gas Safe registered engineer, before starting work, to ensure it is made safe. It is never acceptable to assume that a gas appliance will not be used after a flue has been removed'.

## 11.5.3 Diesel engine exhaust emissions

Diesel engine exhaust emissions (commonly known as diesel fumes) are a mixture of gases, vapours, liquid aerosols and substances made up of particles. They contain the products of combustion, such as those shown below.

- Carbon monoxide.
- Carbon (soot).
- Nitrogen.
- Water.
- Aldehydes.
- Oxides of nitrogen.
- Oxides of sulphur.
- Polycyclic aromatic hydrocarbons.

**Workers refurbishing a large industrial warehouse became ill and were taken to hospital suffering from the effects of carbon monoxide. They were using diesel-power floats and even though the doors were left open there was insufficient ventilation.**

Breathing in diesel fumes can affect workers' health, and exposure to the fumes can cause irritation of the eyes or respiratory tract. These effects are generally short-term and should disappear when away from the source of exposure.

However, prolonged exposure to diesel fumes, in particular to any blue or black smoke, could lead to coughing, chestiness, breathlessness and cancer.

There is evidence that repeated exposure to diesel fumes over a period of years may increase the risk of lung cancer. Diesel engine exhaust is not only an important workplace carcinogen, but also contributes to air pollution. Reduction in diesel engine exhaust could be achieved through engineering controls (such as improved ventilation and regular maintenance of vehicles). Other measures include improving worker practices (such as limiting vehicle numbers, particularly in closed spaces, turning off engines when not in use and, if necessary, using appropriate respiratory protective equipment).

**The risk assessment and method statement for any diesel plant must address the potential hazard of build up of fumes. Diesel fume extraction fans can be hired and carbon monoxide levels monitored by a suitable gas monitor. It is also important to remember that fumes are heavier than air, and can in effect roll into and build up in an open excavation or trench.**

### 11.5.4 Gas Safe register for gas engineers

All gas work carried out in the home and in certain commercial premises should be done by a Gas Safe registered engineer. Gas work includes installing, repairing or servicing a gas boiler and installing or repairing a gas fire, gas cooker or hob.

The Gas Safe register is the only gas engineer registration scheme approved by the HSE under the Gas Safety (Installation and Use) Regulations.

All gas engineers wanting to undertake domestic and certain other gas work need to be registered with the Gas Safe register, to ensure they are competent and qualified to work safely and legally with gas.

**For more information visit the Gas Safe register online.**

*Example of a Gas Safe competency card*

Gas engineers will often have a range of qualifications that allow them to carry out specific types of gas work. It is important to check what work they are qualified to do before you use them. You can find this information using the check an engineer service or by looking on the back of their Gas Safe register ID card.

Every gas engineer carries a Gas Safe register ID card with their own unique licence number, showing the type of gas work they are qualified to do. Before any gas work is carried out, always make sure you ask to see their Gas Safe register ID card.

**For information on how to find a gas engineer refer to the Gas Safe website.**

## 11.6 Monitoring and training

CO detectors can provide an audible, high-pitched alarm when high levels of CO are detected, or can provide an alarm plus a digital display of the concentration of CO detected in units of 'parts per million' (ppm).

*Carbon monoxide sensor*

Three types of carbon monoxide detectors are available.

- ☑ **Chem-optical (gel cell or biomimetic) technology** alarms use a type of sensor that simulates haemoglobin in the blood.
- ☑ **Electrochemical alarms** work by converting the carbon monoxide electrochemically to carbon dioxide, which generates an electrical current that is taken as a measure of the gas concentration. Electrochemical alarms are usually powered by a battery lasting about five years.
- ☑ **Semiconductor technology** alarms use semiconductors or tin dioxide technology to detect carbon monoxide levels. Unlike the alarms above, semiconductor detector alarms do not require any replacement sensors.

It should be noted that all these sets of regulations place a legal duty on the employer to provide employees with adequate information, instruction, training and supervision to be able to carry out any work task safely and without risks to their health.

Information, instruction, training and supervision, as required by the Health and Safety at Work Act and the Management of Health and Safety at Work Regulations must be provided for supervisors and personnel who work in conditions that may expose them to CO. New employees should receive full instruction before starting work and should be familiarised with the following.

*Carbon monoxide alarm*

- ☑ The health risks associated with CO and the preventative measures in operation, as identified by the risk assessment.
- ☑ The correct use and cleaning of protective clothing and equipment.
- ☑ The reasons for monitoring and correct use of monitoring equipment.
- ☑ Their duties in respect of the correct use of equipment and of safe systems of work in operation.
- ☑ The procedures for reporting potential CO exposure and defective or inadequate equipment.
- ☑ The procedures for treating individuals suspected of CO poisoning.

# Appendix A – Example ventilation requirements for domestic fuel-burning heating appliances when upgrading or installing draught-proofing

## Balanced flue (room sealed)

### Air supply

- ☑ No permanent vent required to outside air from room space containing the appliance.

### Action

- ☑ Check flue terminal air inlet and exhaust outlet is not blocked or sealed. If correct proceed with draught-proofing installation.

## Open flue gas fire of rated input over 7 kW

### Air supply, for appliances of rated input over 7 kW

- ☑ A permanent vent is required to outside air. This opening shall be 4.5 $cm^2$ per kW of rated input over 7 kW.

### Action

- ☑ Verify permanent vent to outside air is present, is not blocked or covered and is of the correct dimensions to produce the free areas required for the appliance rating. If correct proceed with the standard draught-proofing installation.
- ☑ If a permanent vent to outside air is not present, or is present but blocked, covered or inadequate, leave a minimum of eight metres of window perimeter without draught-proofing or sealants in the appliance.

Where the window perimeter is less than eight metres, both the window and the internal door from the appliance room to the hallway, stairway or passage, which serves the room, shall not be draught-proofed. Where the external door enters the appliance room via a draught lobby that serves no other room, the draught lobby shall not count as a hallway, stairway or passage and another internal door from the appliance room to another room shall not be draught-proofed.

The area given below is the free area of the vent(s) or the equivalent free area for ventilators of a more complex design. Divide the area given above in $mm^2$ by 100 to find the corresponding area in $cm^2$.

In the diagram below A, D, H and I are permanently open vents on the outside. B, C, F and G are permanently open air vents between an appliance compartment and a room or a space.

| | Open flued | Room sealed |
|---|---|---|
| **Appliance in a room or space** | 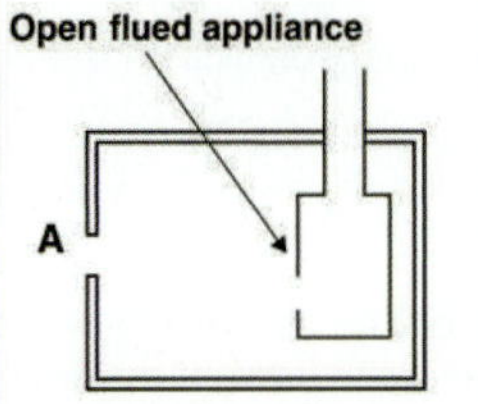<br>A = $500mm^2$ per kW input (net) in excess of 7kW (net) | 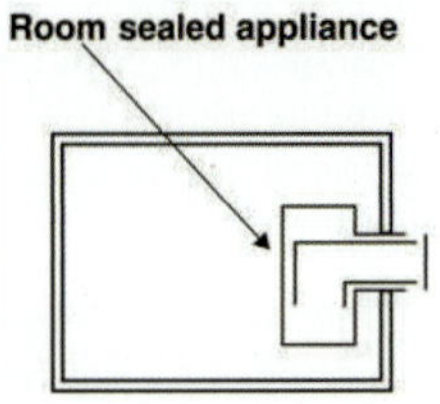<br>No vent needed |
| **Appliance in an appliance compartment ventilated via an adjoining room or space** | 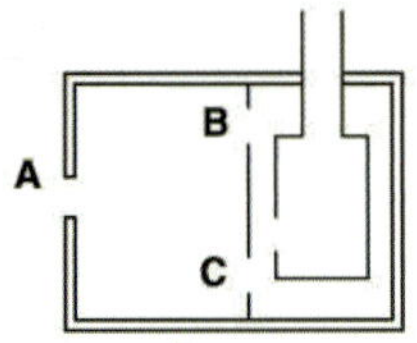<br>A = $500mm^2$ per kW input (net) in excess of 7kW (net)<br>B = $1000mm^2$ per kW input (net)<br>C = $2000mm^2$ per kW input | 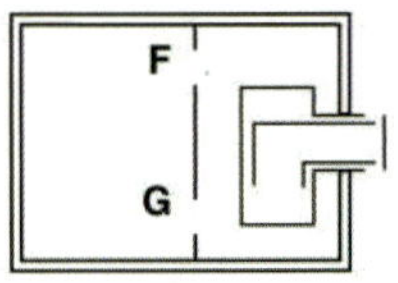<br>F = $1000mm^2$ per kW input (net)<br>G = F |
| **Appliance in an appliance compartment ventilated direct to outside** | 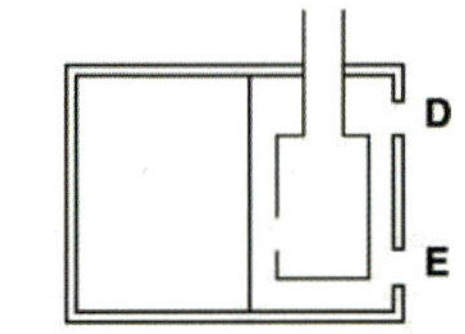<br>D = $500mm^2$ per kW input (net)<br>E = $1000mm^2$ per kW input (net) | 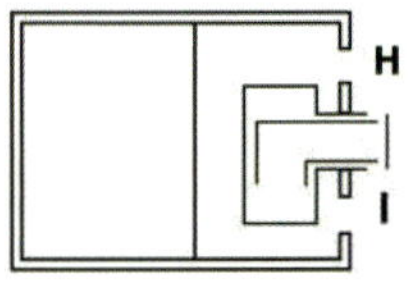<br>H = $500mm^2$ per kW input (net)<br>I = H |

***Note:*** *not to scale.*

## Open flue gas appliance including gas fire with back boiler and decorative fuel effect gas fire

### Air supply

- ☑ A permanent vent is required to outside air from the room space containing the appliance to provide free area of:
  - – 100 $cm^2$ for decorative fuel effect gas appliance
  - – 4.5 $cm^2$ per kW of rated input above 7 kW for any other appliance.

### Action

- ☑ Verify permanent vent to outside air exists and is not blocked or covered and is of correct dimensions. If correct proceed with work.
- ☑ If a permanent vent to outside air is not present, or is present but blocked, covered or inadequate, leave a minimum of eight metres of window perimeter without draught-proofing or sealants in the appliance.

B 11

## Open solid fuel fire with or without back boiler for central heating

### Air supply

- ☑ A permanent vent required to outside air having a free area of at least 50% of the throat opening.

  ***Note:*** *for a typical domestic open solid fuel fire 50% of the throat opening gives an area of approximately 100 cm². This figure is to be used owing to the practical difficulties of measuring the throat opening.*

### Action

- ☑ If a permanent vent to outside air of 100 $cm^2$ is present then complete the standard draught-proofing job after verifying that the vent is clear.
- ☑ If a permanent vent to outside air is not present, or is present but blocked, covered or inadequate, leave a minimum of eight metres of window perimeter without draught-proofing or sealants in the appliance.

## Mobile space heating appliance (LPG, paraffin)

### Action

- ☑ Verify permanent vent to outside air of at least 95 $cm^2$ exists in the room or hallway where the appliance is used. If the permanent vent is not blocked, covered or inadequate, proceed with the standard draught-proofing installation.
- ☑ Where the appliance is used in a room that does not have a permanent vent to outside air or a permanent vent that is blocked, covered or inadequate, then the room must not be draught-proofed.
- ☑ Where the appliance is used in a hallway that does not have a vent to outside air or a permanent vent that is blocked, covered or inadequate, then no draught-proofing shall be installed in this property.

## Flueless fixed gas convector (space heater)

### Air supply

- ☑ A permanent vent is required to outside air from the space containing the appliance to provide a free area of at least 100 $cm^2$, plus 50 $cm^2$ for every kW by which the appliance rated input exceeds 3 kW. A window that can be opened for the release of fumes is also required for these units.

### Action

- ☑ Verify permanent vent to outside air exists and is not blocked or covered and is of the correct dimensions to produce the free areas required for the appliance and rating. Verify opening window can be operated without difficulty and maintained open. If correct, proceed with the standard draught-proofing installation.

B
11

# 12 Lead

Contents



## Supporting information

**G: Checklists and forms**



**GT 700 Toolbox talks**

## Overview

**Old, lead-based paint and dust are still likely to affect the majority of UK buildings, although lead paint was completely removed from retail sale by 1992. Lead surveys are a mandatory requirement under the Construction (Design and Management) Regulations (CDM).**

**Exposure to lead, lead dust and fumes constitutes a major and widely under-estimated hazard to the health of those whose work involves lead, lead products and lead-containing materials (LCMs), such as lead-based paint, or leaded exhaust particle contamination in lofts and roof voids, known as ceiling dust.**

**Lead paint and consequent dust exposure risks are greatest within pre-1970 buildings and structures, especially during repair, maintenance, refurbishment and demolition, if proper precautions are not followed. The build-up of lead 'dust' contamination in lofts, and roof, ceiling and floor voids continued until the general sale of leaded petrol became illegal in 2000.**

**This chapter sets out to explain the risks and controls that are required.**

## 12.1 Introduction

Exposure to lead dust, fumes and vapour constitutes a major hazard to the health of industrial workers, including those in the construction industry, who work with lead, lead products and lead-containing materials (LCMs) (such as old lead-painted surfaces).

Construction workers most at risk are described below.

- ☑ Those carrying out blast-removal and burning of old lead paint.
- ☑ Those stripping old lead paint from doors, windows, and so on.
- ☑ Those carrying out surface preparation of previously lead-painted surfaces. Even stripped surfaces can contain significant lead residues.
- ☑ Those stripping old wallpaper and disturbing underlying lead-based paint.
- ☑ Demolition operatives involved in hot-cutting in demolition and dismantling operations.
- ☑ Plumbers working on lead-flashing, upstands and gutters.
- ☑ Operatives handling old, architectural lead work.
- ☑ Anyone involved in structural renovation or refurbishment, including conservation or heritage projects.

Exposure risks from lead paint, dust and fumes are most likely to occur in pre-1970 buildings but can be present in any building, especially during repair, maintenance, refurbishment and demolition, if proper precautions are not followed. It should be noted that, wherever paintwork or coatings are likely to be damaged or disturbed, the Health and Safety Executive (HSE) advises that, **when preparing paintwork, lead surveys should be completed, regardless of the age of the building or the extent of the works.**

www.

**Information on reducing the health risks in construction work can be found on the HSE website.**

!

**XRF-i lead surveys provide the best data in accordance with HSE guidance to commission.**

The Construction (Design and Management) Regulations (CDM) impose a duty on clients to identify and collect information about hazardous materials likely to affect a project as part of pre-construction information. Lead-containing paint is one such material and the legal requirement for clients to commission lead surveys early on in a project is established in several regulations.

The Control of Lead at Work Regulations (CLAW) and its associated Approved Code of Practice, together with guidance notes and information from the Lead Paint Safety Association (LiPSA) and the Painting and Decorating Association (PDA) have been produced to enable employers to interpret the legal duties placed upon them by the regulations and to take the appropriate actions to protect the health and safety of their employees, who have to work with lead, and other people who may be affected by the way the work is carried out.

Clients have a duty to identify lead hazards before a project commences. An incremental three-stage approach, involving preliminary indicative DIY testing with a simple chemical test, followed by limited professional paint-on-base-material analysis and/or a full lead survey, provides a cost effective approach to meeting this widely unknown requirement.

Employers have a legal duty to protect their employees (and any building occupants). For employees this includes monitoring their blood-lead levels, so that individuals whose work involves *significant* exposure to lead at work (as defined by the CLAW Regulations) can be taken off such work if the legal threshold for blood-lead levels is exceeded.

Lead contaminated waste must be disposed of in accordance with the Hazardous Waste Regulations.

## 12.2 Important points

- Lead and LCMs (such as lead-containing paint) are hazardous. They can become a *significant* exposure risk if lead dust, fumes or vapour are not prevented or adequately controlled. Any work involving lead must be in accordance with the Control of Lead at Work Regulations, also known as CLAW.
- Unless adequate precautions are taken, children and pregnant women are particularly at risk when decorators, for example, are disturbing old lead-containing paint in homes or schools.
- Lead is a cumulative poison that is absorbed into the bloodstream. Over time it will also collect in the kidneys and soft tissues, before accumulating in the bones.
- The ways that lead is likely to get into the body are through the:
  - **inhalation** of fumes or dust
  - **ingestion** of lead particles through hand to mouth contact (especially for smokers)
  - **absorption** through the skin as a result of the slightly acidic environment produced by sweating. (This tends to occur around the seals of full face respiratory protection and in the groin region, where skin is also thinner, softer and less likely to provide an effective barrier.)
- Workers' families may indirectly be exposed to lead as a result of the lead remaining on the workers' clothes when they arrive home.
- All work with lead or LCMs must be subject to a risk assessment, which includes consideration of the amount of lead involved. Hence the legal requirement for lead (paint) surveys.
- General builders, carpenters and decorators who remove or disturb old lead-containing paint, particularly if involved in window replacement, repairs and general refurbishment or demolition, may be exposed to *significant* quantities of lead without realising it. Scaffolders are also a *significant* exposure risk group.
- Where the risk assessment indicates that employees' exposure to lead is likely to be *significant*, certain monitoring actions must be taken with regard to the employees affected and the workplace itself. These include sampling to determine blood-lead levels, air-monitoring for airborne lead-dust levels and surface dust contamination checks.

  ***Note:*** *although there are no legal threshold levels relating to surface dust contamination this is something that HSE inspectors are required to consider during CLAW inspections, as set out in Operational Circular 298/15.*
- *Significant* exposure is defined in the regulations as: **where there is liable to be a substantial ingestion risk.**

  ***Note:*** *it is the ingestion risk that needs to be substantial, not the amount of lead.*
- *Significant* exposure risk also exists where airborne lead-dust levels are greater than or equal to 50% of the occupational exposure limit (OEL) for airborne lead.
- During health surveillance, employees' exposure to lead is most commonly measured by the concentration of lead in their blood. A laboratory analysed saliva check can be used to screen for blood-lead levels.
- Above a certain level of exposure, employers have a legal duty to temporarily suspend the affected worker(s) from further work with lead and lead-containing materials.

www.

**An extract from an observational study undertaken on lead exposure on scaffolders during refurbishment construction activity is available online.**

In the context of this chapter, the main consideration is identifying where and how much lead could be present. This allows appropriate actions to be taken to protect the health of workers exposed to lead risk and, if necessary, other people who may be affected by the work (such as occupant families at home or children at school, or indeed, workers' families).

Although it is possible for lead exposure risks to be contained and controlled in occupied buildings it is worth noting the advice from the Department for Communities and Local Government with respect to stripping and preparing lead-based paint in older homes. It is contained within its lead worked example risk assessment under the *Housing health and safety rating system* (HHSRS):

> **The occupants should be temporarily rehoused during the stripping and re-painting.**

This guidance is consistent with advice in paint manufacturer safety data sheets, which advise:

> **...exclusion of other personnel and especially children from the building during actual work and the subsequent clean-up operations.**

B 12

## 12.3 Control of Lead at Work Regulations

The regulations aim to give greater health protection to people at work, whether directly or indirectly exposed, by reducing their exposure to lead and thus the concentrations of lead in their blood. Where concentrations are too high, employers are required to remove employees from work with lead. This is known as the **suspension level**. If employers cannot transfer employees to other work not involving exposure to lead, they must pay them suspension pay under the Employment Rights Act.

Concentration levels of lead in blood, which are below the suspension level and known as **action levels**, have been set. If these lower levels are breached, employers have a duty to investigate and remedy the cause. Employers are also required to take steps to reduce the concentrations of lead in air to a level not exceeding the occupational exposure limits stated in the regulations.

Women of child-bearing age and young people are particularly at risk of lead poisoning, and therefore have lower blood-lead action and suspension levels than other workers.

**Lead exposure risks are not covered by the Control of Substances Hazardous to Health (COSHH) Regulations. Only the Control of Lead at Work Regulations should be applied to lead hazard and their exposure risk assessment.**

It should be noted that the Control of Lead at Work Regulations place a number of legal duties on employers, as well as limited legal duties on employees.

### 12.3.1 Duties under the regulations

The main requirements of the Control of Lead at Work Regulations are shown below.

- An employer, who is working with lead, or a substance or material containing lead, has to protect from exposure anyone who may be affected by the work as well as their own employees. This includes:
  - the workers of other employers, including those not involved in work with lead (such as maintenance staff and cleaners)
  - visitors to the work site
  - the families of those who are exposed to lead at work who may become affected by lead carried home unintentionally on the clothing and footwear of the employee
  - the occupiers of premises, including private dwellings, irrespective of whether the occupiers are present whilst the work is carried out or they reoccupy the premises later.
- Every employer is required to make a suitable and sufficient assessment of the risk to the health and safety of employees while at work. This includes other people who are not employees but who may be exposed as a result of the way the employer carries out the work concerned.

  The assessment must be reviewed as often as is necessary and in other certain specified circumstances, and a record made of any significant findings if more than five people are employed. Such an assessment is to allow the employer to make a decision whether the work concerned is likely to result in an employee being *significantly* exposed to lead, and to identify the measures needed to prevent or adequately control exposure.

#### 12.3.1.1 Control of exposure

- Every employer must ensure that the exposure of employees to lead is either prevented or, where this is not reasonably practicable, adequately controlled by means of appropriate control measures.
- As the preferred control measure, the employer must consider the use of alternative materials or processes as a means of eliminating or reducing the risks to the health of employees.
- Where it is not reasonably practicable to prevent exposure to lead, the employer must introduce protective measures that are appropriate to the work activity and consistent with the findings of the risk assessment. In order of priority, these must be:
  - the design and use of the work process, systems and engineering controls
  - control of exposure at source, including ventilation systems and wet methods
  - where adequate control cannot be achieved by other means, the provision and use of suitable respiratory protective equipment (RPE) and personal protective equipment (PPE).

**Painters and decorators should be aware that most paint manufacturer MSDS sheets advise the use of wet sanding for surface preparation regardless of whether the surface contains lead or not. Wet sanding prevents airborne dust generation and provides a superior finish.**

☑ The control measure(s) must include:
- the safe handling, storage and transportation of lead and waste that contains lead
- suitable maintenance procedures
- reducing to the minimum required for the task in hand, the number of employees exposed, the level and duration of exposure and the quantity of lead present in the workplace
- control of the working environment, including where appropriate, extract ventilation and appropriate daily clean-up using a combination of HEPA vacuuming and wet mopping
- appropriate hygiene measures, including washing and showering facilities. Decontamination units (DCUs) are an increasingly common choice.

Irrespective of these control measures, where the exposure to lead is, or is likely to be, *significant* the employer must provide suitable and sufficient protective clothing.

☑ Where the inhalation of lead fumes is possible, the control measures will only be regarded as adequate if the:
- occupational exposure limit is not exceeded, or
- employer identifies the reason and takes immediate steps to rectify the situation.

Inhaling lead fumes from the uncontrolled use of heat guns or torches is the most likely cause of acute lead exposure and hospitalisation. Up to 90% of the lead content of any lead fumes can be absorbed through the lungs and passed directly into the bloodstream.

☑ Employers must take reasonable steps to ensure that any control measure provided is properly used or applied.

☑ Employees must make full and proper use of any control measure provided, and:
- take all reasonable steps, where appropriate, to return anything provided as a control measure to its accommodation (storage) after use
- report any defect in any control measure provided to the employer.

☑ Adequate control of exposure to lead covers all routes of possible exposure (such as inhalation, ingestion and absorption through the skin).

☑ When eating, drinking and smoking, adequate steps must be taken to control the ingestion of lead. An employer must ensure that, as far as is reasonably practicable, employees do not eat, drink or smoke in any place which is, or is liable to become, contaminated by lead. In practical terms, employees must be warned against doing so. Furthermore, under this regulation employees have a legal duty not to eat, drink or smoke in any place that they have reason to believe is contaminated by lead. All control measures provided, including RPE and PPE, must be well maintained, kept in a good state of repair and cleaned as necessary. Any defect in the equipment, or failure to use and apply it properly, which could result in a loss of efficiency or effectiveness, thus reducing the level of protection, should be identified and rectified as soon as possible.

Colorimetric (colour change) testing of dust contamination can be used to ensure welfare areas are sufficiently lead-free.

### 12.3.1.2 Air monitoring

Where employees are liable to receive *significant* exposure to lead, employers must establish a programme of personal air monitoring, including keeping records of the findings of such monitoring.

### 12.3.1.3 Medical surveillance

Where exposure to lead is *significant*, as defined in Regulation 2, the employer must ensure the following.

☑ Employees are under medical surveillance by either a medical inspector (employment medical adviser) or a relevant doctor.

☑ Suitable facilities for health surveillance to be carried out are provided, where the procedures are to be carried out at the employer's premises.

☑ Health surveillance records are maintained and then retained for 40 years.

☑ Employees are allowed reasonable access to their personal health records.

☑ Copies of personal health records are provided to the HSE upon request.

☑ All records are made available to the HSE if ceasing to trade.

☑ Steps are taken to determine the reasons why any employee's blood sample exceeds the appropriate action level and appropriate remedial action is taken, where required.

☑ The necessary actions, including reviewing the risk assessment, are taken where an employee's blood or urine sample reaches the suspension level.

**Employees** for whom health surveillance has been arranged must, when required by the employer (and at the cost of the employer), make themselves available for the necessary health surveillance procedures and supply the relevant doctor with such health-related information as the doctor may require.

An initial assessment, including blood-lead levels, should always be carried out on new employees who are employed in an activity liable to expose them to lead, and who are likely to have been exposed to lead at work in a previous job, within the last three months, *irrespective* of whether their exposure to lead in their new employment is likely to be *significant*. The variety and variability of any lead exposure levels in previous employment in refurbishment and related activities are such that it would be safest, at the very least, to check the blood-lead levels of all new employees. If this is not done, then every new project involving activities liable to expose employees to lead should be seen as an opportunity to rectify this oversight and establish a person's base line or reference levels for comparison in case of future problems.

#### 12.3.1.4 Information, instruction and training

Employers who undertake work liable to expose employees to lead shall provide such information, instruction and training as is suitable and sufficient to know the risks to health, and the precautions, which should be taken (*refer to 12.5 Training*).

> **What employers must provide**
>
> In addition to this, the Code of Practice requires that an employer should issue a copy of the HSE's free leaflet entitled *Lead and you* to all employees at the start of their first employment on work with lead, and make copies available for issue at the request of any employees or their representatives.
>
> It is thought that this requirement is often not followed with regard to painters and decorators because the information is not sufficiently trade-specific. The Painting and Decorating Association's (PDA) *Health and safety manual* provides a useful source of more relevant information.
>
> Employers must additionally provide employees with written records of concentrations of lead in air to which they have been exposed, the results of the measurements of lead in their blood or urine, and an explanation of the significance of these results.
>
> ***Note:*** *in construction, blood lead is the most common measure of exposure to inorganic lead (as found in compounds used in old lead paint), with action and suspension levels being expressed in micrograms of lead per decilitre of blood. Urine sampling tends to be used for assessing exposure to organic lead (such as the fumes from tetraethyl lead).*

#### 12.3.1.5 Arrangements for accidents, incidents and emergencies

The employer, in attempting to protect the health of employees (and others) from an accident, incident or emergency, must ensure that procedures, including the provision of first-aid facilities and safety drills, have been prepared and can be put into effect should such an occasion arise. The employer must also ensure that information on such emergency arrangements has been notified to accident and emergency services and that all such information is displayed within the workplace and for occupants in the same premises.

Colorimetric qualitative lead paint and dust-test kits can be kept on site to allow an immediate assessment of likely lead exposure risks when these emerge. Follow-on quantitative analysis should then be used to quantify the severity and extent of the problem.

#### 12.3.1.6 Exemptions

A certificate of exemption may be granted by the HSE. For further information refer to the regulations and seek competent advice.

## 12.4 Approved Code of Practice

The Control of Lead at Work Regulations should be read in conjunction with the supporting Approved Code of Practice (ACoP) and guidance, which interprets the regulations and sets out standards relating to controlling any type of work activity liable to expose employees and any other persons to lead. The regulations achieve this by means of risk assessments, control measures, air monitoring, the setting of an occupational exposure limit (OEL), medical surveillance and the setting of an action level and suspension level for lead in the blood.

## 12.5 Training

With regard to the Control of Lead at Work Regulations (CLAW) (as amended), there is a specific requirement to ensure that the information, instruction and training provided for persons working with lead includes the following.

- ☑ The type of lead being worked, the potential health hazards and symptoms.
- ☑ The relevant occupational exposure limit, action level and suspension level (as explained later in this chapter – *refer to 12.7*).
- ☑ Any other sources of information (such as a lead survey and/or a lead register).
- ☑ Any other legislative provisions relevant to working with lead.
- ☑ The significant findings of the risk assessment (such as the amount of lead involved).
- ☑ The control measures that are in place and that must be used to enable work to be carried out safely.
- ☑ The results of any personal air monitoring or surface dust contamination checks.
- ☑ The results of previous health surveillance, in such a way that the confidentiality of individual cases are not breached.

## 12.6 The effect of lead on health

Lead is a neuro-toxin and should be considered as a potential exposure risk in all of its forms. Lead exposure can initially go unnoticed because there may be no obvious physical symptoms of an underlying problem.

Blood-lead levels (BLLs) are the best measure of current exposure. If the level of lead in the body gets too high, it can cause headaches, tiredness, irritability, constipation, nausea, stomach pains and loss of weight. Continued uncontrolled exposure could cause far more serious symptoms (such as kidney, nerve and brain damage).

The regulations are specifically intended to protect women of child-bearing age and young persons. A developing unborn child is at particular risk from exposure to lead, particularly in the early weeks before a pregnancy becomes known. Thus, women of child-bearing age who may be exposed to lead should take special care to follow good work practices and observe a high standard of personal hygiene.

### 12.6.1 Preventing exposure to lead

The employer has a duty to assess the nature and extent of the exposure to lead and, on the basis of this assessment, to determine the measures necessary to control exposure and comply with the regulations.

Action should be taken to reduce the amount of lead breathed in by operatives to below the lead in air standard.

Although inhalation has always been considered to be the major source of lead exposure, current thinking recognises the much greater contribution of hand-to-mouth contact and the *significant* exposure risk that can arise from ingestion.

Many of the sections of the regulations relate to the prevention of the inhalation or ingestion of lead dust, fumes and vapour. **The basic need is to prevent the liberation of lead dust, fumes or vapour into the workplace.**

If surface finishes are to be disturbed in any way, the potential presence of lead paint should always be established and quantified. The worst should always be assumed (that it is a lead-based paint), as it is not acceptable to take the appropriate precautions if the presence of lead has not actually been checked. The legal requirement is to consider the amount (of lead) involved. This approach, given the substantial variability and severity of lead in paint levels across a project (even on a single component) risks severely under-estimating the problem and how best to manage it. Therefore it is essential that lead content is properly quantified, as it is impossible to undertake a suitable and sufficient risk assessment without this knowledge.

There are a number of ways to test for the presence of lead, shown below.

- A variety of destructive tests for paint sampling, although these can result in damage to painted surfaces in order for samples to be taken.
- Disposable test kits: Instant, on-site lead/no lead result with 95% accuracy. (These are an indicator only, **not** a laboratory-standard test and are unsuitable and insufficient for risk assessment purposes.)
- Paint-sampling kits, which are ready to use (for non-lab professionals) for submission of samples for chemical analysis. (A laboratory-standard test).
- Dust-wipe sampling kits, which are ready to use (for non-lab professionals) for submission of samples for chemical analysis. (A laboratory-standard test).
- Professional sampling for accredited or non-accredited laboratory analysis.
- Hand-portable devices that use XRF-i (x-ray fluorescence isotope) technology to obtain laboratory standard readings instantly, on site.

**When taking physical samples for off-site analysis, it is almost impossible to ensure 100% recovery of all of the lead from a given substrate, whether timber, metal, plaster or any other materials – occupationally *significant* quantities of lead residue tend to be left behind. For this reason laboratory analysis of samples removed from site can significantly understate the severity of the actual on-site hazard – in some cases by up to 500%.**

Paint-on-base-material analysis, instead of the customary use of paint flakes or scrapings, provides the best starting point for determining the full extent of potential lead exposure risks, as found on site. Non-destructive XRF-i analysis lends itself to this methodology.

## 12.7 Controlling exposure to lead

### 12.7.1 Hazards

Lead is a cumulative poison that will find its way into the bloodstream, collect in tissue and be stored in bones. Lead poisoning may occur through exposure to lead in its pure form or exposure to products containing lead.

Lead affects the body's ability to produce haemoglobin, which is the protein in blood that carries oxygen to the tissues.

Inorganic lead, the type likely to be encountered during construction work, can enter the body in one of three ways.

- Inhalation of dust or fumes.
- Ingestion, via the digestive tract from hand-to-mouth transfer of lead particles.
- Absorption, where the presence of sweat can help to dissolve small quantities of lead which, in a liquid state, can be absorbed through the skin.

Although inhalation is generally the most common route of entry, ingestion exposure risk from inadvertent hand-to-mouth contact should not be underestimated. This makes smokers and nail-biters particularly vulnerable. Even though gloves should be worn at all times lead contamination from gloved hands is still easily transferred from hand to mouth.

Whilst the control of exposure through inhalation will be largely controlled by actions taken by the employer, and correct use of lead-safe work methods, the control of exposure through ingestion depends upon the good personal hygiene practices of individual employees working with lead.

## 12.7.2 Risk assessments

Employers must not carry out any work that may expose employees to lead unless a suitable and sufficient risk assessment has been carried out. Given the CLAW requirement to **'consider the amount (of lead) involved'**, a suitable and sufficient risk assessment cannot be based on the assumption that lead-based paint is present. A lead register or lead survey, as required under CDM, is the best place to start the risk assessment process.

The purpose of the risk assessment is to enable the employer to assess whether the exposure of employees to lead is likely to be *significant* and to identify the measures necessary to prevent or control exposure.

## 12.7.3 Control measures

Control measures involve substituting lead with less hazardous substances or, if this is not possible, using engineering and organisational methods, similar to those outlined for COSHH, to control exposure.

The control of exposure to lead (by inhalation) will only be regarded as adequate in the following circumstances.

- If the concentration of lead in the air is kept below the OEL *(see below)*.
- If, where the OEL is exceeded, the employer identifies the reasons and takes immediate steps to remedy the situation.

Where old, lead-based paint is concerned, removal is not necessarily the best option. Leaving it in situ is often safer, especially if it can be encapsulated with a proprietary coating or rigid covering. Encasement behind plasterboard is also an alternative.

## 12.7.4 Air monitoring

Where a risk assessment indicates that employees may be liable to *significant* exposure to lead, the employer must arrange for preliminary personal air monitoring to be carried out to establish the levels of lead in the air at the place of work.

Air monitoring will involve using specialist equipment, fitted to the employee being monitored, to take an air sample from the employee's breathing zone over a set period of time.

Using static air-monitoring equipment to take air samples is not acceptable for preliminary monitoring as the results will not be representative of any employee's personal exposure.

Generally, depending upon the circumstances, monitoring must be carried out for each individual process likely to generate different levels of exposure. The work environment, choice of equipment and the amount of lead in the material being worked on, can all contribute to significant variations. Air monitoring will determine whether the OEL has been breached.

The employer has a duty to retain records of air monitoring results for a period of five years.

Given the temporary nature of construction sites, and the even shorter periods when employees might actually be exposed to lead, this requirement is considered to be largely academic for the construction industry. With tradespeople (such as plumbers and painters) being potentially exposed to lead many times but over relatively short periods, it will be for the employer to decide how frequently air monitoring should be carried out to confirm whether or not existing control measures are adequate.

## 12.7.5 Occupational exposure limit

The standard for inorganic lead in the air is **0.15 mg** (milligrams) or **150 µg** (micrograms) of **lead per cubic metre** of air determined on an eight-hour time-weighted concentration.

### Significant

*Significant* in relation to exposure to airborne lead dust means exposure where any employee is, or is liable to be, exposed to a concentration of lead in the atmosphere exceeding half the occupational exposure limit for lead.

From the above it can be seen that the *significant* level would be **0.075 mg** (milligrams) or **75 µg** (micrograms).

**Units are shown here in micrograms because blood-lead levels are reported in micrograms per decilitre (µg/dL), helping to explain the use and relevance of these numbers and making it easy to relate them to each other.**

This quantifies the standard to be met by the control measures for airborne lead under the regulations.

**Even if the *significant* exposure risk threshold for airborne lead dust is not exceeded, a *significant* lead exposure risk can still exist because of a substantial ingestion risk.**

## 12.7.6 Medical surveillance

Medical surveillance to detect exposure to lead involves measuring the concentration of lead in the blood or urine and therefore necessitates the involvement of suitable, trained medical staff.

### Blood-lead levels (BLLs)

A saliva check or screening test is now available to determine blood-lead levels from the laboratory analysis of saliva samples. This is highly accurate, non-invasive and easy to do. And, because it is a painless, non-medical procedure, it should encourage compliance. As would be the case with an elevated blood-lead analysis result, a high blood-lead level from a saliva test should be followed up by a (second) blood sample.

Where a risk assessment indicates that employees' exposure to lead is likely to be *significant*, the employer has a duty to arrange medical surveillance for the affected employees.

**There is a very important difference between everyday use of the word *significant* and its definition/application under the CLAW Regulations. The amount of lead in an exposure situation can be low or high, but the substantial risk of ingestion can be *significant* in both cases.**

If biological monitoring detects blood-lead concentrations at or above those outlined below, this will trigger continued medical surveillance.

- Women of reproductive capability: **20 micrograms** of lead, or greater, per decilitre of blood.
- All other employees: **35 micrograms** of lead, or greater, per decilitre of blood.

## 12.7.7 Action levels

The action levels for lead are shown below.

- Women of reproductive capability: **25 micrograms** of lead per decilitre of blood.
- Young persons (aged 16–17): **40 micrograms** of lead per decilitre of blood.
- Any other employee: **50 micrograms** of lead per decilitre of blood.

If medical surveillance detects blood-lead concentrations at or above these action levels, the employer must:

- recognise that the employee's blood-lead level is near the suspension level
- investigate the effectiveness of existing control measures and take the necessary actions to reduce employees' blood-lead levels below the action level
- prevent the blood-lead level of affected employees from reaching the suspension level.

## 12.7.8 Suspension levels

If medical surveillance reveals that an employee's blood-lead level has reached or exceeded the levels outlined below, a doctor must decide whether to temporarily suspend them from work that exposes them to lead.

- Women of reproductive capability: **30 micrograms** of lead per decilitre of blood.
- Young persons (aged 16–17): **50 micrograms** of lead per decilitre of blood.
- Any other employee: **60 micrograms** of lead per decilitre of blood.

In such circumstances, the employer must:

- ensure that a doctor makes an entry in the health record of affected employee(s) as to whether, in the doctor's professional opinion, they should be suspended from further work liable to expose them to lead
- review the relevant risk assessment
- review the actions taken to prevent exposure to lead
- provide for a review of the health of any other employees who may have been similarly exposed.

If the doctor thinks that there is no need to suspend the affected employee(s) from work, the doctor must note in their health records the reasons for that decision and any conditions under which working with lead may continue.

Doctors practising in this specialist medical field are familiar with the regulations, and if there are some exceptions to the rule, such doctors will be able to explain them. An employer must act on the doctor's decision and an employee will not be able to work with lead again, or be exposed to it, until the doctor considers it safe to do so.

## Level of concern

The so-called 'level of concern' for the general population is 10 micrograms of lead per decilitre of blood. In some countries a lower threshold of 5 micrograms has been set for children under six years old. Contractors employing operatives with proper training, supervision and equipment should be able to maintain BLLs below 2 micrograms of lead per decilitre of blood. For grit-blasting operations keeping BLLs below 15 micrograms is practicable and achievable.

**Annexes 1–5 and Appendix 6 of the ACoP record details of an employee under medical surveillance because of exposure to lead.**

## 12.7.9 Understanding lead levels

The illustrations below should help visualise that very small amounts of lead can have a significant effect on a person's health, hence why lead exposure must be carefully assessed and controlled.

**1 microgram (μg)= one grain of sugar ÷ 1,000**

One grain of sugar = 1,000 micrograms (μg)

**1 deciliter (dL) = 100 ml**

or 1/10th litre (about half a glass of wine)

For employees the action level is **50 micrograms (μg)** of lead per **decilitre (dL)** of blood.

This is the equivalent of dissolving 1/20th of a grain of sugar into half a glass of wine.

The case study below demonstrates that **36,100 micrograms (μg)** can typically be found in just **1 cm²** of old lead paint.

### Analysis carried out on the window paint of a primary school built circa 1900

*Reading A was taken on exposed timber on a glazing bar where lead paint had flaked off*

Positive result = 8,900 micrograms (μg) per cm²

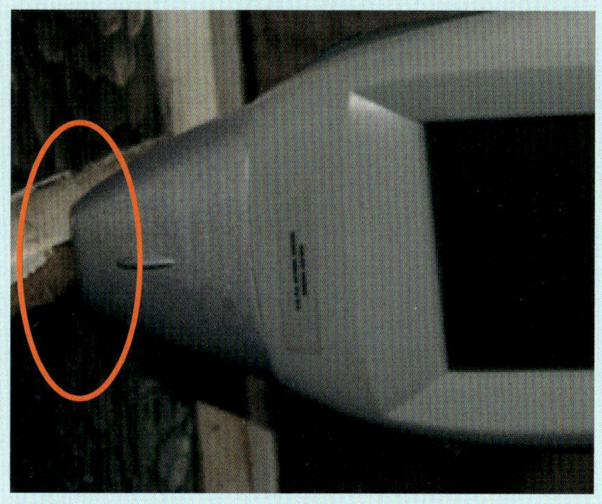

*Reading B was taken on undamaged paint on the same glazing bar*

Positive result = 36,100 micrograms (μg) per cm²

From these readings it can be seen that there is a high risk potential for *significant* lead levels to be released through removal techniques (such as burning off with a blowtorch or dry rubbing down). The same exposure risk situation arises after paint stripping – even if all of the visible paint has been removed.

## 12.7.10 Significant levels

*Significant* exposure to lead can occur in the following circumstances.

- Where any employee is, or is liable to be, exposed to a concentration of lead in the atmosphere exceeding half the occupational exposure limit for lead.
- If there is a substantial risk of any employee ingesting lead.
- If there is a risk of contact between the skin and lead alkyls or other substances containing lead that can be absorbed through the skin.

Employers must provide employees with protective clothing, monitor lead in air-concentrations and place the employees concerned under medical surveillance, including biological monitoring of blood-lead levels.

**The more stringent suspension levels and the action levels introduced by the regulations are intended to tighten controls on exposure to lead and reduce the risk to workers' health. In order to see further improvements in the control of employees' exposure to lead, the HSE has made known its intention to review the suspension levels with a view to reducing the limits further.**

In such cases, all the regulations will apply; blood-lead levels must be monitored and air monitoring must be carried out regularly to confirm the effectiveness of control measures and the results recorded. PPE will be required where control measures are not practicable.

## 12.8 Activities liable to result in significant exposure

Some types of work with lead, carried out as part of construction or decorating (such as in the examples listed below), have the potential to result in *significant* exposure to lead unless the employer provides adequate controls and ensures that they are used. For example.

- Burning off old paint.
- Dry-sanding old paint.
- High temperature lead-work (such as lead-smelting, burning and welding).
- Working with metallic lead and alloys containing lead (for example, soldering).
- Disc abrasion of lead surfaces and cutting lead with abrasive wheels.
- Spray painting with lead-based paints.

- ☑ Grit-blasting operations.
- ☑ Work inside tanks that have contained petrol.
- ☑ Manufacture of leaded glass.
- ☑ Hot-cutting, demolition and dismantling operations.
- ☑ Otherwise removing or disturbing old lead sheet thereby raising contaminated dust.
- ☑ Recovering lead from scrap and waste.
- ☑ Perforating top floor ceilings or ceilings below roof voids holding quantities of settled leaded exhaust particles, known as ceiling dust.
- ☑ Disturbance and/or removal of loft insulation where leaded exhaust particles have settled.
- ☑ Disturbance of floor voids containing accumulated lead particles.
- ☑ Welding galvanised metal and flame cutting steelwork that has been painted with lead-based paint.

**The molten metal in a galvanising bath for hot-dipping steelwork typically used to contain 1% lead (approximately) to assist with run-off after the component had been dipped. In the industry it is well known that older galvanised coatings, once dried, typically had a 0.5% lead content. Although this lead content has been reduced over time it has not yet been completely eliminated. So it is not simply leaded paint that can create or contribute to a person's overall lead exposure risk in this example.**

Those operations that do not usually produce *significant* levels of airborne dust or fumes include low temperature work, ordinary plumbing, soldering, handling clean sheets or pipes of lead and rough painting. In some cases, however, even these can present a substantial ingestion risk, and consequent *significant* exposure risk, if not managed properly.

Examples of types of work producing exposures above and below *significant* levels are given in the ACoP. Frequently, however, these are not sharply divided. For example, if the character of the lead is changed by the work itself, **work with materials containing LESS than 1% lead can be liable to result in *significant* exposure.**

## 12.9 Working with lead-containing paints

The residues of lead-containing paints are a health hazard. Operatives carrying out work involving the disturbance, preparation or removal of old lead-containing paint, and anyone else who might be adversely affected, must be adequately protected when applying or removing it.

Similarly, the occupiers of premises (including the residents of private housing) must be protected by not being allowed to return to their premises (or contaminated parts of those premises) until they have been thoroughly and effectively cleaned.

The findings of a risk assessment by a competent person, with specialist lead knowledge, and carried out before any surface finish is disturbed, will indicate the most appropriate method of removal and the safety precautions that must be taken.

**For a lead risk assessment refer to Section G: *Checklists and forms.***



### 12.9.1 Sanding or flatting

Wet sanding, wet scraping and wet abrasion, regardless of whether or not a coated substrate contains lead, are considered good practice methods for minimising airborne dust and paint chips during surface preparation. Wet residues should be cleaned up before they dry out and become chalky, with the potential to become airborne dust.

Lead-containing paintwork should never be dry-sanded by hand as this activity will liberate lead-rich dust into the air. Mechanical or power sanding should only be used if the sander is fitted with a dust extraction/collection unit incorporating a high-efficiency particulate air (HEPA) filter.

**Not all methods of stripping paint remove the residual lead from the grain of the wood. As a result, the subsequent dry sanding of apparently clean wood can liberate a *significant* amount of lead-containing dust into the air. Whichever of these methods is chosen toxic dust rated RPE (minimum FFP3 or P3) should also be worn.**

### 12.9.2 Burning

Blowlamps or gas torches must not be used to burn off old lead paint as these will heat the paint sufficiently to liberate toxic lead fumes into the air. The use of heat guns, unless very carefully supervised for low-heat use, is likely to generate toxic fumes.

### 12.9.3 Solvents

Lead paint may be removed by using a solvent or water-rinsable paint remover. If a solvent is used, the work area must be well-ventilated and no smoking or naked flames allowed. Suitable RPE and other appropriate PPE should be used.

### 12.9.4 Hot-air gun

These must not be confused with blowlamps and gas torches. Used on a low-heat setting **only** (for example, below 360°C) a hot-air gun will not raise the temperature of the paint sufficiently to allow lead fumes to be released. When using a hot-air gun, the old paint must be scraped off as soon as it is sufficiently soft and before it re-hardens. Care must be taken to ensure that the paint does not burn as this indicates that it is reaching too high a temperature where fumes may be given off. The use of RPE to protect against lead-containing dust may be necessary. Care should also be taken to prevent lead dust and paint from being blown everywhere – especially into people's homes or schools during external redecoration works.

Some hot-air gun manufacturers warn against using their products on lead paint surfaces, others advise low-heat working. Hot-air guns should be avoided on commercial projects because of the near impossibility of supervising their correct use. Unless a device has a pre-set operating temperature that cannot be overridden, allowing hot-air gun use on site is asking for trouble.

### 12.9.5 Infra-red heating

A product is available that safely lifts the old paint from the base material by heating it to a safe temperature using an infra-red heater. Whilst warm, the paint can be safely scraped off. This method is particularly suitable where large, flat surfaces have to be stripped.

The main benefits of using this method, which acts by heating the resins in the wood and breaking the bond between the wood and the first layer of paint, are shown below.

- ☑ All layers of paint are removed in a single hit.
- ☑ As a static heat method, the spread of air-blown lead contamination is avoided.
- ☑ Virtually all residual lead is removed from within the grain of the wood.
- ☑ Large flat surface areas can be safely stripped more quickly than by using other methods.

### 12.9.6 Spraying

Spraying methods should not normally be employed for applying lead-based paints.

### 12.9.7 Cleaning up the work area

All exposed surfaces in areas where lead paint stripping or removal has taken place should be washed down thoroughly, either with a proprietary lead-specific detergent or with a solution of dishwasher detergent in hot water, and then wiped down again with clean water. In areas that will be re-occupied by children, all washed down and rinsed areas should be towel dried to remove or prevent the formation of chalky residues.

Any residual dust and other debris should be removed using a vacuum cleaner fitted with a HEPA filter. Appropriate RPE (FFP3/P3) should be worn whilst doing this.

**Normal vacuum cleaners (domestic or industrial) should not be used as their filters are not sufficiently fine to retain the lead-containing dust. Vacuum cleaners, rated for use with hazardous dust only and fitted with HEPA filters, should be used.**

**For further information refer to Chapter B10 Dust and fumes.**

## 12.10 Personal protective equipment

In the context of this chapter, the regulations require that where a risk of exposure to lead has been identified by a risk assessment and it cannot be adequately controlled by other means, which are equally or more effective, the employer must provide PPE. They must ensure it is properly used by employees.

Users of PPE must be trained in its use and care as appropriate.

In essence, PPE may only be used as a last resort after all other means of eliminating or controlling the risk have been considered and are not reasonably practicable.

### 12.10.1 Respiratory protective equipment

Where control measures do not reduce the lead in air levels to below the control limits, RPE of a type suited to the hazard or process involved must be provided and all employees must be properly trained to use it. All such equipment should be serviced, cleaned, maintained and stored correctly, as is appropriate.

Depending upon whether the hazard is lead dust or fumes, adequate protection will be given by the use of compressed air-line breathing apparatus, self-contained breathing apparatus, or a full face positive pressure-powered respirator fitted with a high efficiency (HEPA) filter. Wearers of RPE must be face-fit tested.

**Half face respirators fitted with P3 filters or their disposable equivalent (FFP3) are suitable for toxic dusts (such as lead), subject to an assessment of the suitability of their assigned protection factor.**

Because lead is both an ingestion and an inhalation risk, airborne lead levels below the OEL (and even below the *significant* exposure level) can nevertheless present a substantial ingestion risk. By providing a physical barrier around the nose and mouth, suitable RPE specified to protect against lead dust can also help to minimise ingestion from hand-to-mouth contact.

Sole reliance on RPE is insufficient to avoid *significant* exposure.

### 12.10.2 Protective clothing

Wherever exposure is substantial, protective clothing must be provided. It must be suited to the hazard or process involved, should resist the permeation of lead dust, and not collect or harbour dust. Laundry facilities should be available so that contaminated clothing is not taken home for laundering. Employees must be instructed to report any damaged or defective ventilation plant or protective equipment, without delay, to their supervisor or safety representative.

All contaminated clothing and footwear should remain on site to prevent the potential of workers' families being exposed to lead – a known problem.

## 12.11 Welfare arrangements

The regulations require the provision of adequate welfare facilities, particularly in respect of personal hygiene. Contractors must provide or make the following items available.

- ☑ Suitable and sufficient washing facilities, including showers if necessary, due to the nature of the work (decontamination units (DCUs) are becoming more commonplace for this).
- ☑ Hot (or warm) and cold water, soap or other cleanser and towels or other effective means of drying.
- ☑ Suitable and sufficient changing rooms.
- ☑ Lockers or other facilities in which to secure work clothing that is not taken home and personal clothing that is not worn at work.
- ☑ Suitable rest facilities where meals may be prepared and eaten.

Regular checks (such as dust wipe sampling), should be made to ensure welfare facilities are sufficiently free of lead contamination.

**In accordance with HSE *Operational circular* OC 298/15 for inspections under CLAW, inspectors may seek from employers evidence of surface contamination levels.**

### 12.11.1 Changing and washing facilities

This includes accommodation for clothing where necessary. To avoid any risk to health or damage to the clothing concerned, the employer must also provide separate accommodation for an employee's own clothing and any protective clothing the employee may have to wear at work. This requirement will normally apply for protective clothing worn for work with lead.

Adequate and suitable washing facilities are required where operatives are exposed to lead. The ACoP requires that, where employees are exposed to lead, washing and changing facilities provided should allow them to meet a high standard of personal hygiene so as to minimise the risk of them ingesting or otherwise absorbing lead.

The design of the washing facilities should be related to the nature and degree of exposure to lead as indicated by the assessment. Where employees are *significantly* exposed to lead, and if washbasins alone would not be adequate, the washing facilities should include showers or baths.

An example would be where work is carried out in dusty conditions that could result in the whole body being contaminated by lead. Then the provision of showers or baths would be essential.

Washing facilities should provide the following, as a minimum.

- ☑ One washbasin for every five persons. Basins should be of sufficient size to permit arms to be immersed up to the elbow.
- ☑ A constant supply of hot (or warm) and cold water (running water where reasonably practicable).
- ☑ Soap or other cleaning materials.
- ☑ Nail brushes.
- ☑ Warm air dryers or roller towels; communal towels should not be used.

For certain types of work (such as lead paint removal work), carried out at premises or sites where such work is not regularly done (for example, certain tank cleaning, lead burning and grit-blasting operations), mobile caravan type washing/showering DCU facilities of suitable design should be provided.

### 12.11.2 Eating, drinking and smoking

The regulations specifically require employers to reduce the risk of ingestion of lead by ensuring that employees do not eat, drink or smoke* in places that are contaminated, or likely to be contaminated, by lead arising from work. Therefore, employers should reduce the risk of employees ingesting lead by ensuring that they are given adequate information on the specific areas that might be contaminated by lead and in which they should not eat (including chewing gum or tobacco), drink or smoke.

The information should be reinforced by displaying a prominent notice to identify those areas in which employees may, or may not, eat, drink or smoke.

The following points should be noted.

- ☑ Clean areas, canteens or mess rooms should be isolated from lead-contaminated work areas and checked regularly for levels of surface lead-dust contamination.
- ☑ Protective clothing should be removed before entering these areas.
- ☑ Washing should take place before eating meals or drinking.
- ☑ The employer must advise employees where they may not eat, drink or smoke.
- ☑ A legal duty is placed on employees not to eat, drink or smoke in any place where there is risk of contamination by lead.

** The legal ban on smoking in enclosed places of work may, in many cases, render this legal requirement irrelevant.*

Even with a total ban on smoking in enclosed workplaces, those who work with lead but smoke elsewhere (such as at home) must be aware of the need to remove all traces of lead from their hands and clothes at some time between carrying out the two activities.

**Smokers are likely to ingest between 200-400% more lead than non-smokers.**

### 12.11.3 Personal hygiene

Anyone who works with lead, lead-containing materials and old lead paint, should take simple personal hygiene measures to prevent the inhalation or ingestion of lead during and after work.

Interestingly, the ACoP that supports the Control of Lead at Work Regulations indicates that nail-biting and roll-your-own cigarettes are often implicated in high levels of lead absorption.

## 12.12 Provision and use of work equipment

The regulations require that an employer only supplies work equipment that is correct and suitable for the job for which the equipment is going to be used.

The regulations also require that users of work equipment are trained in its use, as appropriate.

## 12.13 Reporting of diseases

The regulations require the responsible person to report to the enforcing authority (normally the HSE) any case of lead poisoning suffered by any person at work that results from exposure to lead whilst at work.

Lead poisoning, when diagnosed by a medical practitioner, is a reportable occupational disease under RIDDOR and must be reported in accordance with requirements of the regulations.

The regulations contain strict provisions as to medical surveillance and require that employers ensure that basic details of all those who need to be under medical surveillance are recorded. (*A copy of this form is reproduced in Section G: Checklists and forms.*) There are additional forms specified by the regulations in respect of the following.

- The initial medical assessment, which also contains the past occupational medical and clinical details of the employee, including a smoking history.
- A surveillance record for persons exposed to lead.
- A notification to an employer of biological test results and a record of medical surveillance.
- A certification of unfitness or fitness to return to work.
- An annual return of persons under medical surveillance, to be completed by employers.

**For further information on the Reporting of Injuries, Diseases and Dangerous Occurrences Regulations (RIDDOR) refer to Chapter A13 Accident reporting and investigation.**

## 12.14 Supporting information

### 12.14.1 Lead Paint Safety Association

The Lead Paint Safety Association (LiPSA) is a not-for-profit organisation. It is at the forefront of efforts to promote awareness and good practice in lead paint safety and compliance. Its overall objective is to prevent, and ultimately eliminate, unnecessary childhood and occupational lead poisoning. Inadequate knowledge and non-compliance with established regulations are widespread.

**For further information visit the LIPSA website.**

### 12.14.2 Painting and Decorating Association

The Painting and Decorating Association (PDA) represents thousands of painters and decorators across the UK and is the largest trade and employers' association for contractors. The PDA offers health and safety advice to all its members.

**For further information visit the PDA website.**

## Appendix A – XRF-i lead surveys outperform traditional paint testing

A new technology is transforming the way that lead surveys are carried out. Hand-held x-ray fluorescence 'isotope' (XRF-i) devices were developed specifically for lead paint surveys. On-site lead paint hazards can now be measured in-situ, without causing surface damage and associated exposure risks. **Be aware:** non-'isotope' XRF devices are unsuitable for lead paint surveys.

The two most important considerations when risk assessing for lead exposure potential are:

- ☑ lead content: 'total' lead in paint
- ☑ area: extent of paint involved.

XRF-i lead surveys quantify lead paint content in units of mass per unit area, typically in micrograms or milligrams of lead per square centimetre (μg/cm$^2$ or mg/cm$^2$). So if you need to blast 1m$^2$ of paintwork with a 10 microgram/cm$^2$ lead content you're likely to disturb at least 100,000μg per m$^2$ of lead. The *'significant'* exposure for airborne lead is 75μg/m$^3$.

'Traditional ' laboratory analysis of paint flake samples removed from site describe lead content in units of μg/g, mg/kg or parts per million (ppm) which all tend to be converted into a much more easily understood percentage (%) figure. But quantifying the amount of lead relative to the total weight of the paint sample in which it is found (w/w% or mass/mass%) makes it impossible to apply a 'total' lead content figure to the paintwork that needs to be risk assessed.

In short, 'traditional' laboratory results which express lead in paint content as a percentage are unusable for full risk assessments. They are also compromised by sample quality and consistency:

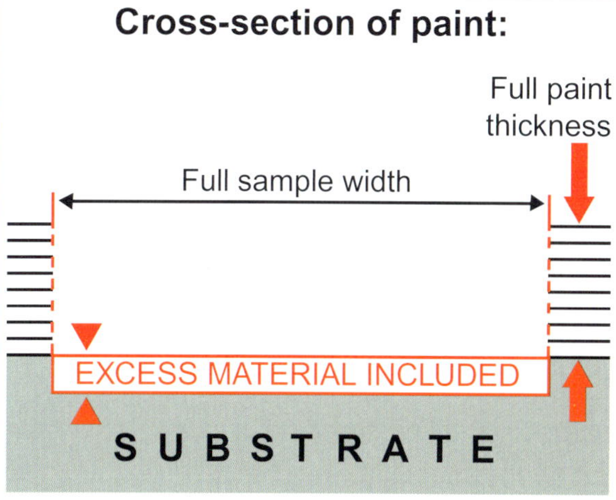


**Over-sampling.** Excessive sample material dilutes the lead fraction and the results understate actual 'total' lead in paint levels found on-site.

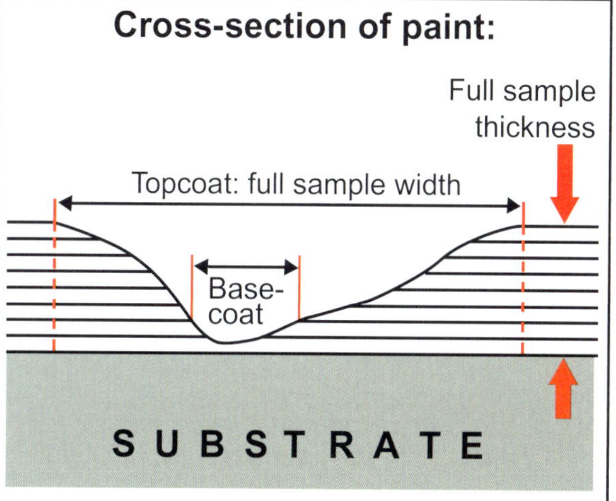


**Unrepresentative &/or undersampling of paint.** Excess surface paint layers, compared with less paint from deeper layers, skew laboratory results. This understates the actual lead hazards on-site as well as the likely exposure risks.

With the emergence of XRF-i lead survey devices, 'traditional' paint testing methods are difficult to justify, even if the analysis and results come from an accredited laboratory.

www. **For further information refer to the Lead Paint Safety Association.**

B 12

# 13 Noise

Contents



## Supporting information

**GT 700 Toolbox talks**

## Overview

**Noise is often taken for granted as an everyday feature of working on construction sites. Construction work can create levels of noise that have the potential to cause permanent damage to the hearing of those affected, if protective measures are not taken.**

**In addition to the long-term health implications, noise can also affect safety on site by interfering with spoken communications to the point where the risk of accidents is increased.**

## 13.1 Introduction

High levels of noise on construction sites often come from machinery used for demolition, excavation or piling, from compressors and concrete mixers, and so on. Other operations (such as hammering, riveting and the use of cartridge-operated fixing tools) may also be a source of excessive noise.

The degree of nuisance or damage caused by noise is related to the nature of the noise generated as well as its loudness. Intermittent noise is often more disruptive than a continuous noise and high-pitched sounds are more disturbing than low frequency ones. Exposure to high levels of noise can cause permanent damage to hearing in the form of hearing loss, tinnitus and partial or total deafness.

As well as hearing problems, excess noise is also known to cause the following problems.

- Annoyance and irritation.
- Loss of concentration.
- Reduced efficiency.
- Fatigue.
- Headaches.
- Stress.
- Increased accident-proneness.
- Masking of warning signals.

## 13.2 Important points

- Noise experienced at work, in the home and social environments can cause permanent damage to hearing.
- There are often early signs that the hearing is being damaged; these should not be ignored.
- Employers should seek to control noise by other, equally or more effective, ways before resorting to personal protective equipment (PPE).
- Effective pre-planning of off-site work and the active management of noise during the construction process can significantly reduce noise exposure on site.
- In addition to hearing damage, excessive noise can have other health and safety implications (such as not being able to hear alarms or shouted warnings).
- Establishing the noise levels on-site might not necessarily involve arranging for noise measurements to be taken.
- The 2008-09 labour force survey (LFS) reported that an estimated 17,000 individuals, who were working in that previous 12 months, believed their most serious work-related illness was hearing problems.
- 150 new claims for noise-induced hearing loss disablement benefit were assessed in 2011 *(Source: IIDB)*.
- Since 2007 all new cases of the noise-induced hearing loss disablement benefit have been awarded to males.
- Construction is one of the industries that has new cases of noise-induced hearing loss.
- The LFS suggests that the average total case numbers of noise-induced hearing loss caused or made worse by work from 2009-10 to 2011-12 is 19,000 cases.

**... research indicates that only around 60% of workers wearing hearing protection actually get the right amount of protection from it.**



## 13.3 Noise and Vibration Partnership Group

Industry bodies, specifically in the energy, extraction, manufacturing and construction sectors, along with the HSE, have formed a Noise and Vibration Partnership Group. This industry led group will work together, long-term, to increase awareness of the risks associated with noise and vibration in the workplace and promote effective management and control.

The purpose of the group is to reduce the incidence of noise-induced hearing loss and hand-arm vibration syndrome in workers. They aim to do this by further raising awareness, using pictorial images (such as posters and calendars), of the risks of exposure to noise and vibration in the workplace. This will improve the workers' knowledge and motivate them to share, promote and encourage good control practices in the workplace. The ultimate intention is to create a change in attitudes and behaviours to workplace noise and vibration.

Posters relating to noise and vibration are available on the HSE website.

## 13.4 Noise at Work Regulations

The aim of the regulations is to ensure that workers' hearing is protected from excessive noise at their place of work, as this could cause them to lose their hearing and/or suffer from tinnitus.

The regulations stipulate that the following requirements must be met.

- ☑ Employers must assess the risk to workers' health and provide them with relevant information at 80 dB(A).
- ☑ Hearing protection must be provided at 85 dB(A).
- ☑ The exposure limit value is 87 dB(A), and workers must not be exposed to noise levels that exceed this level.

**Refer to Appendix A for a summary of employers' duties, as required under the Noise at Work Regulations.**

## 13.5 Nature of noise

**Sound** is the transmission of air vibrations at different frequencies. **Noise** is sometimes defined as unwanted sound. The ear is a pressure-sensitive mechanism, detecting small changes of air pressure over a wide range of frequencies of 20–20,000 cycles per second. The unit of frequency is the hertz (Hz). Those with impaired hearing due to age or other forms of hearing loss are less likely to be able to hear the higher frequency range.

Audiometry is the technique used to determine the capacity of the ear to detect sounds of varying loudness over a range of frequencies. It can be used to measure an individual's hearing capacity against a recognised standard. Successive audiometric checks can confirm whether or not a person is suffering from progressive hearing loss.

**When judging the level of noise, the rules of thumb are that if you have to raise your voice to make yourself understood at two metres from the other person, the background noise is around 85 dB(A). If the distance is only one metre, the noise is around 90 dB(A).**

A peak sound pressure of 137 dB(C) will be produced by many impact tools (such as cartridge-operated tools).

Two types of noise may damage the hearing of the people who are exposed to it.

- ☑ **Continual or periodic noise**, which even if varying over the course of time, can be measured and averaged out over an eight-hour (or in some circumstances a weekly) reference period. This is known as the daily (or weekly) personal noise exposure, as referred to in the regulations. This is the common everyday noise that is experienced on many construction sites.
- ☑ **Sudden, short bursts of loud impulsive noise** (such as that experienced during the driving of piles, the use of explosives or the use of some hand tools). The references in the regulations to peak sound pressure are to this type of noise.

## 13.6 Effects of noise at work

Noise levels may fluctuate widely or be relatively steady. A reasonably steady sound level is where the level fluctuates through a total of less than 8 dB(A) on a slow response scale.

The HSE has provided recordings demonstrating how hearing is gradually lost over a working life, considering the effects of both noise exposure and ageing on hearing.

### 13.6.1 Hearing loss

Hearing loss can be temporary or permanent. Temporary deafness is often experienced after leaving a noisy place. It is often accompanied by a ringing in the ears. Although hearing usually recovers within a few hours, this symptom should not be ignored. It should be taken as a sign that further or continued exposure to noise is likely to result in permanent damage. Permanent hearing damage can also be caused immediately by sudden and loud noises (for example from explosives or cartridge-operated tools).

Hearing loss due to prolonged exposure to noise is usually gradual. It may only be when damage caused by exposure to noise over the years combines with normal hearing loss due to ageing that people realise how deaf they have become.

This incurable hearing loss may mean that they cannot hear the television clearly when set at a comfortable volume for the rest of the family, they cannot keep up with conversations in a group or they have trouble using the telephone. Eventually, all sound becomes muffled and people find it difficult to distinguish between 't', 'd' and 's', so they confuse similar words. Social situations become very difficult, as does communication at work.

Prolonged exposure to noise can also cause **tinnitus**, which can be described as a permanent ringing, whistling or buzzing in the ears. This distressing condition can lead to disturbed sleep which, in turn, can lead to fatigue even before an employee arrives at work.

### 13.6.2 Other adverse effects of noise

At work, noise can also be a safety hazard, interfering with communication, the understanding of instructions and, most serious of all, making warnings harder to hear. Noise can also cause stress. The Control of Noise at Work Regulations do not deal with these problems specifically, but the subject of noise and its attendant problems should be borne in mind when considering the overall subject of occupational health.

Exposure to noise can have the following consequences.

- ☑ It can cause annoyance and irritation.
- ☑ It may affect concentration and efficiency.
- ☑ It may cause fatigue and the likelihood of accident-proneness.
- ☑ It can mask out other sounds, preventing a person's ears from registering instructions and warnings.
- ☑ It can result in temporary hearing loss.
- ☑ Regular exposure to loud noise can cause damage to the ear and permanent loss of hearing.

There is also growing evidence that continued exposure to noise has consequential effects on some other illnesses.

## 13.7 Establishing noise levels

### 13.7.1 Measurement

The measurement of noise is a specialist activity. An individual's exposure depends not only on the level of noise, which will usually vary as different works start and stop, but also on the length of time during which they are exposed to noise.

The unit of measurement for sound levels (noise) is called a decibel (dB). This scale is logarithmic and means that 90 dB is ten times the intensity of 80 dB and one hundred times the intensity of 70 dB.

An increase of 3 dB doubles the energy in the sound. This means that, for example, 87 dB is actually twice as damaging as 84 dB, even though the 3 dB difference in sound level is difficult to perceive.

The various action values are meaningless to anyone who does not have a way of accurately calculating the noise levels on site, taking into account the time factor. There are, however, two rules of thumb that should give a rough indication of noise levels.

- ☑ **One-metre rule.** If two people standing one metre apart (about an arm's length), who are not wearing hearing protection, have to raise their voices to hear each other, the noise level is around or above 90 dB. Hearing protection must be worn to reduce the noise at the ear to below the exposure limit (ELV) or the noise reduced to the ELV by other means. Employers must identify why ELV has been breached and modify organisational and technical measures.
- ☑ **Two-metre rule.** If two people standing two metres apart (double arm's length) have to raise their voices to hear each other, the noise level is around 85 dB and hearing protection must be worn.

There is also a third rule that, if there is any doubt, everyone affected by the noise should be wearing hearing protection in the interests of their health.

Where there is likely to be a persistent noise problem, employers should arrange for noise surveys to be carried out across the whole scope of their operations.

**! These surveys must only be carried out by a competent person who has received proper training in noise measurement techniques and has the appropriate noise measuring equipment.**

Sound level meters, used for measuring noise levels, have standard filters built into them that attenuate or emphasise signals at different frequencies in order to simulate how the sound affects the ear. This is known as frequency weighting.

An instrument with a frequency weighting known as an 'A' weighted scale is commonly used on construction sites to measure noise from the working environment. Readings are expressed as dB(A).

Sudden impact noises (such as hammer blows) are measured in terms of maximum pressure. In this case measurements are 'C' weighted and therefore expressed as dB(C).

Noise meters vary considerably depending on type, size, complexity and cost, but even the inexpensive range will give a reasonable indication of noise levels being produced and priorities for action. Risk assessments should be based on measurements of the 'Leq', which is an average of the level of noise for the duration of the measurement.

**e.g.** 

### Sound levels

There is a lot of equipment that produces high levels of noise in the building and construction industry. Sound levels are measured in decibels (dB) and some typical examples include:

- electrical hand tool – 95 dB
- hammer drill – 102 dB
- circular bench saw – 107 dB
- bulldozer/grader – 121 dB.

**Employers have a duty to reduce the risk of damage to employees' hearing to the lowest level that is reasonably practicable. For further information on calculating personal noise exposure refer to Appendix D.**

## 13.7.2 Survey of noise levels

If it is necessary to resort to the measurement of noise, someone who is competent in evaluating the type of workplace, the use of the equipment and the interpretation of the results must be engaged. They must be able to draw valid conclusions from the information obtained and advise management on the actions needed to comply with the requirements of legislation.

The aim of the noise assessment is as follows.

- To identify workers who may be at risk of hearing damage to enable an action plan to be prepared to control the noise exposure.
- To determine the daily personal noise exposure (LEP,d) of workers (including times when not actually working (for example, rest areas) and from non-occupational sources, such as personal entertainment systems).
- To identify additional information to comply with legislation (for example, whether noise control measures or hearing protection are needed and, if so, where and what type).

The following are requirements of the employer.

- Keep a record of the noise assessments and the employees who are exposed to the noise.
- Regularly review those assessments. This should be done biannually or whenever it is considered that the assessment is no longer valid (for example, whenever there is new equipment or a change to the process that may alter noise levels).
- Use the assessment to develop an action plan for introducing noise control measures.
- Deal with the immediate risk by providing personal hearing protectors (this should only be until other controls have been investigated and implemented).
- Identify what steps are reasonably practicable to reduce the noise exposure of employees by engineering or other organisational means.
- Establish priorities for action and consider what changes may need to be phased in over the course of time.

Ideally, one person, with sufficient authority, will be given the responsibility for ensuring that the legislation is complied with and for co-ordinating and monitoring the noise reduction programme where necessary.

A points system has been developed by the Health and Safety Executive (HSE), which allows for quick estimates of the noise exposure for a worker. Each process is assigned a number of points per hour. Adding the points from each process carried out (calculated by multiplying the points per hour by the number of hours use) provides an estimate of the total exposure. The upper exposure action value corresponds to 100 points; the lower exposure action value corresponds to 32 points.

**!** **Training should cover the correct use of PPE, including how to communicate clearly whilst wearing it.**

| | SOUND INTENSITY RATIO | SOUND LEVEL IN dB(A) | SOUND SOURCE |
|---|---|---|---|
| | | | PAIN THRESHOLD |
| Harmful range | 100 000 000 000 000 | 140 | Jet engine |
| | 10 000 000 000 000 | 130 | Riveting hammer |
| | | | THRESHOLD OF FEELING |
| Critical zone | 1 000 000 000 000 | 120 | Propeller aircraft |
| | 100 000 000 000 | 110 | Rock drill |
| | 10 000 000 000 | 100 | Plate fabrication shop |
| | 1 000 000 000 | 90 | Heavy vehicle |
| Safe range | 100 000 000 | 80 | Very busy traffic |
| | 10 000 000 | 70 | Private car |
| | 1 000 000 | 60 | Ordinary conversation |
| | 100 000 | 50 | Quiet office |
| | 10 000 | 40 | Soft music from radio |
| | 1 000 | 30 | Quiet whisper |
| | 100 | 20 | Quiet urban dwelling |
| | 10 | 10 | Rustle of a leaf |
| | 1 | 0 | THRESHOLD OF HEARING |

*Typical sound intensities*

**For examples of sound levels of construction and piling equipment refer to Appendix E.**

## 13.8 Risk assessment

### 13.8.1 Action and limit values

The regulations specify the following three levels of exposure to noise, each of which requires that certain actions are taken.

- **Lower exposure action value.** This is reached when a daily or weekly personal exposure reaches 80 dB(A) or a peak sound pressure of 135 dB(C) occurs.
- **Upper exposure action value.** This is reached when a daily or weekly personal exposure reaches 85 dB(A) or a peak sound pressure of 137 dB(C) occurs.
- **Exposure limit value.** This is the maximum level of noise to which anyone at work may be exposed. It is set at 87 dB(A) at the ear, measured on a daily or weekly basis as appropriate or when a peak sound pressure of 140 dB(C) occurs.

If any employee is likely to be exposed to noise **at or above the lower exposure action value**, the employer must carry out a risk assessment, which may or may not result in the need for a competent person to measure the actual level of noise exposure.

### Assessing noise levels

Other methods of assessing noise levels should be used by employers before resorting to the actual measurement of noise levels. Any new tool or equipment that generates a potentially harmful level of noise should state the actual level of noise generated, either on the tool itself or in the accompanying documents. This can be useful in identifying potentially problematic tools, but it is important to remember that the actual noise experienced by the operator depends on many factors (such as the acoustics of the working environment, tool configuration and material being worked).

The most effective way of controlling exposure is to eliminate the source of noise, thereby removing the risk of damage to hearing. This is often not practical although sometimes a change of work process is possible.

Where noise elimination is not practical, there are several control techniques that might be applied. Which method is chosen will depend upon the nature of the equipment, the way in which it is used and the work environment.

### 13.8.2 Five stages to assessing risk

#### 13.8.2.1 Stage 1. Arrangements

Decide how the company intends to manage the risk of hearing damage. The arrangements can be used as a tool to help monitor and review safety performance, and ensure that it continues to control risks effectively.

The arrangements for dealing with noise risks should link with the overall health and safety policy.

Ask the following questions.

- ☑ **Purpose/aim.** What will the arrangements achieve? Will they prevent anyone being exposed to loud noise?
- ☑ **Scope.** Who do the arrangements affect?
- ☑ **Legal duties.** What are the legal duties specific to noise?
- ☑ **Objective(s) and targets.** What are the objectives and how can you measure progress? It is important to choose objectives and set sensible targets to measure progress and, where relevant, to specify and measure a baseline to assess how much progress has been made.
- ☑ **Risk control measures.** How can you encourage the workforce to work with you to reduce the risks?
- ☑ **Information and training.** How can you train and encourage your workforce to reduce the risks? Should you provide some incentives, formal training, toolbox talks, and/or on the job training?
- ☑ **Monitoring.** How will you check that the arrangements manage risk effectively? Is there any work that you particularly need to review and monitor? How and when will you monitor the health of those who are still exposed to a risk?
- ☑ **Audit and review.** When and how will you review the arrangements?

### 13.8.2.2 Stage 2. Assess health risks

The risk assessment is to help decide how to ensure the health and safety of workers who are exposed to noise. Requirements of the risk assessment are shown below.

- ☑ Identify where there might be a risk from noise.
- ☑ Clarify who is likely to be affected.
- ☑ Contain a reasonable estimate of your employees' exposures.
- ☑ Identify what you need to do to comply with the law (for example, whether additional control measures are needed and, if so, where and what).
- ☑ Identify any workers who need health surveillance.

It should be possible to do a basic risk assessment without the need for measurement. It will show whether exposures are likely to exceed the exposure action values and allow planning and prioritising of control actions effectively.

It is quite common for people to use the one and two metre rules *(refer to Measurement 13.7.1)* to indicate whether there is a potential noise problem. Alternatively, use manufacturers' noise data or have actual measurements taken as a basis for estimating exposures. A detailed exposure assessment may help with the following.

- ☑ Deciding which control actions might be most effective and practicable in reducing noise exposure.
- ☑ Clarifying whether exposures are likely to exceed the action or limit values.
- ☑ Checking whether controls are effective.

The regulations require that reasonably practicable steps are taken to control noise. In many cases you will not need a detailed assessment to identify which steps to take initially.

Exposure depends on a combination of noise level and exposure time. Be wary about just relying on self-reported estimates of exposure because these are unlikely to be accurate. Observe the work; it is just as easy to over as well as underestimate exposure. Take account of background noise that may add to your workers' exposures (for example, construction work near a high-speed road).

It may be useful to observe work, measure the exposure time over part of a day and then use the information to estimate exposure for a full shift. If an employee is exposed to noise from more than one tool or work process during a typical day, you will need to collect information about the likely noise level(s) and exposure time for each source.

www.

**The HSE has provided noise calculators to help work out the daily and weekly noise exposure, and estimate the performance of hearing protection.**

Once the relevant noise data and exposure times have been collected it may be helpful to use an exposure calculator to assess each employee's daily exposure.

The Supply of Machinery (Safety) Regulations require manufacturers and suppliers to design equipment that will minimise noise risks. Equipment should be CE marked to show that it complies with these requirements, and health and safety information should feature in the instructions that are supplied with a machine. This should include the following.

- ☑ Information on safe use and, where necessary, training requirements.
- ☑ Information on how to maintain the equipment.
- ☑ A statement of the noise emission (where the equipment noise level exceeds 70 dB at the operator position), together with information on the test method.

Manufacturers' information can indicate whether further assessment and action might be required. However, general data is unlikely to fully represent the actual conditions of use.

### Buy quiet

The HSE has launched an initiative called *Buy quiet*. It aims to help manufacturers, importers, suppliers and users of equipment to work together to reduce the risk of noise-induced hearing loss in the workplace.

It supports users in their duty to avoid high noise equipment when suitable lower noise equipment is available. It also supports manufacturers in their duty to minimise noise by technical means.

- ☑ *Buy quiet* to reduce noise in your workplace.
- ☑ *Buy quiet* for a simple, common sense process that will help you to protect your workforce from noise risks.
- ☑ *Buy quiet* and there are likely to be significant cost benefits over time.
- ☑ *Buy quiet* and you will be helping to stimulate manufacturers to develop lower-noise machinery.

**For further information on the *Buy quiet* initiative refer to the HSE website.**

### 13.8.2.3 Stage 3. Eliminate risk

The purpose of the Control of Noise at Work Regulations is to make sure that people don't suffer damage to their health from noise – so controlling the risks from exposure to noise should be where you concentrate your efforts.

Clients and designers can have a big influence over eliminating noise risks on site (for example, by specifying prefabricated components or work methods that avoid the need for noisy tools and processes).

Where noise exposures are below the lower exposure action value (LEAV) 80 dB, the risk of damage to health is generally lower and so will only be expected to take actions that are simple and inexpensive.

Where the assessment shows that employees are likely to be exposed at or above the exposure action values, a planned programme of noise control must be implemented. It is rarely acceptable just to rely on hearing protection alone, except as a short-term measure.

**Refer to the HSE website for a case study relating to hearing damage.**

- ☑ Look for alternative work methods that eliminate or reduce exposure to noise. Trade associations, industry contacts, equipment suppliers and trade journals may help to identify good practice.
- ☑ Mechanise or automate work so that the operator is removed from the noisy environment (such as excavator cab).
- ☑ Make sure that equipment is suitable and can do the work efficiently. Equipment that is unsuitable, too small or not powerful enough is likely to take longer to complete the task and increase exposure to noise.
- ☑ Select tools that produce the least noise.
- ☑ Limit the use of high-noise tools wherever possible.

### Ways to reduce noise and vibration

- ☑ To cut large holes in brickwork, use a diamond-tipped hole-cutter with a rotary action rather than a tungsten-tipped bit, which requires rotary and hammer action. This reduces both vibration and noise exposure.
- ☑ Use vibration-dampened stone-cutting saw blades. Construction processes that lead to high levels of hand-arm vibration are often high-noise processes too.

When work equipment gets damaged or worn seek replacement kit that is suitable for the work, as well as being quiet and efficient. Ensure that your purchaser specifies low noise and vibration equipment.

**Refer to the HSE website for good practice relating to low noise machines.**

### 13.8.2.4 Stage 4. Control risk

Power tools and other work equipment should be serviced and maintained in accordance with manufacturers' instructions and maintenance schedules. This should help to prevent unnecessarily high noise levels and ensure efficient operation. Maintenance includes:

- ☑ keeping cutting tools sharp
- ☑ correctly dressing abrasive wheels
- ☑ replacing worn parts

- carrying out balance checks and corrections as necessary
- checking and replacing defective vibration dampers, bearings and gears
- sharpening chainsaw teeth and keeping the correct chain tension
- tuning and adjusting engines.

#### 13.8.2.5 Stage 5. Manage remaining risk

You can manage any remaining health risks by using a range of measures (such as PPE, information, health surveillance and routine monitoring).

For work schedules, job rotation can be used to share a noise exposure between several people. Some examples are shown below.

- Limit the time that each worker is exposed to noise.
- Where tools require continual or frequent use, introduce rotas to limit individual exposure times.
- Weekly averaging may be used to ensure that exposures are managed; include quiet days in the rotas.

Effective job rotation is more complex if workers use more than one tool or process that involves a noise exposure.

There are generally two types of hearing protection available: ear defenders or muffs, and earplugs – and there is plenty of choice. Different products may not offer the same level of protection so, when purchasing PPE, check the product information for details.

Workers need to understand the risks of noise exposure. Where workers are exposed above the lower exposure action values the following should be explained.

- The likely noise exposure and the risk that this creates.
- What you are doing to control risks and exposures.
- Where and how people can obtain hearing protection.
- How to report defective noise control equipment and hearing protection.
- What their duties are under the Control of Noise at Work Regulations.
- What they should do to minimise the risk (such as the proper way to use noise control equipment and hearing protection, storage and maintenance).
- Health checks and surveillance.

**Further information can be found online in the HSE publication *Noise. Don't lose your hearing!***

Working with safety representatives and employees' representatives is a useful way to communicate about health and safety. For example, discuss the risk assessment and action plan, including any proposal to average exposure over a week, selection of hearing protection, any hearing protection zones and the health surveillance programme.

**Involving employees in decisions can help improve working relationships, make employees more receptive to new ideas and help control exposure to noise.**

## 13.9 Avoiding exposure to noise

### 13.9.1 Planning against excess noise levels

Attention should be given at the planning stage to developing a noise control strategy that considers the following.

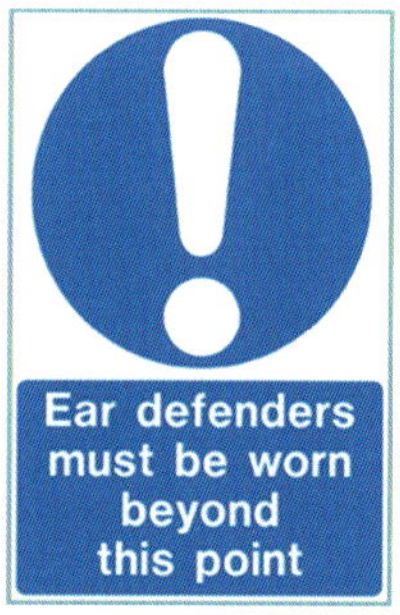


- Design of the project and of the processes and equipment that will be involved.
- Phasing of differing operations, especially if a number of contractors are working on site.
- Requirements of the Local Authority.
- Location of the site; or sites if the project involves more than one location.
- Noise levels that are likely to be produced by the work being carried out.
- Layout of the site, including the siting of access points, batching plants, and so on.
- Hours of working that are planned (or perhaps limited by the Local Authority).
- Provisions available for controlling noise on site.
- Possibility of disturbance to nearby residents and properties (if this is likely, the situation and measures to be taken to reduce noise should be explained to persons likely to be affected).

Failure to plan the control of noise may lead to delay and increased cost later. Where appropriate, noise levels must be a consideration for designers under the CDM Regulations.

Attention should be given to the Local Authority powers under the Environmental Protection Act, which deal with noise as a statutory nuisance, and the Control of Pollution Act, which relate particularly to work on construction sites.

## 13.9.2 Managing noise levels during construction

Exposure to noise can be eliminated or reduced by the following methods.

- ☑ Controlling noise at source.
- ☑ Employing engineering controls where possible.
- ☑ Using a purchasing/hire policy for plant, equipment and tools that takes noise into account.
- ☑ Introducing alternative methods and processes that eliminate or reduce noise levels.
- ☑ Giving consideration to the careful siting of noisy plant and equipment.
- ☑ Where practical, storing bulk materials to form an acoustic screen.
- ☑ Carrying out job rotation for employees to reduce exposure to noise.
- ☑ Providing rest rooms or acoustic refuges for staff during breaks from work.
- ☑ Rearranging work locations for staff, if possible, away from noisy equipment.
- ☑ As a last resort, providing personal hearing protectors.

## 13.9.3 Control of noise at source

Controlling the noise at its source can be achieved by a variety of means.

- ☑ The design and manufacture of the equipment.
- ☑ The use of acoustic covers and exhaust silencers for equipment.
- ☑ The use of alternative, less noisy equipment or methods of working.
- ☑ Enclosing noisy equipment within temporary structures.
- ☑ Regular inspection and maintenance of the equipment being used.
- ☑ Fitting noise-absorbent mountings to reduce the transmission of noise through adjacent structures.

**For an example of how sound levels vary with distance from source refer to Appendix C.**

## 13.9.4 Engineering controls

Measures that can be taken include ensuring that all equipment, which has the potential to create excessive noise, is well maintained, kept in good order, including ensuring that there are no loose panels or casing and that exhaust mufflers are in good condition, and not left running when it is not actually in use.

## 13.9.5 Siting or location

Effective siting or location includes:

- ☑ removing the source of the noise to a distance whenever possible
- ☑ orientating plant to direct the noise away from the work area
- ☑ placing site buildings, stores, and so on between the noise source and noise sensitive areas
- ☑ screening the noise source with a barrier, wall, acoustic screen, spoil heap, or by locating the source behind partly completed buildings.

The effectiveness of a noise barrier will depend on its dimensions, its position relative to the source and the listener, and the material used in the construction of the barrier. Care must be taken to ensure that barriers do not, by reflecting sound, transfer the noise nuisance from one sensitive area to another and so create a health problem for someone else.

## 13.9.6 Demolition

Where demolition operations are carried out in locations likely to affect the general public, the Local Authority may request the contractor to submit an application under Section 61 *Prior consent* of the Control of Pollution Act (COPA). It allows developers and contractors to apply for a prior consent for noise generating activities during the construction phase of a development. A prior consent will not be issued if construction, including demolition work (other than minor preparatory or enabling work agreed in advance) has already commenced. If work has started then the Local Authority is likely to serve a Section 60 notice setting out their own terms and conditions.

In accordance with the Control of Noise at Work Regulations, where noise levels are above (or expected to be above) the lower exposure action value, the demolition contractor must ensure that a noise assessment has been carried out and that, where possible, people are kept out of the danger area.

Any machinery that is to be used in the demolition process should, as far as possible, be fitted and used with soundproofing equipment (for example exhaust silencers). Generators, particularly those powering cabins outside of working hours, should be super silent or sited within a noise enclosure.

Where it is necessary for people to work within the area of noisy operations, adequate hearing protection must be provided and used as necessary. If the upper exposure action value is exceeded, or likely to be exceeded, hearing protection must be worn and hearing protection zones clearly indicated.

Where the findings of a risk assessment indicate that the hearing of any employee is at risk due to noise exposure at work, health surveillance, including hearing checks, must be provided.

**The most significant number of complaints regarding noise arise during out of hours working. Local Authority by laws must be adhered to. Failure to do so is an offence and will cost time, money and loss of reputation.**

## 13.10 Personal hearing protectors

All hearing protectors produced or imported by reputable companies are manufactured to British and European Standards. As with all PPE for use at work, ear protectors should be selected by a competent person who can ensure, in discussion with the supplier, that it possesses the necessary performance characteristics. Most leading manufacturers and suppliers will offer their own advisory service.

- Personal hearing protectors must be provided on an individual basis.
- A competent person must be responsible for any training that may be necessary in the correct use of personal hearing protectors.
- Personal hearing protectors should normally be provided as an interim measure while more effective and permanent methods of control are sought.
- Employees must be trained in the use, care and storage of ear protectors.
- Ear protectors must be suited to the user, suitable for the type of noise and provide an effective seal.
- They should be stored in a clean place when not in use, unless disposable.
- They should be inspected regularly for deterioration or damage and replaced when necessary, unless disposable.
- Personal hearing protectors should not over protect, whereby users can become isolated from their work environment and be unable to hear warnings.

**PPE cannot be used for long-term noise risk management.**

Competence in the selection of this type of PPE is particularly important, as ear protectors that give good protection against noise at a high frequency may not offer very much protection against low frequency noise, and vice versa.

All reasonably practicable methods must be used to reduce noise levels, but where these remain at or above the upper exposure action value, after control measures have been implemented, ear protectors must be made available and worn. Ear protectors are not a substitute for other methods of noise control; they are an absolute last resort.

Employees may initially be reluctant to wear ear protection, and those who are at risk must be made aware of the potential for hearing loss that can be caused by exposure to excessive noise levels.

**Comfort, motivation and supervision are the paramount factors that determine the wear rate and therefore the protection that is achieved in practice.**

**A check should be made to ensure that hazard warning signals are audible to individuals wearing ear protectors, and the volume, tone, or method of signalling changed if necessary.**

### 13.10.1 Types of personal hearing protectors

The two basic types of protector are earplugs and ear defenders.

#### 13.10.1.1 Earplugs

**Disposable earplugs** are made of very fine mineral fibre or foam, sometimes ready shaped. They must be inserted correctly and, if taken out, should not be reused. They should only be handled with clean hands.

**Reusable earplugs** are made of rubber or plastic, and need regular, careful washing. The initial supply and fitting should be carried out by trained persons. Different sizes may be required for each ear and must be a good fit. They must be fitted with clean hands as any contamination by dirt, grease or swarf may cause ear irritation. Earplugs are therefore unsuitable on site for intermittent use (such as can occur when operating a breaker).

*Disposable earplugs*

*Reusable earplugs*

#### 13.10.1.2 Ear defenders

Ear defenders (or muffs) completely cover the ear and are sealed to the head with a foam or liquid-filled seal. Badly designed or badly produced defenders may give little or no protection against noise. Other points are listed below.

- ☑ Pressure from the seal may cause wearers to complain of tightness, but loose defenders lose most of their protective capability and are ineffective.
- ☑ Damage and deterioration to seals also results in ineffectiveness and loss of protection.
- ☑ In fitting, account needs to be taken of people with different sized or shaped heads or ears, hair styles and spectacles.
- ☑ Facial hair and the arms of spectacles may interfere with the seal on ear defenders.
- ☑ Defenders fitted to safety helmets may cause problems by not fitting tightly to the ear, or by moving as the helmet moves.
- ☑ Defenders must be chosen to deal with a particular noise problem; ones that offer protection against low frequency sound may be ineffective at high frequency, and vice versa.

Ear defenders that incorporate a sound enhancement system are available. When noise levels are low, sound detected by a microphone is replayed to the wearer enabling them to communicate normally. When noise levels are high, the sound replay system is automatically cut, such that the defenders act as regular ear protectors. Such products are particularly suitable for those exposed to unpredictable, short bursts of noise.

Ear protectors are only effective while they are being used. If protectors are worn for only half the shift, only some 10% protection is gained; if worn for 7¾ out of eight hours, the protection factor is still only 75%.

**For information on the differences between exposure levels refer to Appendix B.**

B
13

## Appendix A – Summary of the Noise at Work Regulations

A summary of legal requirements can be found in the table below.

**For further details on the regulations and guidance refer to the HSE website.**

| Employers' duties | Exposure below the lower exposure action value of 80 dB(A) | Exposure at or above the lower exposure action value of 80 dB(A) or peak sound pressure of 135 dB(C) | Exposure at or above the upper exposure action value of 85 dB(A) or peak sound pressure of 137 dB(C) | Exposure at or above the exposure limit value of 87 dB(A) or peak sound pressure of 140 dB(C) |
|---|---|---|---|---|
| **Assessment of noise exposure**<br>▪ Risk assessment to be carried out and reviewed as necessary. | | ✔ | ✔ | ✔ |
| ▪ Record of significant findings and control measures put in place. | | ✔ | ✔ | ✔ |
| ▪ Risk assessment to include extra considerations in higher risk situations. | | | ✔ | ✔ |
| **General duty to reduce risk**<br>▪ Risk of hearing damage to be eliminated or reduced to the lowest level reasonably practicable. | | ✔ | ✔ | ✔ |
| ▪ Implement organisational and technical control measures, excluding issue of personal hearing protection. | | | ✔ | ✔ |
| ▪ Reduce exposure below exposure limit value (ELV), if ELV breached, identify why and modify organisational and technical measures. | | | | ✔ |
| ▪ Ensure noise exposure in rest facilities is kept to acceptable level. | | ✔ | ✔ | ✔ |
| ▪ Adapt control measures as necessary to take account of employee(s) who may be particularly at risk from exposure to noise. | | ✔ | ✔ | ✔ |
| ▪ Consult with employees or their representatives on protective measures taken. | | ✔ | ✔ | ✔ |
| **Provision of hearing protection**<br>Ensure that personal hearing protectors are:<br>▪ provided to employees who ask for them | | ✔ | | |
| ▪ provided to all those exposed | | | ✔ | ✔ |
| ▪ used by all those exposed. | | | ✔ | ✔ |
| Create hearing protection zones, designated by appropriate signs and:<br>▪ restrict access if justified by the level of risk | | | ✔ | ✔ |
| ▪ ensure as far as is reasonably practicable that all who go into a marked hearing protection zone use hearing protection. | | | ✔ | ✔ |
| **Maintenance and use of equipment**<br>Ensure so far as is reasonably practicable that:<br>▪ all equipment provided under the regulations, except personal hearing protectors, are fully and properly used | | | ✔ | ✔ |
| ▪ all equipment is maintained in an efficient state and good working order. | ✔ | ✔ | ✔ | ✔ |

| Employers' duties | Exposure below the lower exposure action value of 80 dB(A) | Exposure at or above the lower exposure action value of 80 dB(A) or peak sound pressure of 135 dB(C) | Exposure at or above the upper exposure action value of 85 dB(A) or peak sound pressure of 137 dB(C) | Exposure at or above the exposure limit value of 87 dB(A) or peak sound pressure of 140 dB(C) |
|---|---|---|---|---|
| **Information instruction and training**<br>Provide adequate information, instruction and training and update it as necessary, on: | | | | |
| ■ the nature of the risks to hearing from noise | | ✔ | ✔ | ✔ |
| ■ the organisational and technical measures taken | | ✔ | ✔ | ✔ |
| ■ the action and limit values | | ✔ | ✔ | ✔ |
| ■ the significant findings of the risk assessment | | ✔ | ✔ | ✔ |
| ■ how to obtain a personal hearing protector | | ✔ | ✔ | ✔ |
| ■ how to detect and report signs of hearing damage | | ✔ | ✔ | ✔ |
| ■ the entitlement to health surveillance | | ✔ | ✔ | ✔ |
| ■ the results of any **collective** health surveillance. | | ✔ | ✔ | ✔ |
| Provide information, instruction and training for anyone who has responsibilities for ensuring the employer's legal duties are carried out. | | ✔ | ✔ | ✔ |
| **Health surveillance**<br>Provide as appropriate if the risk assessment indicates there to be a risk to employees' health resulting from noise at work. | | ✔ | ✔ | ✔ |
| Keep and maintain records of health surveillance and enable employees access to their own health surveillance records and allow the HSE to access records as necessary. | | ✔ | ✔ | ✔ |
| Where employees are found to have hearing damage:<br>■ ensure the employee is informed by a suitably qualified person | | ✔ | ✔ | ✔ |
| ■ review the risk assessment and control measures | | ✔ | ✔ | ✔ |
| ■ consider assigning the employee to alternative (non-noisy) work | | ✔ | ✔ | ✔ |
| ■ continue with health surveillance. | | ✔ | ✔ | ✔ |
| **Employees' duties** | | | | |
| **Use of equipment**<br>Employees must:<br>■ make full and proper use of personal hearing protectors | | | ✔ | ✔ |
| ■ use any other control measures provided by the employer | | ✔ | ✔ | ✔ |
| ■ report any defects discovered in the protective measures to the employer. | ✔ | ✔ | ✔ | ✔ |
| **Health surveillance**<br>Attend health surveillance procedures as required by the employer in working hours and at the employer's expense. | | ✔ | ✔ | ✔ |

## Appendix B – Exposure levels

### The effect on maximum working times due to exposure without protection

| Average noise level dB(A) | Maximum exposure in one working day if 80 dB(A) (LEP,d) is not exceeded |
|---|---|
| 80 | 8 hours |
| 83 | 4 hours |
| 86 | 2 hours |
| 89 | 1 hour |
| 92 | 30 minutes |
| 95 | 15 minutes |
| 98 | 7.5 minutes |
| 101 | 3.75 minutes |

### Increase of protection gained in relation to time if ear protectors are worn

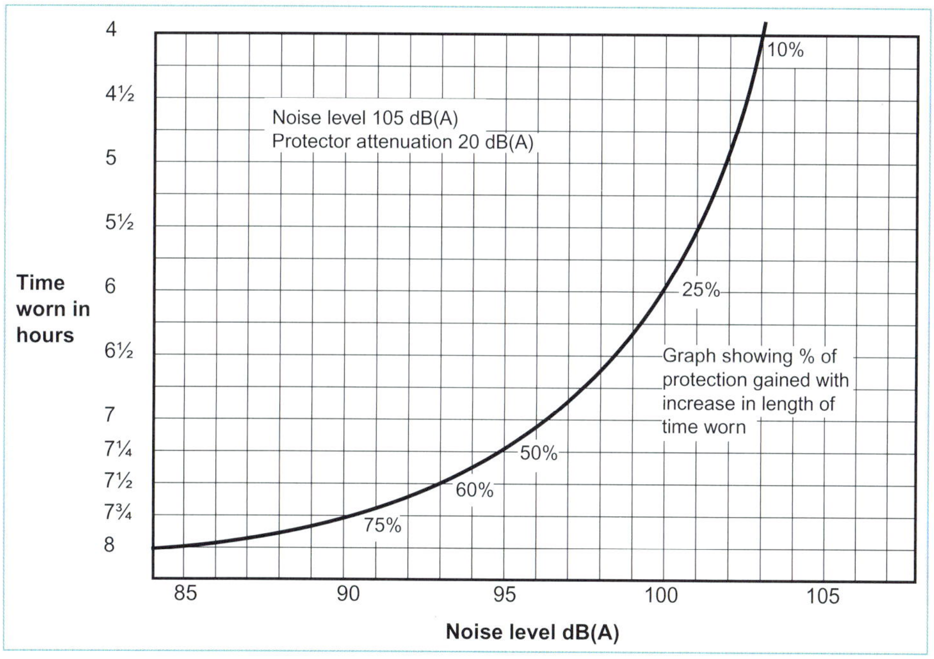


B 13

## Appendix C – Sound levels

### How sound levels vary with distance from source

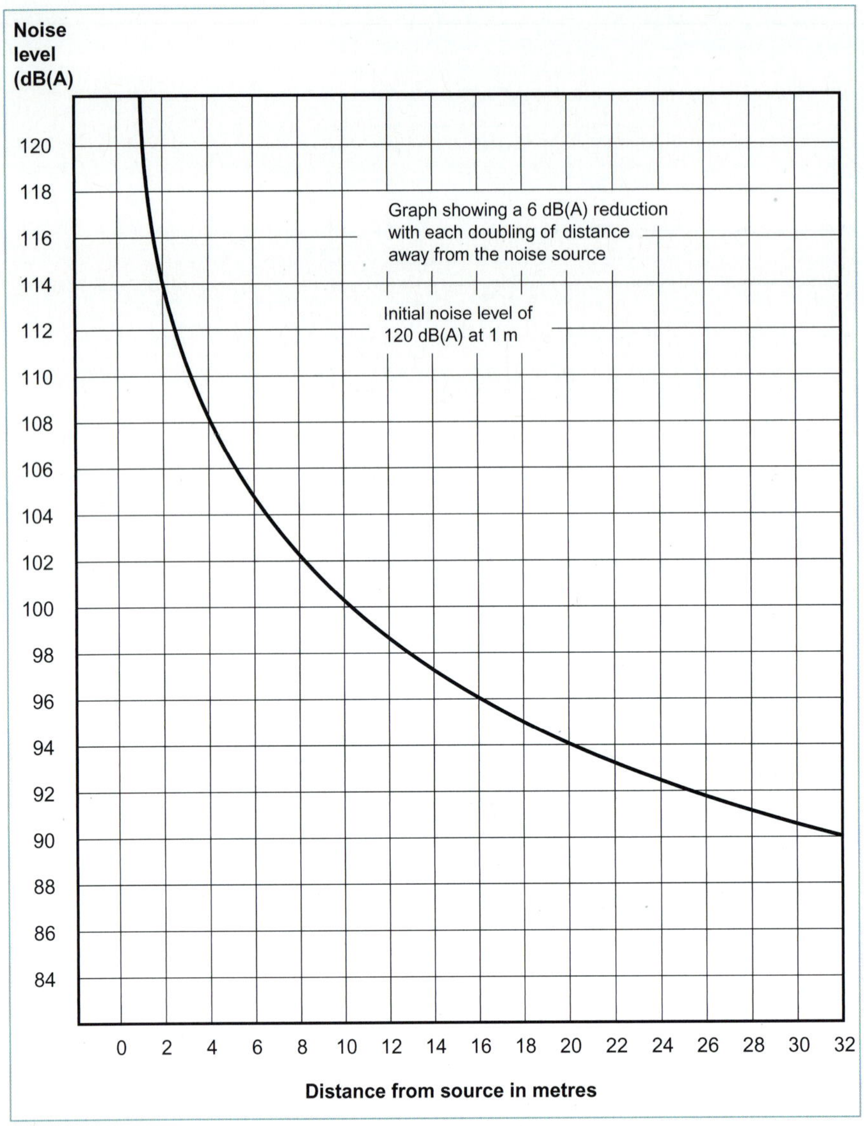

## Appendix D – Calculating personal noise exposure

**Two personal exposure calculators are available on the HSE website.**

Microsoft Excel is required to use these calculators, which enable users to calculate the daily or weekly exposure of individuals to noise. An on-site measurement of sound pressure (noise) must first be taken, which requires specialist knowledge and equipment. The daily noise exposure calculator enables an individual's exposure to noise to be apportioned across up to eight different tasks carried out within any one day, each with different levels of exposure.

A third calculator on the same web page enables users to establish the protection factor required in any hearing protection that they provide. In this case, by knowing the noise levels within the workplace and the protection information on the hearing protection, its suitability can be determined.

Two noise exposure ready reckoners (for daily or weekly exposure) can be accessed through the same web page (Adobe Acrobat required). The noise level on site must again be known.

### Exposure calculator

| Job/task | Noise level ($L_{Aeq}$ dB) | Exposure duration (hours) | Exposure points (job/task) | Exposure points per hour |
|---|---|---|---|---|
| 1. | | | | |
| 2. | | | | |
| 3. | | | | |
| 4. | | | | |
| 5. | | | | |
| 6. | | | | |
| 7. | | | | |
| 8. | | | | |
| | Total duration | | | |
| | Daily noise exposure ($L_{EP,d}$) | | | |

**Exposure points can be used to prioritise noise control. The highest exposure points are given by the jobs and tasks, which make the greatest contributions to daily noise exposure. Therefore, tackling these noise exposures will have the greatest effect on daily noise exposure.**

### Instructions for exposure calculator

Enter the $L_{Aeq}$ (in dB) and select the daily exposure duration (in hours) in the white areas for up to eight jobs or tasks carried out by a person during their working day.

Rounding noise levels to the nearest decibel and durations to the nearest 15 minutes (0.25 hours) is sufficiently precise.

Exposure points will appear for each entry and the overall daily personal noise exposure ($L_{EP,d}$) will be displayed.

The lower exposure action value (an $L_{EP,d}$ of 80 dB) is represented by 32 exposure points, the upper exposure action value ($L_{EP,d}$ of 85 dB) by 100 points.

## Appendix E – Some typical sound levels of construction and piling equipment

(Levels given are average at source).

| Sound level dB(A) | Construction equipment | Piling equipment |
|---|---|---|
| 95 | Hand tools – electric | |
| 100 | Hand tools – air | |
| 101 | Forklifts | |
| 102 | Hammer drill | |
| 103 | Dumpers | |
| 104 | Concrete mixer | |
| 105 | Hand tools – petrol | |
| 106 | Tower cranes | |
| 107 | Circular bench saw | |
| 108 | Trucks | |
| 109 | Excavators | 6 tonne drop hammer (cased piles) |
| 110 | Crawler cranes | |
| 111 | Heavy lorries | |
| 112 | Ready mix | |
| 113 | Hoists – diesel | |
| 114 | Loading shovel | |
| 115 | Rock drill | |
| 116 | Batching plant | Trench hammer (sheet piles) |
| 117 | Generators | Rotary bored piles |
| 118 | Loaders | Screen drop hammer (sheet piles) |
| 119 | Cranes – lorry mounted | |
| 120 | Compressors – compactors | Impact boring (driving case method) |
| 121 | Bulldozers – graders | 2 tonne drop hammer (pre-cast concrete piles) |
| 125 | | Vibration system (sheet piles) |
| 126 | | Resonant system 'h' section |
| 128 | | Single acting air hammer (pre-cast concrete) |
| 136 | | Diesel hammer (sheet piles) |
| 138 | | Double acting air hammer (sheet piles) |

These sound levels are for guidance only. Information should be sought from the manufacturer or the plant hire company regarding machines on site.

By virtue of Section 6 of the Health and Safety at Work Act 1974, manufacturers and suppliers are required to provide information about the noise levels generated by the equipment made or supplied if the noise level is at or above the first action level or peak action level.

Noise levels emitted from the machines will be affected by the competence of the operator and the quality of maintenance.

For accurate measurement of site noise, a survey is necessary. GB04 Hearing protection selection

# Appendix F – Hearing protection selection

## Types of personal hearing protectors

**Disposable earplugs** should be discarded after each use.

**Reusable earplugs** should be washed in warm, soapy water and thoroughly dried before reuse.

**Ear defenders** (or muffs) completely cover the ear and are sealed to the head with a foam or liquid-filled seal. Badly designed, badly produced or poor fitting defenders may give little or no protection against noise.

## Standards for hearing protection

Personal hearing protection must be CE marked showing it meets the relevant European Standard BS EN 352.

| **EN 352-1** – Hearing protectors – earmuffs |
|---|
| In addition to the standard number, maker and model identification:<br>■ indication of orientation of the earmuff, where required (for example 'TOP' and/or 'LEFT' and 'RIGHT'). |
| **EN 352-2** – Hearing protectors – earplugs |
| Markings may only appear on the packaging. In addition to the Standard number, maker and model identification:<br>■ whether disposable or re-useable<br>■ fitting instructions<br>■ nominal size of formable plugs, in range 5 to 14 mm<br>■ left-right differentiation for custom moulded plugs. |
| **EN 352-3** – Hearing protectors – earmuffs attached to an industrial safety helmet |
| ■ As for EN 352-1. |
| **EN 352-4** – Hearing protectors – level-dependent earmuffs |
| ■ As for EN 352-1. |
| **EN 352-5** – Hearing protectors – active noise reduction earmuffs |
| ■ As for EN 352-1. |
| **EN 352-6** – Hearing protectors – earmuffs with electrical audio input |
| ■ As for EN 352-1. |
| **EN 352-7** – Hearing protectors – level dependent earplugs |
| ■ As for EN 352-2. |
| **EN 352-8** – Hearing protectors – entertainment audio earmuffs |
| ■ As for EN 352-1. |

### e.g. Selection of hearing protection

In order to select the correct type of hearing protection you need to know the noise level on site and be able to select the right type of hearing protection required to reduce the noise exposure to a safe level (which is below 80 dB).

For example, 100 dB would need to be reduced by 20 dB to bring it to 80 dB. This reduction is known as attenuation or single noise reduction (SNR) and this value is shown on manufacturers' products.

The HSE recommends providing hearing protectors that perform 4 dB better than the required minimum, in order to take into account real world factors (such as poor fitting). This means that to protect the worker against 100 dB of noise, you need to select hearing protection with attenuation or SNR of 24 dB.

Personal hearing protectors should not over-protect, whereby users can become isolated from their work environment and be unable to hear warnings, reversing vehicles, and so on.

The optimum value with hearing protection is between 70 dB and 80 dB. Thus, in this example, select hearing protection with an attenuation or SNR of between 24 dB and 34 dB.

B
13

# 14
# Vibration

**Contents**



## Supporting information

**G: Checklists and forms**



**GT 700 Toolbox talks**

## Overview

**A considerable number of the tools and other pieces of equipment that are currently used in the building and construction industry have a rotary or percussive action and therefore have the potential to cause hand-arm vibration. The seriousness of the situation will depend largely on how frequently and for how long vibrating tools are used although other factors contribute to the potential for ill health.**

**This even applies to some widely used small tools (such as hand drills) that have a hammer action. Other examples of tools that create vibration include pneumatic breakers, vibrating pokers, vibrating rollers, plate compactors and scabbling.**

## 14.1 Introduction

The control of vibration at work makes good business sense for employers. Employees who are able to work are of far greater benefit to the employer than those who are off sick as a result of work-related ill health, or those who cannot work to maximum effect due to ill health sustained as a result of using vibrating tools and equipment incorrectly or for too long (for example, hand-arm vibration syndrome (HAVS), vibration white finger (VWF) or whole-body vibration (WBV)).

## 14.2 Important points

- ☑ Exposure to hand-arm vibration has the potential to cause disabling injuries.
- ☑ WBV can cause severe back pain.
- ☑ Employers have a legal duty to reduce the risks to the health of employees by either eliminating exposure to vibration or reducing it to an acceptable level.
- ☑ Employers have various means at their disposal of estimating exposure to vibration before resorting to having measurements carried out.
- ☑ If it is necessary to have vibration measurements taken, it is essential that the person doing so is trained and competent.

Some of the things that can be done to control the potentially harmful effects of exposure to hand-arm vibration are listed below.

- ☑ Adopting alternative (non-vibrational) work methods.
- ☑ Ensuring that tools are either low-vibration by design and/or well-maintained.
- ☑ Adapting work patterns.
- ☑ Ensuring that ergonomic factors are taken into account.
- ☑ Preventing those person(s) exposed to vibration from becoming cold and/or damp.
- ☑ Training workers how to minimise the risks from vibration.

## 14.3 Control of Vibration at Work Regulations

The Control of Vibration at Work Regulations came into force in July 2005 and implement the requirements of the European Directive regarding the exposure of employees to vibration. They impose duties on employers to protect employees (and others) who may be exposed to the risk of ill health because of vibration at work.

The vibration regulations are, in places, very technical, particularly in relation to the measurement of vibration. It is anticipated that the services of a qualified technician or occupational health professional may be needed in those sectors of the industry where the measurement of vibration is a significant issue.

The regulations place legal duties on employers and employees with regard to the control and management of employees' exposure to vibration.

## Definitions

The regulations give a number of definitions, knowledge of which will help readers better understand the requirements of the regulations.

**Hand-arm vibration (HAV)** means mechanical vibration that is transmitted into the hands and arms by a work activity.

**Whole-body vibration (WBV)** means mechanical vibration that is transmitted into the body through the supporting surface when a person is seated or standing during a work activity.

**Mechanical vibration** means vibration occurring in a piece of machinery, equipment or vehicle as a result of its operation.

**Daily exposure** means the extent of the mechanical vibration to which a worker is exposed during a working day, which takes account of both the magnitude and duration of the vibration.

**Exposure action value (EAV)** means the level of daily exposure that, if exceeded, requires specific action to be taken to reduce the risk.

**Exposure limit value (ELV)** means the level of daily exposure for any worker that must not be exceeded.

**Working day** means a daily working period, irrespective of the time of day, when it begins or ends, or whether it begins or ends on the same day.

**Health surveillance** means an assessment of the state of health of an employee as related to their exposure to vibration.

## 14.3.1 Exposure limit and action values

The regulations introduce action and limit values for hand-arm and whole-body vibration.

### 14.3.1.1 Hand-arm vibration

- The **daily exposure action value** is 2.5 metres per second squared (2.5 $m/s^2$ A(8)), at which level employers should introduce technical and organisational measures to reduce exposure.
- The **daily exposure limit value** is 5 metres per second squared (5 $m/s^2$ A(8)), which should not be exceeded.

### 14.3.1.2 Whole-body vibration

- The **daily exposure action value** is 0.5 metres per second squared (0.5 $m/s^2$ A(8)).
- The **daily exposure limit value** is 1.15 metres per second squared (1.15 $m/s^2$ A(8)).

**The 'A(8)' notation after each value indicates that the measurement of exposure to vibration is time weighted over an eight-hour period.**

**The regulations allowed for a transitional period for the exposure limit value for hand-arm vibration until 2013. This allowed for work activities, where older tools and machinery were being used, which could not keep exposures below the exposure limit value. This period has now expired.**

## 14.3.2 Employers' duties to non-employees

**Further information on duties of employers can be found in the flowchart at Appendix B.**

Where these regulations place a duty on employers with respect to the health and safety of employees, the employer shall, so far as is reasonably practicable, also be under a similar duty to **anyone else, whether at work or not,** who may be affected by the vibration created by the employer's work. This is applicable, except for the provision of health surveillance, and information, instruction and training (unless the non-employees are at the same place of work as where the noise is being created).

## 14.3.3 Employers' duties to employees

If employees are likely to be exposed to risks from vibration in the course of their work the employer must ensure the following.

- ☑ An assessment of the risks to the health and safety of the employees exposed to vibration is carried out. The risk assessment must identify the measures that need to be taken to meet the requirements of these regulations.
- ☑ As part of the risk assessment, the daily exposure of employees to vibration is assessed by:
  - observing work practices
  - referring to information on the probable level of vibration corresponding to the equipment used in those particular conditions
  - if necessary, arranging for vibration levels to be measured.
- ☑ Assess whether any employee is likely to be exposed to vibration at or above the **exposure action value** or the **exposure limit value.**
- ☑ Ensure that exposure to vibration is eliminated at source or reduce it to the lowest level that is reasonably practicable.
- ☑ Where exposure is likely to be at or above the exposure action value, reduce exposure to vibration to as low a level as is reasonably practicable, by implementing organisational and technical measures that are appropriate to the work activity being carried out.
- ☑ Ensure that the actions taken to comply with the above two requirements are based upon the principles of prevention set out in the Management of Health and Safety at Work Regulations and must include consideration of:
  - alternative work methods that eliminate or reduce exposure to vibration
  - alternative work equipment or an appropriate ergonomic design which, taking account of the work to be done, produces the least vibration
  - the design and layout of the workplace, including any rest facilities
  - the provision of extra equipment that has the effect of reducing injuries caused by exposure to vibration
  - the effective maintenance programmes for equipment that can create vibration, the workplace itself and workplace systems
  - the provision of information and training for at-risk employees, such that they are aware of how to use work equipment correctly and safely in order to minimise exposure
  - limiting the duration and intensity of exposure to vibration
  - adjusting work schedules and ensuring adequate rest periods
  - the provision of work clothing to protect at-risk employees from cold and damp.

### 14.3.3.1 Risk assessment considerations

- ☑ The magnitude, type and duration of exposure to vibration, including intermittent vibration and repeated shocks.
- ☑ The effects that the vibration might have on employees whose health is particularly at risk from exposure.
- ☑ Any effects that vibration might have with regard to work equipment, such as the:
  - proper handling of controls
  - reading of indicators
  - stability of structures
  - security of joints.
- ☑ Any information provided by the manufacturers of the equipment that creates the vibration.
- ☑ The availability of alternative equipment that is designed to reduce exposure to vibration.
- ☑ Exposure of employees to WBV when not actually working (such as in rest areas and canteens).
- ☑ Specific working conditions (such as working in low temperatures).
- ☑ The availability of appropriate information obtained from health surveillance including, where possible, published information (such as various HSE publications).

The employer must regularly review the risk assessment if there is reason to believe that it is no longer valid or there has been a significant change in the work to which the assessment applies, in which case immediately implement changes to the risk assessment as identified by the review process.

Where the risk assessment shows a risk to the health of employees who are (or are liable to be) exposed to vibration at or above the exposure action value, the employer must provide the employees and their representatives with suitable and sufficient information, instruction and training. This must include the following.

- ☑ The organisational and technical measures taken to eliminate or control exposure to vibration.
- ☑ The exposure limit value and the action values.
- ☑ The significant findings of the risk assessment, including details of any measurements taken, with an explanation of the findings.
- ☑ Why and how to detect and report signs of injury resulting from exposure to vibration.
- ☑ The employees' entitlement to health surveillance.
- ☑ How to work safely to minimise exposure to vibration.
- ☑ The collective results of any health surveillance carried out. These must be anonymous so as not to reveal the personal health record of any individual.

The information, instruction and training provided as above must be updated by the employer to take account of any significant changes in the type of work carried out or method of working.

### 14.3.3.2 Employers' records

The following items must be documented by the employer.

- ☑ The significant findings of the risk assessment, as soon as is practicable after the risk assessment has been carried out or changed.
- ☑ The measures taken to eliminate or control exposure to vibration.
- ☑ The measures taken to provide information, instruction and training for at-risk employees.

### 14.3.3.3 Exposure to vibration

The employer must ensure that employees are not exposed to vibration above the exposure limit value or, if they are, immediately complete the following.

- ☑ Reduce exposure to below the exposure limit value.
- ☑ Identify the reasons for the exposure limit value being exceeded.
- ☑ Take appropriate actions to prevent it occurring again.

These points do not apply where the exposure of an employee to vibration is usually below the exposure action value but varies markedly from time to time and may **occasionally** exceed the exposure limit value, as long as the following apply.

- ☑ The exposure to vibration averaged over one week is less than the exposure limit value.
- ☑ There is evidence to show that the risk from the actual pattern of exposure is less than the corresponding risk from constant exposure to the exposure limit value.
- ☑ The risk from exposure is reduced to as low a level as is reasonably practicable.
- ☑ The employees concerned are subject to increased health surveillance, where appropriate.

Any measures taken to comply with this regulation must be adapted where necessary to take account of any employee(s) who is particularly at risk from exposure to vibration.

If the risk assessment indicates that there is a risk to the health of employees who are exposed to vibration, or those employees are likely to be exposed to vibration at or above the exposure action value, then the employer must ensure that those employees are placed under suitable health surveillance, where appropriate.

### 14.3.3.4 Health surveillance

The health surveillance will be appropriate in the following circumstances.

- ☑ If a link can be established between exposure to vibration and an identifiable disease or any other adverse effect on health.
- ☑ Where it is probable that the disease or other effect on health may occur under particular working conditions.
- ☑ If there are valid ways of detecting the disease or other effect on health.

The employer must ensure the following.

- ☑ A record is kept and maintained for each employee who undergoes health surveillance and that records are readily available in a suitable form.
- ☑ Employees are allowed to see their health surveillance records, having given reasonable notice.
- ☑ Copies of the records are provided to the enforcing authority (usually the HSE) upon request.

Where, as a result of health surveillance, an employee is found to have an identifiable disease or other adverse effect on health, which is considered by a doctor or other occupational health professional to be the result of exposure to vibration, the employer must ensure the following.

- ☑ The employee is informed, by a suitably qualified person, including advice regarding a need for further health surveillance.
- ☑ The employee is informed of any significant findings of the health surveillance, allowing for medical confidentiality.
- ☑ The risk assessment is reviewed.
- ☑ Existing control measures are reviewed, taking into account any advice given by a doctor, occupational health professional or enforcing authority.
- ☑ Consider reassigning the employee to other work, where there is no risk from further exposure, taking into account any advice given as above.
- ☑ The health of any other employee(s) who has been similarly exposed is reviewed, including the provision of a medical examination where recommended by a doctor, occupational health professional or the enforcing authority.

**! The employer must ensure that any person, whether an employee or not, who has been given the responsibility to ensure that the employer's duties are carried out (for example a site manager or project manager) receives suitable and sufficient information, instruction and training to enable compliance with the regulations.**

## Summary of employers' legal responsibilities

The regulations require that the employer ensures the following.

- Assesses the risks to the health of their employees from vibration, and to effectively plan for its control.
- Properly manages the risks.
- Provides suitable work equipment for their employees, having regard for technical developments in tool design and vibration suppression.
- Maintains equipment fully and correctly.
- Gives employees and supervisors information and training on the risks to health caused by vibration, and on the safe use of the work equipment that is provided.
- Provides health surveillance and/or health monitoring where risks cannot be completely eliminated.
- Reports any confirmed cases of HAVS or VWF to the Health and Safety Executive (HSE).
- Consults employees and their appointed representatives on proposals for dealing with vibration.

### 14.3.4 Employees' duties

Under these regulations, employees have a legal duty to make themselves available for health surveillance checks (during working hours) as required by the employer, the health surveillance being at the employer's expense.

## Compensation and civil claims

Cases are now regularly reaching the civil courts in which employees are pursuing claims for compensation after having reportedly developed HAVS, VWF or similar conditions from the use of plant and equipment that generated vibration.

*Use of technology and planning reduces the risk of exposure*

Complying with the Control of Vibration at Work Regulations, following the guidance on the regulations and implementing an occupational health programme that monitors and manages employees' exposure to vibration will help to reduce the number of employees suffering from symptoms, and thus help reduce such court cases and their potential costs to an employer, as well as perhaps having some influence on the level of future insurance premiums.

It should be noted that records of compliance need to be kept.

## 14.4 Hand-arm vibration

The most common form of vibration affecting those who work in construction is hand-arm vibration syndrome (HAVS), which has the potential to damage the circulation, nerves, joints and bones in the hands and arms.

Listed below are some tools and plant used in the construction industry that could cause exposure to risks from hand-arm vibration.

- Road and concrete breaking drills.
- Concrete pokers.
- Plate vibrators/wacker plates.
- Demolition picks.
- Compressor guns.
- Pneumatic drills.
- Angle grinders.
- Percussive (hammer) drills.
- Sanders, and similar reciprocating tools.
- Cut-off saws or disc cutters.
- Power hammers and chisels, including Kango hammers.
- Needle guns/scabblers.
- Chainsaws.
- Strimmers.
- Woodworking machinery.

This is irrespective of the tools' power source. Other equipment that may occasionally be used and that is a source of vibration includes rotavators, lawnmowers, brush-cutters and leaf blowers.

*Examples of tools that could cause hand-arm vibration if control measures are not implemented*

Factors that can influence the degree of severity of HAVS are shown below.

- ☑ The frequency at which the tool vibrates.
- ☑ The exposure pattern (length and frequency of work and subsequent rest periods).
- ☑ The sharpness and suitability of the cutting tool or blade to cut the material being worked on.
- ☑ The grip, push and other forces used to guide and apply the vibrating tools. The tighter the grip, the more vibration energy is transferred to the hands (vibration may increase as a tool becomes blunt and the user pushes harder).
- ☑ Other factors that potentially affect blood circulation (such as workplace temperature, whether the person smokes and individual susceptibility).
- ☑ The hardness of the material being worked.
- ☑ The posture of the tool user, because tense muscles are more susceptible to hand-arm vibration (for example, using vibrating tools at arm's length increases the effect).

HAVS can develop into a severe and potentially disabling condition known as vibration white finger (VWF). Symptoms of VWF are usually triggered by the cold and some of the early signs are shown below.

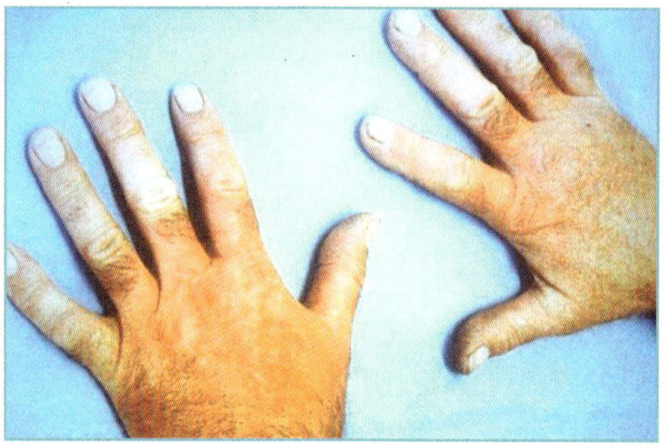

*Vibration white finger*

- ☑ Pale fingertips.
- ☑ Loss of sense of touch.
- ☑ Severe pain and numbness.
- ☑ Pins and needles.
- ☑ Loss of grip.
- ☑ Loss of dexterity (such as when doing up buttons, and so on).

In the longer-term, VWF can result in disabling conditions, including ulceration and gangrene.

Vibration damage to the fingers, hands or body is very much dose-related. The greater the exposure to vibration, the more likely there is to be damage. Increased exposure could be due to being exposed to greater magnitudes of vibration or being exposed for longer durations.

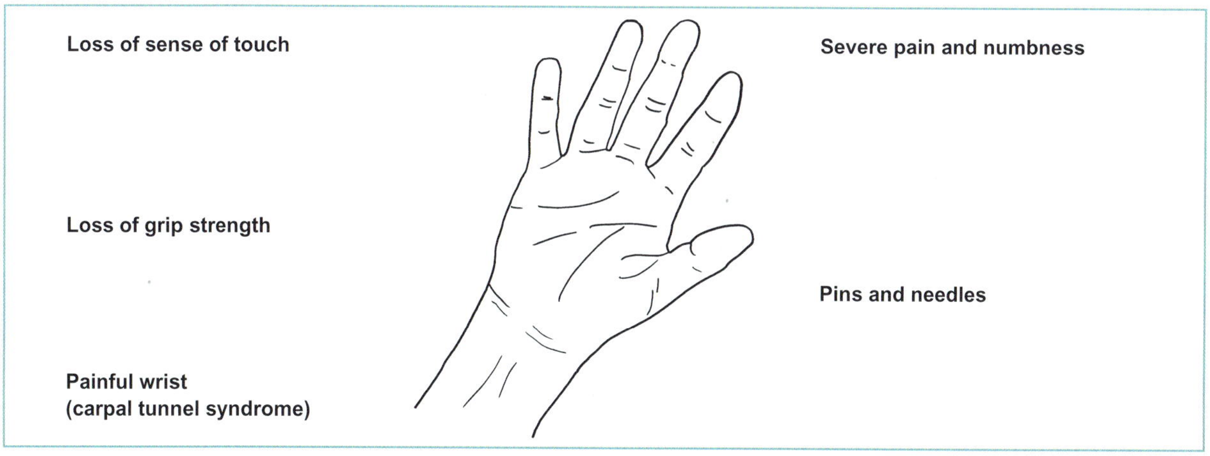


*Vibration damage to areas of the hands and wrists*

Other factors (shown below) can influence the risk of developing HAVS.

- ☑ The grip, push and other forces used to guide and apply the vibrating tools or pieces of work equipment. The tighter the grip, the more vibration energy is transferred to the hands.
- ☑ Tools with blunt cutting edges usually require more time to complete the task, higher grip and push forces, and often result in greater vibration emission.
- ☑ The exposure pattern, length and frequency of work and rest periods.
- ☑ How much of the hand, and other parts of the body, is exposed to the vibration.
- ☑ Factors that potentially affect blood circulation (such as workplace temperature, smoking and individual susceptibility).
- ☑ The hardness of the material being worked.
- ☑ Tool maintenance, which is important in order to keep it running smoothly and efficiently.

**HSE guidance is available for employees using hand-held power equipment.**

**Use a breaker attachment on an excavating machine to break concrete rather than using a hand-held breaker.**

## 14.5 Whole-body vibration

WBV, as its name suggests, is vibration or jolting of the whole body through the surface that is supporting the body (such as a machine seat or floor).

WBV, which often results from driving or operating some types of construction plant or vehicles, has the potential to cause back injury or make an existing back condition more painful.

Back pain can be caused by many work and non-work activities. It can lead to time off work, loss of productivity and compensation claims. Mobile machine operators and drivers (especially those who work off-road) are at increased risk from back pain.

There are things that you can do to help your employees avoid the problem, but you cannot prevent all back pain, so early reporting of symptoms, proper treatment and suitable rehabilitation is essential.

Most exposure to WBV at work is unlikely on its own to cause back pain. It may pose a risk when there is unusually high vibration or jolting, or the vibration is uncomfortable for a long time on most working days. In such situations, the risk from vibration is related to the overall time the operator or driver is exposed to the vibration and the number of shocks and jolts they experience each day.

Listed below are some tools and plant used in the construction industry that could cause exposure to risks from WBV.

- ☑ Rough-terrain forklift trucks and telehandlers.
- ☑ Vibratory rollers.
- ☑ Mobile crushers.
- ☑ Dumper trucks and other forms of earth-moving machinery.
- ☑ Delivery vehicles if required to travel on rough terrain.

Among those most likely to experience high vibration exposures are regular operators and drivers of off-road machinery.

- ☑ Construction, mining and quarrying machines and vehicles, particularly earthmoving machines (such as scrapers, bulldozers and building site dumpers).
- ☑ Tractors and other agricultural and forestry machinery, particularly when used in transportation, tedding (turning hay), primary cultivation and mowing.

WBV can be controlled in different ways, for example, improved technology in mobile plant (such as improved suspension and driver's seat), operator training, smooth operation of machines and job rotation.

*Equipment that could produce whole-body vibration*

## 14.6 Control measures

### 14.6.1 Health surveillance

If the findings of the risk assessment, feedback from employees or other sources of information show that there is a risk to the health of employees because of their use of vibrating tools, or that employees are exposed to vibration in excess of the exposure action value, then the employer must ensure that the employees are under suitable medical surveillance where it is appropriate.

The HSE recommends a five-stage system of health surveillance for HAV.

| | |
|---|---|
| **Stage 1** | An initial questionnaire to be answered when employees first move into any job that involves exposure to vibration *(refer to Section G: Checklists and forms)*. |
| **Stage 2** | A short questionnaire answered annually by employees exposed to vibration *(refer to Section G: Checklists and forms)*. |
| **Stage 3** | A formal HAVS health assessment carried out by a qualified person (for example, an occupational health nurse). |
| **Stage 4** | A formal diagnosis made by a doctor who is qualified in occupational health, and who will assess fitness for work. |
| **Stage 5** | (Optional) if considered necessary, the doctor refers the employee for certain tests for HAVS to assist the doctor in making the judgements required in Stage 4. |

www.

**The HSE's five steps to manage health risk can be found on its website.**

Employers who consider that their employees are at a potential risk from HAVS should appoint a person to manage the health surveillance programme and be actively involved in the initial stages. Requirements of that person are shown below.

- ☑ Does not need to be medically qualified.
- ☑ Should not attempt diagnosis or be judgemental as to the causes of HAVS with regard to individual cases.
- ☑ Should receive training from an occupational health professional.
- ☑ Must be able to describe the symptoms of HAVS.
- ☑ Should have experience of the working environment.
- ☑ Must be able to gain the trust and co-operation of employees, and understand the importance of confidentiality.

The HSE recommends that employees who are known to be at risk of HAVS but report no symptoms for three consecutive years on their annual questionnaire (Stage 2), should be referred to an occupational health nurse for an independent view of symptoms that may have been overlooked by the individual.

For WBV, detailed health surveillance is not possible, as there are many non-vibration causes of back pain. Therefore, the HSE recommends health monitoring, which is a structured system for self-reporting of symptoms.

**For an example of a health monitoring questionnaire refer to Section G: *Checklists and forms*.**

### 14.6.2 Keeping records

Health surveillance records should be stored in-house, in a way that retains their confidentiality, possibly under the control of the person nominated to manage the health surveillance system.

Employers should create a health record for each individual who is exposed to vibration and keep them for at least as long as they are under health surveillance, and possibly longer.

Health records should be kept up to date and should include full details of the employee's exposure to vibration and any questionnaires that have been completed.

The records can be kept in any form providing it is possible to produce a copy if required by the enforcing authority, usually the HSE.

It is considered to be good practice if employees are offered a copy of their health records when they leave their employer.

### 14.6.3 Work patterns

One of the most simple but also one of the most effective ways of minimising risks arising from vibration is by reducing the time when operatives are actually exposed to vibration.

If the use of a vibrating tool is shared between a team of employees, as opposed to it only being used by one person, the tool may be kept in productive use for the day.

Moving any employees not operating the tools at that time onto other areas of work will considerably lessen the effects of vibration on users, by splitting and rotating the work. This will also assist the maintenance of blood circulation, thus lessening the chances of injury or ill health being caused to users by the vibrating tool.

**Organise employees to work in teams where they switch tasks within the team to avoid individuals having unnecessarily high exposure to vibration.**

### 14.6.4 Maintaining blood circulation

Keeping the hands and body warm is essential to help maintain good blood flow to the fingers and reduce the risk of injury due to HAV. Specific measures might include those listed below.

- Wearing gloves.
- Using proprietary heating pads for the hands.
- Using tools with heated handles.
- Avoiding tools that have pneumatic exhausts that discharge towards the hands.
- Allowing operatives to warm up before starting work, and helping them to stay warm.
- Wearing warm, weatherproof clothing in cold, wet areas.
- Massaging and exercising fingers during work breaks.

### 14.6.5 Personal protective equipment

Some retro-fit products are available that are designed to protect operators from vibration. Only those approved by the machine manufacturers should be used.

**The wearing of anti-vibration gloves is not recommended**, due to the problems below.

- Reduced flexibility at the hands resulting in higher grip and push forces and loss of precise tool control.
- The possibility of gloves amplifying the tool vibration in some cases (these cases are very difficult to predict).
- Some anti-vibration gloves only cut out the high frequency levels of vibration, which aren't harmful.
- Anti-vibration gloves are only tested in one direction and vibration occurs in three directions.
- Field trials of gloves have shown that the vibration isolation materials are not always durable.

However, if anti-vibration gloves are to be tried, it is essential that they carry the CE mark and are selected by a competent person. One benefit from gloves is that they keep the hands warm and offer other protection.

Therefore, if an employer intends to provide items of PPE as part of their strategy to reduce the risks from vibration, it is important to understand that PPE will not fully protect the worker. The aim of specifying gloves should be to keep the operator's hands warm and not to expect gloves to reduce exposure to vibration.

All PPE produced or imported by reputable companies is manufactured to British and European Standards. As with all PPE for use at work, gloves or anti-vibration protection should be selected by a competent person who can ensure, in discussion with the supplier, that they meet the appropriate standards. Most leading manufacturers and suppliers will offer advice on the selection of different types of gloves and other PPE.

Ear defenders should be worn to lessen the effects of the noise created by vibrating tools, and eye protection should be worn to avoid the risks from dust or flying particles.

## 14.7 Managing vibration

### 14.7.1 Vibration risk assessment in practice

A general risk assessment can be briefly defined as a systematic examination of a work process, carried out by a competent person on behalf of an employer.

A vibration risk assessment follows the same principle, but with the emphasis solely on vibration and its potential to cause ill health in employees.

The principle of risk assessment is not new. In fact, it is quite likely that many employers have been carrying out risk assessments, including vibration risk assessments, during the day-to-day course of their business, possibly without thinking of the process in terms of a risk assessment.

**To cut large holes in brickwork, use a diamond-tipped hole-cutting drill bit with a rotary action rather than a tungsten-tipped hole bit, which requires rotary and hammer action.**

## 14.7.2 Changing the process

*Mechanisation removes the risk*

*Machine-mounted pick replaces hand-operated breakers*

### 14.7.2.1 Identifying at-risk persons

A survey of what work is carried out, using what tools and equipment, and by whom, will establish who is at risk. If there is any doubt as to whether a particular job has the potential to cause vibration-induced health problems or injury, it is better to assume that it has, initially at least.

Having established who could be at risk it is necessary to examine work in detail to determine which work is of genuine concern. As outlined in the summary of the Control of Vibration at Work Regulations, only when all other investigative methods have been exhausted should it be necessary to carry out vibration measurements.

Some of the many sources of information available to employers are shown below.

- ☑ The users of vibrating tools themselves; they are the ones who may have experienced the early symptoms of HAVS.
- ☑ Free online vibration measurement databases, which are based on the actual vibration measurements achieved during the testing of hundreds of tools of different types in different conditions.
- ☑ The HSE's vibration management publications.
- ☑ Tool manufacturers' published vibration data, although this should be treated with caution as it can be based upon laboratory testing rather than field trials, and usually underestimates exposures under real work conditions.

www.

**The HSE web-based vibration calculators are available through its website.**

In construction, it is likely that those exposed to WBV will exceed the **exposure action value** if they operate machines for several hours per day. The **exposure limit value** should only be exceeded if the machine is operated very aggressively or with non-approved attachments.

For HAV, the guidance from the HSE is that an employee is probably at risk from HAVS if they are using hammer action equipment for more than 15 minutes each day, or rotary equipment for more than one hour each day.

Employees who fall into these categories, as well as other at-risk employees, should be asked to complete a short health surveillance questionnaire.

**An initial hand-arm vibration screening questionnaire can be found in Section G: *Checklists and forms*.**

**An important factor in establishing who is at risk is the actual time that someone is using a vibrating tool, commonly referred to as the trigger time. This is the actual time the tool is operating, not the time holding the tool. When asked, it is usual for users to overestimate the length of time that they actually use the equipment. Their response may be 'I use the equipment all day' when in fact what they mean is that they use it on-and-off all day with, for example, a total trigger time of less than 60 minutes per day.**

### 14.7.2.2 Eliminating or controlling exposure to vibration in the workplace

On the basis of the general principles and hierarchy of control measures, employers must ensure that employees' exposure to vibration is either eliminated or reduced so far as is reasonably practicable.

Where it cannot be eliminated the employer must introduce a programme of organisational and technical measures (control measures) consistent with their risk assessment.

This must include the following considerations.

- ☑ Alternative methods of carrying out the work that eliminate or reduce employees' exposure to vibration (for example, stripping off surface coatings by chemical treatment rather than power-sanding).
- ☑ Choice of work equipment that, because of its design or features, or the nature of the work to be done, produces the least possible vibration.
- ☑ The provision of ancillary equipment that reduces the risk of injury being caused by vibration (for example, manufacturer approved vibration absorbent handles for hand-held equipment).
- ☑ Proper maintenance arrangements for the work equipment, workplace and workplace systems (for example, maintaining ground surfaces over which vehicles regularly travel) .
- ☑ The design and layout of workplaces, workstations and rest facilities.
- ☑ Suitable and sufficient information and training for employees so that they may use the equipment safely and correctly in order to minimise their exposure to vibration (such as training mobile machine operators how to correctly adjust their seats and the benefits of driving less aggressively).
- ☑ Limitation of the duration and intensity of the vibration (for example, by job rotation).
- ☑ Appropriate work schedules with adequate rest periods.
- ☑ The provision of clothing to protect employees from cold and damp.
- ☑ Arranging for operatives to stay warm by providing heating for the workplace where needed and possible, together with suitable clothing and gloves.
- ☑ Ensuring that any new tools have vibration control measures built in.
- ☑ By adopting a buy smooth/hire smooth policy, in which a commitment is made to choose tools that incorporate low vibration technology.
- ☑ The reduction of vibration transmission in the path between the source and the handles or other surfaces gripped by operatives' hands.
- ☑ The minimisation of the amount of force required to apply and control the tools, and keeping them in good order.

The HSE has developed a points system that allows for quick estimates of the hand-arm vibration exposure for a worker. Each process is assigned a number of points per hour. Adding the points from each process carried out (calculated by multiplying the points per hour by the number of hours' use) provides an estimate of the total exposure.

- ☑ For HAV the **exposure action value** corresponds to 100 points and the **exposure limit value** corresponds to 400 points.
- ☑ For WBV the **exposure action value** corresponds to 100 points and the **exposure limit value** corresponds to 529 points.
- ☑ Points from HAV and WBV should not be combined. Exposure times are actual trigger times, and not the time holding the tool or carrying out the task.

**Further guidance on estimating exposure is contained in Appendix A.**

A further benefit gained as a result of controlling vibration can be a reduction in noise levels; in some circumstances reducing noise will also reduce vibration, hence many noise control techniques also involve techniques for controlling vibration.

**HSE information on practical ways to avoid or reduce use of vibrating equipment can be found on its website.**

## 14.7.3 Information and training for employees

If the risk assessment shows that there is a risk to the health of employees because of vibration, or they are exposed to vibration in excess of the exposure action value, then the employer must give employees and their representatives information, instruction and training on the following.

- ☑ How the employer is managing vibration in the workplace.
- ☑ The exposure limit values and exposure action values.
- ☑ The significant findings of the risk assessments, including details of any measurements taken.
- ☑ What employees should look for in themselves as regards HAVS, VWF and low-back pain and how they should inform their employer.
- ☑ The entitlement to health surveillance.
- ☑ The safe working practices in place to minimise employees' exposure to vibration.
- ☑ The collective (as opposed to individual) results of any health surveillance undertaken.

## Vibration reduced breaker

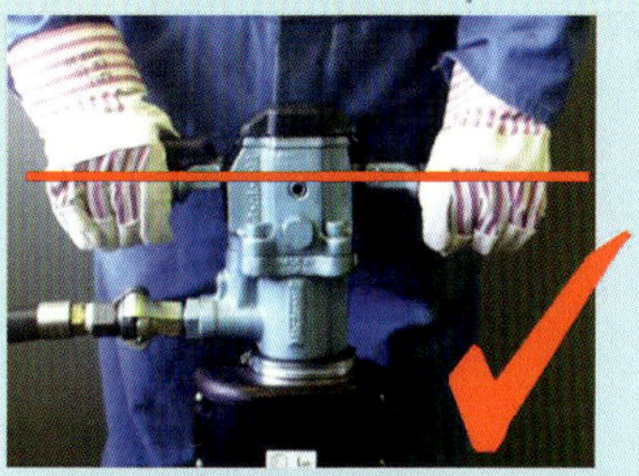

- ☑ Keep the moil point sharp.
- ☑ Break a little at a time, don't get jammed.

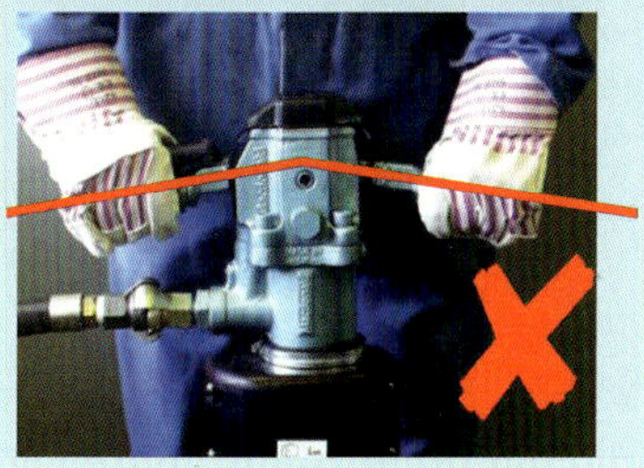

- ☒ Don't force anti-vibration handles.
- ☒ Stop breaker before pulling out.

## 14.7.4 Work equipment

### 14.7.4.1 Selection of tools and equipment

All equipment that is liable to vibrate, and that is manufactured for use as work equipment, should be designed to have low vibration operating characteristics.

Manufacturers are required to provide information on all aspects of their equipment, including details of any vibration that may be expected. In particular, suppliers must provide information on vibration levels if the tool or machine is likely to subject workers to levels of vibration exceeding the exposure action value of 2.5 metres per second squared.

The Supply of Machinery (Safety) Regulations require that suppliers provide purchasers with information on the amount of vibration generated by an item of equipment during normal expected use, so that an informed judgement may be made when purchasers are selecting tools and machinery.

However, as some manufacturers may base their vibration figures on laboratory simulation rather than field trials, the figures quoted may be unrealistically low. In many cases information is also available from independent real or simulated work measurements.

Vibration emission is one of many important factors to consider when selecting a tool. For example, a very heavy tool might not emit much vibration but could cause manual handling risk. Similarly, some tools might emit less vibration than others but be relatively inefficient, resulting in increased exposure times, higher grip and push forces. Always select the right tool for the job.

### 14.7.4.2 Regular maintenance of tools

Correctly installed and smooth running machines will, in time, vibrate as the machinery parts become worn.

The parts of machinery and vehicles that contribute to vibration are shown below.

- ☑ Worn bearings.
- ☑ Dirty fan blades (unbalanced fans).
- ☑ Worn mountings or worn anti-vibration pads.
- ☑ Misaligned shafts.
- ☑ Unbalanced rotating parts.
- ☑ Loose bolts.
- ☑ Damaged gear teeth.
- ☑ Blunt cutting tools and blades.
- ☑ Worn suspension components.
- ☑ Incorrect tyre pressures.
- ☑ Damaged seats.
- ☑ Damaged tyres/tracks.

The lack of correct maintenance and lubrication will produce increased vibration magnitudes. Machines should, therefore, be maintained at regular intervals and any detected faults rectified as soon as possible, thus reducing the risk of vibration problems. Cutting tools or blades should be kept sharp by maintenance or replacement, as appropriate.

### 14.7.4.3 Measuring vibration

The measurement of vibration is usually carried out by specialist companies, although some larger construction companies have bought their own vibration measuring equipment and trained their staff to carry out in-house vibration measurements. There is an obligation to physically monitor the use of plant per operative (for example, use the breaker for five minutes then rest for 45 minutes), a chart should be completed and signed by a supervisor to record that monitoring has taken place. The legislation specifies two levels of vibration that require employers to take action.

- **Exposure action value** is a level of vibration that if reached, as determined by vibration measurements, requires that employers put in place control measures to manage the exposure of employees.
- **Exposure limit value** is a measure of vibration, again determined by measuring vibration, above which employees may not be exposed and therefore the activity must stop.

**Where a heavy grinder is used at a permanent workstation to do repetitive work, suspend it from a counterbalance system to reduce the load on the operator's arms and the tightness of grip needed.**

## Appendix A – Estimating exposure to hand-arm vibration

You may be able to get suitable vibration data from the equipment handbook, or from the equipment supplier. See Table 1 for examples of vibration levels HSE has measured on equipment in use. There are also some databases on the internet that may have suitable vibration data.

If you plan to use the manufacturer's vibration data you should check that it represents the way you use the equipment (see 'Duties of manufacturers and suppliers') since some data may underestimate workplace vibration levels substantially. Ask the manufacturer for an indication of the likely vibration emission of the tool when your employees are using it. If you are able to get vibration data from the manufacturer that is reasonably representative of the way you use the equipment, it should be suitable for you to use in estimating your employees' exposure. **However, if the only information available to you is the vibration emission declared in the equipment's handbook, it may be safer to double this figure before using it for estimating daily exposures.****

You also need to check, by observing them, how long employees are actually exposed to the vibration (that is the total daily trigger time with the equipment operating and in contact with the employee's hand(s)). Employees are unlikely to be able to provide this information very accurately themselves. You could observe and measure the trigger time over, for example, half an hour and then use the result to estimate the trigger time for the full shift. Alternatively, where the work task is repetitive, for example drilling large numbers of holes in masonry, you could measure the trigger time when drilling several holes and multiply the average by the number of holes typically drilled in a shift.

** *This sentence does not apply to machinery manufactured after December 2009 due to the introduction of standard tests as required by the Supply of Machinery (Safety) Regulations.*

### Table 1. Some typical vibration levels for common tools

| Tool type | Lowest | Typical | Highest |
|---|---|---|---|
| Road breakers | 5 m/s$^2$ | 12 m/s$^2$ | 20 m/s$^2$ |
| Demolition hammers | 8 m/s$^2$ | 15 m/s$^2$ | 25 m/s$^2$ |
| Hammer drills/combi hammers | 6 m/s$^2$ | 9 m/s$^2$ | 25 m/s$^2$ |
| Needle scalers | 5 m/s$^2$ | – | 18 m/s$^2$ |
| Scabblers (hammer type) | – | – | 40 m/s$^2$ |
| Angle grinders | 4 m/s$^2$ | – | 8 m/s$^2$ |
| Clay spades/jigger picks | – | 16 m/s$^2$ | – |
| Chipping hammers (metal) | – | 18 m/s$^2$ | – |
| Stone-working hammers | 10 m/s$^2$ | – | 30 m/s$^2$ |
| Chainsaws | – | 6 m/s$^2$ | – |
| Brushcutters | 2 m/s$^2$ | 4 m/s$^2$ | – |
| Sanders (random orbital) | – | 7–10 m/s$^2$ | – |

If the employee is exposed to vibration from more than one tool or work process during a typical day, you will need to collect information on likely vibration level and trigger time for each one.

www.

**Once you have collected relevant vibration data and exposure times you will need to use an exposure calculator to assess each employee's daily exposure (see the HSE vibration web pages).**

Alternatively, you can use the simple exposure points system in Table 2 to estimate the daily exposure.

### Workplace vibration measurements

If you want to obtain vibration measurements for your own tools you will need to arrange for a competent person to carry out measurements for you using specialised equipment. Measurement results can be highly variable, depending on many factors, including the operator's technique, the condition of the work equipment, the material being processed and the measurement method. The competence and experience of the person who makes the measurements is important so that they can recognise and take account of these uncertainties in producing representative vibration data.

## Table 2. Simple exposure point system

| Tool vibration ($m/s^2$) | 3 | 4 | 5 | 6 | 7 | 10 | 12 | 15 |
|---|---|---|---|---|---|---|---|---|
| Points per hour (approximate) | 20 | 30 | 50 | 70 | 100 | 200 | 300 | 450 |

Multiply the points assigned to the tool vibration by the number of hours of daily trigger time for the tool(s) and then compare the total with the exposure action value (EAV) and exposure limit value (ELV) points.

100 points per day = exposure action value (EAV)

400 points per day = exposure limit value (ELV).

*(The above text is an extract from the HSE's free leaflet Control the risks from hand-arm vibration (INDG175 rev2), which is reproduced under licence from the Controller of Her Majesty's Stationery Office.)*

www.

**Further advice on estimating and managing exposure to hand-arm vibration can be found on the HSE website.**

## Appendix B – Vibration – Actions by employers

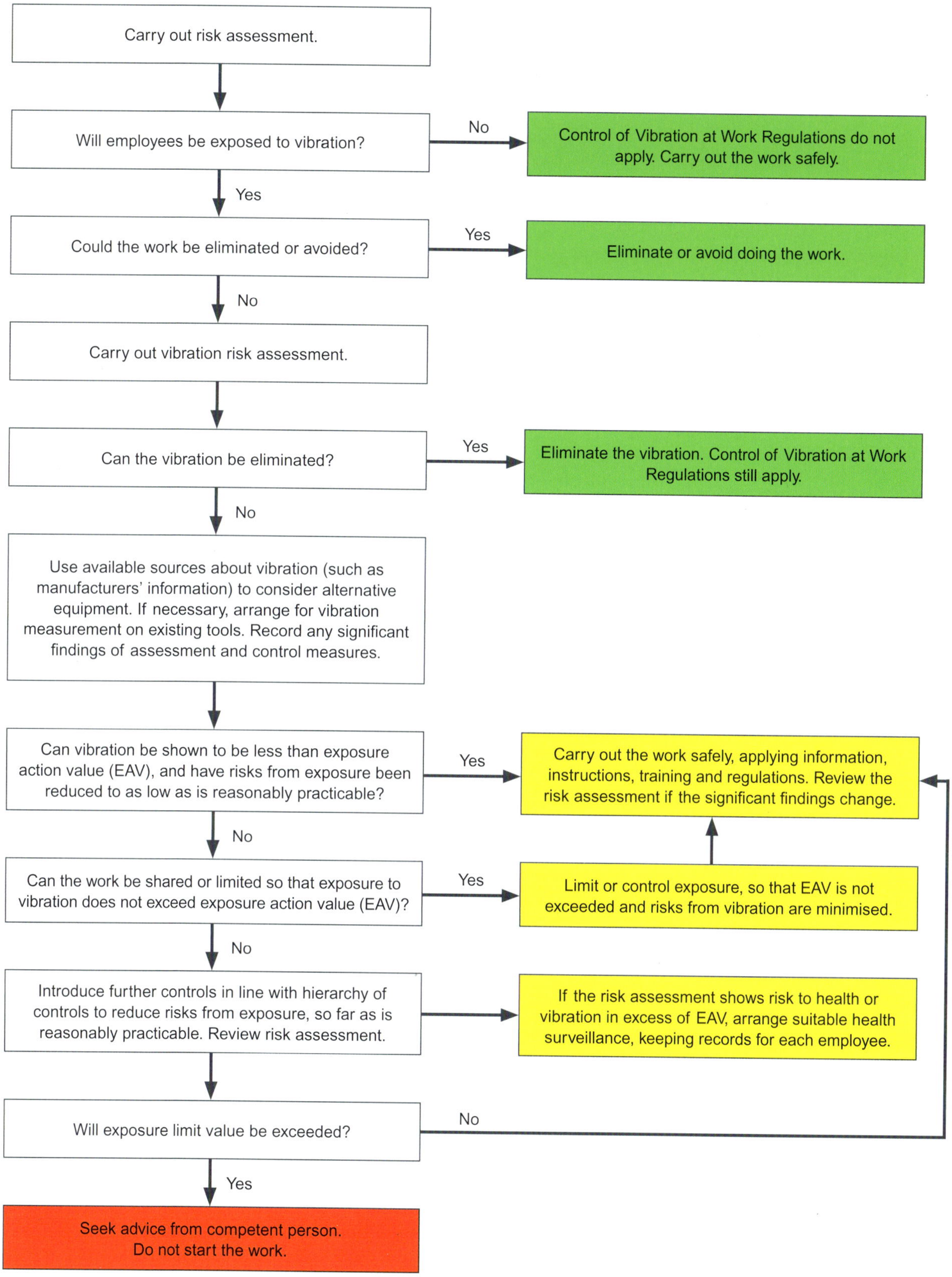


| | HAV | WBV |
|---|---|---|
| Exposure action value (EAV)= | 2.5 m/s² | 0.5 m/s² |
| Exposure limit value (ELV) = | 5.0 m/s² | 1.15 m/s² |

# 15

# Manual handling

Contents



## Supporting information

**G: Checklists and forms**



**GT 700 Toolbox talks**

## Overview

**All construction and building work involves lifting and handling to some extent. The first consideration should always be whether the load needs to be handled. Where this cannot be avoided, consideration should be given to minimise the handling of the load. Where manual handling cannot be avoided mechanical lifting aids should be used.**

**The risk of injury can be greatly reduced by a knowledge and application of correct lifting and handling techniques.**

## 15.1 Introduction

More than a quarter of all reported accidents each year result from poor manual handling techniques. Many cause absence from work, and in the worst cases, permanent disability and physical impairment.

Giving employees the appropriate training in the correct manual handling techniques and the use of mechanical lifting aids is highly cost effective.

Adequate supervision is necessary to ensure that employees then use the proper equipment and techniques and do not take shortcuts. This will reduce accidents, the amount of time lost on site, and the disruption to work that is caused when something goes wrong.

The part of the body most vulnerable if bad manual handling techniques are used is the back, particularly the lower back. Once it has been damaged, it is usually weakened for the rest of a person's life.

All the other major joints and muscle groups can also be easily damaged if the correct manual handling techniques are not used.

The consequences of an injury due to bad manual handling, or a musculoskeletal injury or illness as they are often called, can be a long-term or permanent inability to work. The cost to the employer is reduced productivity and having to find others to carry out the work.

## 15.2 Important points

- ☑ Poorly thought out or badly performed manual handling is the cause of many injuries to construction workers.
- ☑ Manual handling includes lifting, lowering, pulling, pushing or carrying a load by physical effort.
- ☑ Factors which determine whether it is safe for an individual to manually handle a load include the task, individual, load and environment (TILE).
- ☑ Employers must:
  - avoid, so far as reasonably practicable, their employees having to carry out manual handling likely to result in an injury
  - where that is not reasonably practicable, assess the risks to the employee
  - put in place control measures to prevent such an injury occurring.
- ☑ Employees must:
  - make full and proper use of the employer's safe system of work
  - use (lifting) equipment and machinery in accordance with instruction and training given
  - report to the employer any situation where it is considered the system of working is not safe.
- ☑ Where manual handling cannot be avoided mechanical lifting aids should be used where possible.
- ☑ The Health and Safety Executive (HSE) has developed two online assessment tools to assist employers:
  - a manual handling assessment chart (MAC), to help assessors carry out general manual handing assessments
  - an assessment of repetitive tasks tool (ART), to assist where employees have to carry out rapid repetitive tasks.

## 15.3 Manual Handling Operations Regulations

Regulation 4(1) sets out a hierarchy of measures to reduce the risks of manual handling. These are shown below.

- ☑ Avoiding hazardous manual handling operations, as far as is reasonably practicable.
- ☑ Assessing any hazardous manual handling operations that cannot be avoided.
- ☑ Where a risk is identified, which cannot be avoided, reducing the risk of injury, so far as is reasonably practicable (for example, by implementing risk reduction control measures).

The regulations do not have an ACoP due to the immense diversity covered by the regulations. However, the regulations are supported by guidance that should be followed.

### 15.3.1 Employers' duties

Each employer shall, so far as is reasonably practicable, avoid the need for employees to undertake any manual handling operations at work, that involve a risk of their being injured; or where this is not reasonably practicable, each employer shall:

- make a suitable and sufficient assessment of all such manual handling operations to be undertaken by their employees, having regard to those points contained in the manual handling checklist *(refer to Section G: Checklists and forms)*
- take appropriate steps to implement control measures, thereby reducing the risk of injury to those employees undertaking any manual handling operations, to the lowest level which is reasonably practicable
- take appropriate steps to provide any of those employees who are undertaking any manual handling operations with general indications and, where it is reasonably practicable to do so, precise information on:
  - the weight of each load
  - the heaviest side of the load whose centre of gravity is not positioned centrally.

Any assessment that an employer has made must be reviewed where there is reason to suspect that it is no longer valid, or there has been a significant change to the manual handling operations to which that assessment relates.

Where changes to an assessment are required, as a result of any review, an employer shall make them.

When determining for the purposes of this regulation whether manual handling operations at work involve a risk of injury, and to determine the appropriate steps needed to reduce that risk, particular care shall be taken to check the following.

- The physical suitability of the employee to carry out the operation.
- The clothing, footwear and other personal effects worn by the employee.
- The employee's knowledge and training.
- The results of any relevant risk assessment carried out under the Management of Health and Safety at Work Regulations.
- Whether the employee is within a group of employees identified by that assessment as being especially at risk.
- The results of any health surveillance provided under the Management of Health and Safety at Work Regulations.

The **Management of Health and Safety at Work Regulations** requires that a general risk assessment is undertaken. If this risk assessment identifies there is a possibility of injury from manual handling, then a separate manual handling assessment should be carried out.

In addition, employers must provide the following.

- Safe systems and places of work.
- The safety of their employees and, where possible, the absence of risks in the handling, storage and transport of all types of articles and substances.
- The information, instruction, training and supervision necessary to ensure the health and safety of their employees.

### 15.3.2 Employees' duties

The following duties are required of each employee, while they are at work.

- Make full and proper use of any system of work provided for use by the employer in connection with manual handling.
- Use any machinery or equipment provided by the employer in accordance with any training or instruction received.
- Inform the employer, or anyone else responsible for safety, of any dangerous work practice or shortcomings in the employer's arrangements for safety.

## 15.4 Common injuries

Injuries resulting from unsafe or incorrect manual handling can affect the following part of the body.

- Whole body.
- Back.
- Shoulders.
- Arms.
- Hands.
- Feet and toes.

Back injuries are the most common, but hernias, ruptures, sprains and strains are all conditions that can result from poor manual handling techniques.

Legislation requires that adequate and appropriate protective clothing and equipment be provided by the employer and worn by the employee. Gloves, footwear, hard hats and overalls all play an important part in reducing the type and severity of accidents arising from manual handling.

There are conflicting views on the benefits of wearing a back-support belt. Some authoritative bodies believe that wearing one may render some people more likely to suffer an injury. There is no evidence to support the theory that they reduce manual handling injury rates. There may be some benefit derived from the fact that wearing a back support will keep the lower-back muscles warm.

The cost of physical injury can be very high for the employer through lost production and raised costs, and legal liabilities leading to possible prosecution. For the employee, the physical injury may cause pain and even permanent disability, leading to lost wages.

Anyone who believes that they have suffered a manual handling injury, particularly a back injury, should be encouraged to seek prompt medical advice.

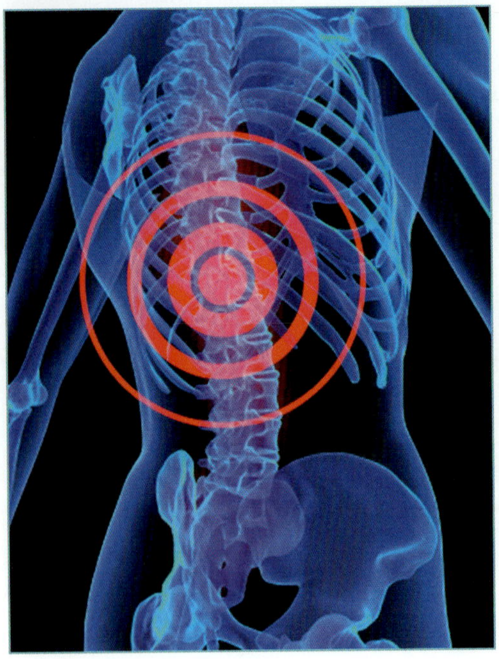

Radiated pain from a spinal injury

- **Musculoskeletal disorders** (MSD) covers any injury, damage or disorder of the joints or other tissues in the upper limbs or the back, neck and shoulders; less often they affect the lower limbs. Health problems range from discomfort and minor aches and pains to more serious medical conditions.
- **Strains and sprains to muscles and joints, torn ligaments and tendons, disc trouble and hernias.** These are often caused by sudden and awkward movements (for example, twisting or jerking while lifting or handling heavy loads). They are also caused by persons attempting to lift loads beyond their physical capabilities. The muscles of the abdominal wall are particularly vulnerable, and excessive strain may lead to ruptures.
- **Cuts and abrasions from rough surfaces, sharp or jagged edges, splinters, projections, and so on.** Personal protective equipment (PPE) and clothing should be worn as necessary (such as leather gloves to protect the hands).
- **Back injuries** are most frequently sustained while lifting and handling manually. They may be the cumulative effect of repeated minor injuries, or the result of an abrupt strain. Stoop lifting (see below) should be avoided; it greatly increases the chances of sustaining back injuries. Laboratory tests show that the stresses imposed on a rounded back during stoop lifting is six times that experienced if the trunk is kept straight while bending at the knees.
- **Crushing of limbs** by falling loads, or fingers, hands or feet becoming trapped by loads. Correct positioning of hands and feet in relation to the movement of the load is essential. Timber wedges or other blocks should be used when beginning to raise or lower heavy loads.

The risk of injury is reduced by knowledge of correct lifting techniques and by not attempting to lift excessively heavy loads without assistance.

**Manual handling and lifting injuries are often for life.**

## 15.5 Manual handling assessment

An ergonomic approach to the problems of manual handling and lifting can help to overcome many of the problems.

Ergonomics have been described as *fitting the job to the person, rather than fitting the person to the job*. This requires attention to the following.

- **Task.** What has to be achieved and by when?
- **Individual.** Male or female, large or small frame, age, stature and state of health or previous injuries?
- **Load.** Is it too heavy to lift and, if so, can it be broken down into smaller loads? Can two people lift it?
- **Environment.** Consider hazards en-route (such as uneven floor surfaces, slopes, steps and narrow passages).

**Task, individual, load and environment can be remembered using the acronym TILE.**

Where the assessment indicates potential risks to the health of employees from the manual handling of loads, the employer must develop a safe system of work that avoids the risks.

**A load must be a movable object. An implement (such as a chain saw, tool or breathing apparatus) is not considered to be a load under these regulations.**

The employer must consider the following.

- **The task.**
  - Can manual handling be avoided completely?
  - Can the distance a load has to be moved be reduced by better on-site planning?
  - Can lifting aids be used?
  - Does the load have to be raised to, or lowered from, above head height?
  - Does the task involve repetitive lifting?
  - Is it possible to avoid lifting from the floor?
  - Can the centre of gravity move (fluid loads)?
  - Can it be carried close to the body?
  - Should it be carried by two (or more) people?
- **The individual.**
  - Do they need manual handling training?
  - Do they need additional PPE?
  - Is there any known reason why they might not be suitable for the job?

*Safe working using a mechanical aid*

- **The load.**
  - Can it be broken down into smaller loads?
  - Is the weight known and, if not, can it be found out?
  - Are there adequate handholds?
  - Does it have sharp edges?
  - Can lifting accessories be built or cast in, or fixed into position?
  - Is it evenly balanced (centre of gravity)?
  - Are there any manufacturers' recommendations or constraints for methods of lifting?
- **The environment.**
  - Is the floor surface sufficiently level?
  - Are there any space constraints or trip hazards that should be removed?
  - Is the level of lighting adequate?
  - Is the workplace temperature satisfactory?
  - Is the surface slippery? (Consider varying weather, such as frost, ice and dew in the mornings.)

**Employees must co-operate in the following way.**

- By using the appropriate equipment supplied in accordance with their training and instructions.
- By following the systems of work laid down by their employer.

## 15.5.1 Online assistance

www.

**The HSE has developed two online tools to assist employers to carry out manual handling assessments.**

- **Manual handling assessment chart (MAC).**
- **Assessment of repetitive tasks (ART).**

The **manual handling assessment chart** tool helps users identify high-risk manual handling by helping them to understand, interpret and categorise the level of risk of the various known risk factors associated with manual handling. This incorporates a numerical and colour coded scoring system to enable priorities to be identified.

As its name suggests the **assessment of repetitive tasks** tool, which uses a numerical score and a traffic light system, assists employers in assessing the risks of musculoskeletal disorders arising out of repetitive tasks.

## 15.6 Lifting and handling

The weight that can be lifted by any individual will vary according to personal physique, age, condition of health and practice, and the techniques employed. Lifting capacity declines with age and an older person may not be capable of lifting the same load as a younger person; this, however, can be offset to some extent by employing a better technique.

The general rule is that the load should not be lifted if it causes a feeling of strain. Assistance should be available if required, and employees must not be required to lift loads beyond their capacity.

Youthful exuberance and bravado often tempt younger employees to try to lift loads that are too heavy. While they may succeed in the short-term, long-term damage may be done to the ligaments, muscles and back.

After taking account of expert opinion and the long history of complaints over handling heavy blocks, the Construction Industry Advisory Council has concluded that there is a high risk of injury in the single-handed, repetitive manual handling of building blocks or other loads heavier than 20 kg.

If single person handling is needed, either blocks or other materials of 20 kg or lighter should be specified and used, or other precautions should be implemented to reduce the risk by, for example, the provision of mechanical handling.

With blocks or other materials weighing less than 20 kg, manual handling risks are still significant and suitable precautions should be taken to minimise these risks as much as possible.

Some of the solutions listed below will require a degree of training and expertise; indeed some will require a driving licence.

### 15.6.1 Avoiding manual handling

Reducing the risk of injury can be helped by using the following types of mechanical aids.

- ☑ Genie lifts.
- ☑ Kerb lifters.
- ☑ Sack trolleys.
- ☑ Pallet trucks.
- ☑ Skids.
- ☑ Telehandlers.
- ☑ Correct delivery locations.
- ☑ Built-in lifting attachments.
- ☑ Wheelbarrows.
- ☑ Stillages.
- ☑ Conveyor belts.
- ☑ Suction pads.
- ☑ Temporary handles/grips.
- ☑ Material hoists.
- ☑ Excavators/dumpers.

*Kerb layer used to reduce manual handling*

**Bricklaying – stacking bricks and mortar on a platform at waist height allows more of the work to be done between waist and shoulder height, thus avoiding stooping.**

### 15.6.2 Preparing to lift

Before lifting and handling any load, the following points should be established.

- ☑ What has to be moved?
- ☑ Does it really have to be moved?
- ☑ What does it weigh?
- ☑ Can it be broken down into smaller loads?
- ☑ Can the process that requires it to be moved be changed?
- ☑ Where is the load's centre of gravity?
- ☑ Can it be safely handled by one person?
- ☑ Will assistance be required?
- ☑ Can the move be carried out more safely with mechanical assistance?
- ☑ How far does it have to be moved and from where to where?
- ☑ Is the route clear of obstructions?
- ☑ Can it be put down safely?

Suitable protective clothing should be worn. This may include gloves, safety footwear, safety helmets, and special overalls if hot or corrosive substances are to be carried.

Ensure that the lifting and lowering areas are clear of tripping hazards, and likewise check the route over which the load is to be carried.

## 15.6.3 The load

Large, heavy loads should, if possible, be broken down into smaller, lighter and more manageable sizes. It is obviously easier to lift 10 kg five times than to try to lift 50 kg once.

Where the load has to be moved by a woman, the weight should be reduced by approximately 30%.

As a rough guide, where lifting is repetitive, weights should be reduced as shown in the table below.

| Special factors in operation | Rough guide |
| --- | --- |
| Operation repeated once or twice a minute. | Reduce weight by 30%. |
| Operation repeated five to eight times a minute. | Reduce weight by 50%. |
| Operation repeated more than 12 times per minute. | Reduce weight by 80%. |
| 'Average' female. | Reduce weight by 30%. |
| Handler twists through 45 degrees. | Reduce weight by 10%. |
| Handler twists through 90 degrees. | Reduce weight by 20%. |
| Handler seated and twisting. | Less than 5 kg. |
| Handler seated. | About 5 kg. |
| Pushing or pulling a load (assuming that force is applied). | About 25 kg for starting or stopping a load. |
| With hands between knuckle and shoulder height. | About 10 kg for keeping a load in motion. |

The size and shape of a load may be as significant as its weight in determining whether assistance is required. Large awkward loads that require the arms to be extended in front of the body place more strain on the back and abdomen than compact objects carried close to the body.

The absence of natural or designed handling points can also make it difficult to raise and carry objects without strain so barrows or other lifting and handling aids may be required to move the load.

Not all loads need to be carried, of course. It may be easier to roll or push them, depending on the contents. Even so, assistance might still be required to avoid the risk of injury.

## 15.6.4 Manual handling techniques

### 15.6.4.1 Plan the task

- ☑ What has to be moved?
- ☑ Where to; where from; how far; is the route suitable, safe and clear of obstructions?
- ☑ Is it safe for one person to do it alone?
- ☑ Will help be required? If so, how much and for what purpose?

### 15.6.4.2 Use your body wisely

- ☑ Let the leg and thigh muscles do the work. They cope better than the back muscles.
- ☑ Try to keep your spine straight (not necessarily vertical, but straight) and the muscles relaxed. However, slight bending of the back, knees and hips is permitted if necessary to maintain the natural curve of the spine, and is certainly preferable to fully flexing the back (stooping) or fully flexing the hips and knees (deep squatting).
- ☑ Once you have started to lift (taken the full weight) don't flex your back any further, which can happen if you begin to straighten before you have raised the load.
- ☑ Avoid twisting the back or leaning sideways, especially whilst the back is bent.
- ☑ Use the movement of your own body weight to get things moving. Do not snatch the load.

### 15.6.4.3 Bend your knees

Feet slightly apart; one foot slightly forward; balance; keep the back straight. Avoid tight clothing that prevents you from bending your knees.

### 15.6.4.4 Get a good grip

Use your hands – not fingers. Tilt the load slightly to get a secure grip as close to the body as possible. Keep your elbows tucked in.

### 15.6.4.5 Lift with your legs

Do not jerk or snatch. Let the thigh muscles do the bulk of the work. Lift in stages, if necessary from the ground onto a low platform.

*Good practice method for lifting a load*

### 15.6.4.6 Putting the load down – plan before you start

- ☑ To floor level: It will probably be a reversal of the lifting process. Attention must be given to the positioning of the feet and back.
- ☑ To a higher level: Depending upon the height of the surface to which the load is to be positioned, it may be less of a stress on the body to lower the load and assistance may be required.
- ☑ If loads are to be manually handled, heavier loads should be stored at waist height.

*Good practice method for lifting and placing a load*

**There is a case study on the HSE website for reducing plasterboard manual handling, which could be delivered as a toolbox talk.**

### 15.6.4.7 Team lifting

*A good example of a team lift*

If the load is large, heavy or awkward – get assistance, preferably from someone of about the same size, and build as yourself to help maintain the balance of the load during lifting. Always plan the lift with your helper and agree who will give directions as to when and how you will lift.

### 15.6.5 Simple mechanical aids

Steel pipes and round timbers make effective rollers or mechanical aids, and should be used when necessary, but great care must be takento ensure the following.

*Hoist being used for loading out roof materials*

- ☑ The movement of the load is co-ordinated with the positioning of the rollers.
- ☑ The hands of the person who positions the rollers are kept well out of the way of the moving load.

The use of a wheelbarrow or sack truck will make the manual handling of suitable loads that much easier. Using lifting straps or hand-held suction devices will assist in moving some sheet materials.

The use of simple mechanical aids lowers the level of risk, can prevent accidents and avoids unnecessary fatigue and strain.

Whenever practical, mechanical handling and lifting should replace manual techniques. This will reduce the risk of fatigue, improve efficiency and reduce the risk of accidents.

#### e.g. Handling building blocks

- ☑ Specify/order blocks that weigh less than 20 kg.
- ☑ Store blocks where they will not get wet (and increase their weight).
- ☑ Arrange work so that lifting over shoulder height is not carried out.
- ☑ Deliver blocks as close to the point of laying as possible.

### 15.6.6 Scaffolds

Manual handling will be an activity linked to the erection, alteration and dismantling of scaffolds. It is also likely that those who work from scaffolds will be involved in manual handling during the course of their work.

Employers carrying out scaffolding work must assess the risks arising out of manual handling. This is usually undertaken as part of the general risk assessment and method statement/scaffold plan.

Specific manual handling techniques and skills are required for scaffolding. These enabling skills are comprehensively covered by the CISRS training courses. Labourers, trainee scaffolders and scaffolders who have not been trained through CISRS scheme should receive specific manual handling training.

# Index